THE 1798 REBELLION IN IRELAND
A BICENTENARY EXHIBITION

Record of an Exhibition

at the

ULSTER MUSEUM, BELFAST

3 APRIL - 31 AUGUST 1998

COMPILED AND EDITED BY W.A. MAGUIRE

Published by the Ulster Museum.
Supported by Belfast City Council.

ISBN 0 900761 35 0

Up in Arms!
The 1798 Rebellion in Ireland

ULSTER MUSEUM PUBLICATION No. 277

DESIGNED BY JAMES HANNA

COVER:

Thomas Robinson (d.1810)
The Battle of Ballynahinch
By kind permission of the Commissioners
of Public Works in Ireland

Contents

LENDERS TO THE EXHIBITION

Royal Academy of Arts, London
Armagh Public Library
Bell Gallery, Belfast
Lady Mairi Bury
Trustees of the British Museum, London
Chester Beatty Library, Dublin
Mr Neil Clayton
Dublin City Council
English Heritage
Mr J.A. Gamble
Grand Orange Lodge of Ireland
Historical Portraits Ltd, London
Irish Linen Centre and Lisburn Museum
Mrs A. Jardine
National Army Museum, London
National Gallery of Ireland, Dublin
National Library of Ireland, Dublin
National Maritime Museum, London
National Museums of Scotland (Scottish United
Services Museum), Edinburgh
National Portrait Gallery, London
Newtownabbey Borough Council
Office of Public Works, Dublin
Public Record Office of Northern Ireland
P. & B. Rowan
Representative Church Body, Dublin
Royal Artillery Museum, London
Scottish National Portrait Gallery, Edinburgh
Trinity College Dublin Library
Ulster Museum, Belfast
University of Ulster (Magee College Library)
Mrs and Mrs Neville Whittley
and a private collector

FOREWORD

Following the success of 'Kings in Conflict', an exhibition in 1990 commemorating the tercentenary of the Battle of the Boyne, the Trustees of the Ulster Museum resolved to mark the bicentenary of the 1798 Rebellion by an exhibition of similar scope and style. Like the earlier exhibition, 'Up in Arms' is intended to set the events it describes in the context - national and international - of their own time. The result is another major presentation, researched and created almost entirely in-house, but drawing on exhibits from a large number of institutional and private sources as well as those of the Museum itself, and dependent on help from many quarters. I want to thank particularly all the Museum staff whose dedication and teamwork have brought the exhibition into existence and I wish it all the success their hard work deserves.

The Board of Trustees records its thanks first to the lenders, without whose generosity such an exhibition would be impossible. Secondly, in these lean times, when any large exhibition needs additional funding, or help in kind, the joint support of Belfast's two morning newspapers, the *News Letter* and the *Irish News*, is both welcome and appropriate. Thirdly, the Board welcomes the very substantial financial support that has come from the European Union's Special Support Programme for Peace and Reconciliation, via the Northern Ireland Community Relations Council. This has enabled the appointment of an Exhibition Outreach Officer to work with community groups, an important extension of the work of our Education Department. Our special thanks are due to Mark Adair, the CRC Development Officer.

Lastly, every temporary exhibition, however well-devised and well-presented, comes to an end and fades from the memory. Some less ephemeral record of the event is needed. As in 1990, Belfast City Council has made this possible by a grant of such generosity that we have been able to produce a splendidly-illustrated historical catalogue at a very reasonable price. We particularly thank the Lord Mayor, Aldermen and Councillors for this invaluable support.

Marshall McKee
Acting Director
April 1998

ACKNOWLEDGEMENTS

First and foremost, I have to thank Chris Bailey, Arts Officer of Belfast City Council, for his help and advice in securing the generous grant that has made it possible to produce this volume. As to the contents, most of the catalogue entries and other text were written by the Editor and members of the permanent staff of the Ulster Museum (Trevor Parkhill, Robert Heslip, Tom Wylie and Winifred Glover in Human History; Martyn Anglesea, Elizabeth McCrum and Elise Taylor in Art). A number, however, were kindly provided by other individuals, namely Dr Allan Blackstock ('The Irish Yeomanry', pp 147-150); Dr Anthony Buckley and Mrs Linda Buckley (115); Allan Carswell (184-203); Jane Leonard (130, 206-216, 259, 290, 291); John McCabe (207); and Bryn Owen (230). I am most grateful for their help.

Of the many people who provided valuable help with research or illustrations the following deserve particular mention: Frazer Agnew and Norman Dunn (Newtownabbey Borough Council), Nelson Bell (Bell Gallery), Dr Peter Boyden and Clare Wright (National Army Museum), Peter Carr (Whiterow Press), Harry Carson (Armagh Public Library), Mary Clark (Dublin City Archives), Dr David Craig (National Archives, Dublin), Jack Gamble (Emerald Isle Books), Stephen Lloyd (Scottish National Portrait Gallery), Professor Edith Johnston, Adrian Le Harivel (National Gallery of Ireland), Brian Mackey (Irish Linen Centre and Lisburn Museum), Dr A.P.W. Malcomson and Ian Montgomery (Public Record Office of Northern Ireland), Dr Bernard Meehan (Trinity College, Dublin), Philip Mould (Historical Portraits, London), Donall O'Luanaigh and Colette O'Daly (National Library of Ireland), Dr Peter Rowan (P. and B. Rowan), Dr Michael Ryan (Chester Beatty Library, Dublin), Simon Stephens (National Maritime Museum), Patrick Teskey (Magee College Library), Brigadier Ken Timbers (Royal Artillery Museum) and Neville Whittley.

I owe special thanks to those Ulster Museum staff who have been most directly engaged in the preparation of the book. James Hanna, its designer, did his work not only with great competence but in a remarkably short time. Peter Crowther and Trevor Parkhill gave invaluable assistance with the vital matter of proof-reading and did much to improve the text. Pat McLean and the Museum's photographers - Bill Anderson-Porter, Michael McKeown and Bryan Rutledge - responded with agreeable efficiency to all my unreasonable demands for images. Robert Heslip provided an index at very short notice. Lastly, I must record a particular debt to Pauline Dickson who, working well beyond the call of normal duty in the work of preparing the text, displayed great technical skill, endless patience and remarkable good humour.

W.A. Maguire

CREDITS

Ashmolean Museum, Oxford 3; Biblothèque Nationale, Paris 35, 49, 94. 96, 98, 264; Trustees of the British Museum 60-66, 101, 160-161, 168, 227, 250, 271, 282-284; Girdaudon/Bridgeman Art Library 2, 10, 51; Bridgeman Art Library 48; A.C. Cooper, Ltd 113; Dublin Corporation 13; Dundee City Council 156; English Heritage 279; Historical Portraits, London 172; Historic Scotland 272; Irish Linen Centre & Lisburn Museum 242; Musée de la Marine, Paris 90; National Army Museum, London 6, 204, 205, 220, 221, 234, 252; National Gallery of Ireland, Dublin 45, 46, 75-78, 88, 131, 147, 149, 173, 218, 228, 232, 241, 245, 251, 256, 269, 270, 278, 281, 288, 301; National Library of Ireland, Dublin 22, 50, 222, 226, 229, 255; National Maritime Museum, London 102, 103, 153; Board of Trustees of the National Museums and Galleries on Merseyside, Liverpool 5; Courtesy of National Museums of Scotland 184-203; Courtesy of National Museum of Wales, 230; Courtesy of National Portrait Gallery, London 34, 52, 134, 225; Photothèque des Musées de la Ville de Paris 97; Rijksmuseum, Amsterdam 154; Royal Academy of Arts, London 1; R & R, Hull 33; Scottish National Gallery, Edinburgh 53, 132, 155, 157-159; Service Historique de l'Armée de Terre, Paris 260-262; Trinity College Library, Dublin 297, 303; Ulster Museum, Belfast all others except 56 and 163.
We are grateful to the following copyright owners for permission to use their material: Mr Alan Carey (240 and 248) and Dr Michael Purser (302).

The Ulster Museum wishes to acknowledge that several works in the exhibition, drawn from its collections, were purchased with the support of grant aid as follows:
National Heritage Memorial Fund 19
National Lottery, through the Heritage Lottery Fund 23
National Art Collections Fund 19, 20, 23
Esmé Mitchell Trust 19, 23
Friends of the National Collections of Ireland 20

ACADEMIC ADVISERS TO THE EXHIBITION

Professor Thomas Bartlett (University College Dublin)
Professor Marianne Elliott (University of Liverpool)
Dr A.T.Q. Stewart (formerly Queen's University Belfast)

'UP IN ARMS' EXHIBITION PROJECT

The exhibition was devised and researched by Trevor Parkhill and Bill Maguire and designed by Roy Service. Peter Crowther managed the project team, which consisted of staff from the departments of Conservation, Education, Registry, Marketing and Warding & Security, as well as those from History and Design & Exhibition Services.

Select Bibliography

The following sources have proved to be particularly useful in compiling this volume:

A. Webb, *Compendium of Irish Biography* (Dublin, 1878)
Dictionary of National Biography
Encyclopaedia Britannica, 11th edition and 15th edition
E. Bénézit, *Dictionnaire des Peintres, Sculpteurs, Dessinateurs et Graveurs* (Paris, 1976)

J.C. Beckett, *The Making of Modern Ireland, 1603-1923* (London, 1961)
Eileen Black, *Irish Oil Paintings, 1572-c.1830. A Catalogue of the Permanent Collection 3* (Ulster Museum, Belfast, 1991)
D.A. Chart (ed), *The Drennan Letters, 1776-1819* (Belfast, 1931)
W.H. Crawford and B. Trainor (eds), *Aspects of Irish Social History, 1750-1800* (Belfast, 1969)
Anne Crookshank and The Knight of Glin, *The Painters of Ireland c.1660-1920* (London, 1978).
Charles Dickson, *Revolt in the North: Antrim and Down in 1798* (Dublin and London, 1960)
David Dickson, Dáire Keogh and Kevin Whelan (eds), *The United Irishmen* (Dublin, 1993)
Marianne Elliott, *Partners in Revolution: The United Irishmen and France* (London and New Haven, 1982); and *Wolfe Tone: Prophet of Irish Independence* (London and New Haven, 1989)
W.J. Fitzpatrick, *The Secret Service under Pitt* (London, 1892)
E.M. Johnston, *Great Britain and Ireland, 1760-1800* (Edinburgh, 1963)
John Keane, *Tom Paine: A Political Life* (London, 1995)
Dáire Keogh and Nicholas Furlong (eds), *The Mighty Wave: The 1798 Rebellion in Wexford* (Dublin, 1996)
Frank MacDermot, *Theobald Wolfe Tone: A Biographical Study* (London, 1939)
R.B. McDowell, *Ireland in the Age of Imperialism and Revolution, 1760-1801* (Oxford, 1979)
Mary McNeill, *The Life and Time of Mary Ann McCracken, 1760-1866* (Dublin, 1980, reprint Belfast 1988)
R.R. Madden, *The United Irishman, their Lives and Times*, 4 vols (London, 1857-60)
Thomas Pakenham, *The Year of Liberty* (London, 1969)
A.T.Q. Stewart, *A Deeper Silence: The Hidden Origins of the United Irishmen* (London, 1993); and *The Summer Soldiers: The 1798 Rebellion in Antrim and Down* (Belfast, 1995)
Theobald Wolfe Tone, *The Autobiography of Theobald Wolfe Tone*, ed. R. Barry O'Brien, 2 vols. (London, 1893)

THE FRENCH REVOLUTIONARY CALENDAR

In October 1793 the Convention of the French Republic abolished the Gregorian Calendar and replaced it with a new one which started from the foundation of the Republic on 22 September 1792. L'an 1 (Year 1) thus began on that date.

The year was divided into twelve 'months' of thirty days each, plus five extra days known as sans-culottides. Each month was divided not into weeks but into three décades of ten days.

The months of the new calendar were named (by the poet who devised it) after the characteristics of the natural year. Autumn consisted of Vendémiaire (the vintage month), Brumaire (the foggy) and Frimaire (the frosty). Winter consisted of Nivôse (the snowy), Pluviôse (the rainy) and Ventôse (the windy). Spring consisted of Germinal (seed time), Floréal (the flowery) and Prairial (the grassy). Summer consisted of Messidor (harvest), Thermidor (the warm month) and Fructidor (the month of fruit).

The Revolutionary calendar was abolished by Napoleon in 1806.

PREFACE

The 1790s were arguably the most important decade in modern Irish history, a turning point at which though in one sense history failed to turn, yet after which nothing was ever to be the same again. The year 1798 was the bloody climax of a violent period, and the seed-bed of both unionism and republican nationalism.

Any interpretation of 1798 that does not take proper account of the context in which events in Ireland took place will at best distort and at worst falsify what really happened. The Rebellion took place against the background of the French Revolution, and, more particularly, the Revolutionary War, in which Ireland was strategically vital to Britain's survival as a great power. The fact was that retaining control of Ireland was always more important to the British than 'liberating' it ever was to the French. To encourage their followers to think otherwise, and to gloss over the likely consequences of a successful French invasion, was at best naive of the leaders of the United Irishmen.

The savagery of 1798 - casualties were reckoned to amount to at least 20,000, perhaps even 30,000 - arose from the dangerously combustible mixture of local enmities this wider context ignited. In varying degrees for the people concerned, the Rebellion was a war of ideas, a struggle for national independence, a sectarian conflict, a rural jacquerie and a civil war. Though set in motion by Protestants and supported by many northern Presbyterians in particular, it was fought in its main theatre mainly by Catholics. Despite the large part played by Catholics of the Irish Militia in suppressing it, Catholics in the end got most of the blame. For everyone involved it was a tragedy: Catholic and Dissenter rebels experienced the bitterness of defeat, the Protestant Ascendancy saved their property but lost the 'independence' they had gained in 1782, sectarian divisions were sharpened rather than assuaged.

1 RIVAL POWERS

One of the most enduring features of relations between the great powers of Europe throughout the eighteenth century was the rivalry between Great Britain and France. In all the major European wars of the period - the War of the Spanish Succession, the War of the Austrian Succession, the Seven Years War - the two powers were on opposite sides, not only in Europe itself but also far away in North America, the West Indies, the Indian Ocean and India, where they were rivals for trade and colonies. Even in parts of the world not yet exploited by European powers - especially the great Pacific Ocean - they were rivals in exploration.

For most of the century, the hostility between the two powers was underpinned by differences in government and outlook. Until 1789, France was an absolute monarchy and a Catholic power; Great Britain prided itself on having a limited monarchy and was a Protestant power. Under the *ancien régime*, as it came to be called, the peasantry of France (the vast majority of her people) were oppressed by the feudal system; the people of Great Britain were comparatively free and on the whole better off.

In some significant respects Ireland, which was in theory a separate kingdom but whose monarch was also ruler of Great Britain, was an exception to these remarks. Because of its strategic location and peculiar history it had long been seen by any great power at war with Britain as a way of invading - or at least threatening to invade - by the back door. This was as true in the eighteenth century for France as it had been in the sixteenth for Spain.

From 1789, the French Revolution changed France and Franco-British relations a great deal, but in one respect at least things remained the same: when it came to war, Ireland remained a potential threat for Great Britain and a potential opportunity for France.

1 *George III (1738-1820)*

BY AGOSTINO CARLINI (C.1718-90)
PORTRAIT BUST, IN MARBLE, 80 CM HIGH, SIGNED AND DATED 1773
ROYAL ACADEMY, LONDON

George III (George William Frederick), born 4 June 1738 in London, the son of Frederick Louis, Prince of Wales and Augusta of Saxe-Gotha, was king of Great Britain and Ireland 1760-1820 and elector (from 1814 king) of Hanover, in one of the longest reigns in British history. During that time, Britain won an empire by her victory over France in the Seven Years War, lost another by the revolt of her American colonies, and emerged after a long struggle against Revolutionary and Napoleonic France as a leading power in Europe. He succeeded his grandfather, George II, as king in 1760. The following year he married a German princess, Charlotte Sophia of Mecklenburg-Strelitz. In the early years of his reign his well-intentioned but clumsy efforts to 'glory in the name of Briton' (as opposed to German) were badly received and exposed him and his first prime minister Bute - who encouraged rather than moderated his delusions - to the scurrilous attacks of the radical John Wilkes. When even the Peace of Paris, which triumphantly ended the Seven Years War against France and her allies in 1763, was criticised as like the peace of God in that it passed all understanding, Bute resigned. Tactless and inexperienced, George had difficulty in finding a suitable replacement for Bute until 1770, when Lord North became his prime minister.

One of the results of the complete defeat of the French in North America and the annexation of their colony in Canada was that Britain's American colonies no longer had so much to fear from the French and their Red Indian allies. The war had also created a financial crisis, but when British governments tried to make the colonists contribute to their share of the debt and meet the cost of governing them, by duties such as a Stamp Act (1765) and import taxes on commodities such as tea, there was increasing resistance.

The British parliament was determined to make them pay, and when George III identified with this policy he became hated by many colonists. The American War of Independence which followed went badly for the crown and its supporters in the end, especially after 1788 when France intervened on the side of the colonists. The continuation of the war long after the cause was lost was largely George's fault; for one thing, he argued, if the Americans were allowed to disobey, the Irish might be encouraged to follow their example. North was forced to resign in 1782. Subsequently he returned to office with the liberal Whig Charles James Fox (an inveterate critic of royal power and policies) as his coalition partner. At this stage George's spirits were so low that he contemplated abdicating. Yet within a year he had turned the tables on his enemies, dismissing Fox and North and appointing as prime minister William Pitt the Younger, aged only twenty-four and leader of a minority group in the Commons. In the general election of 1784 the country supported the King's action. With one short interval Pitt was to be prime minister till he died in 1806.

The stress and strain of governing, at which he worked hard, might in itself have caused the King's health to break down, especially when his sons added to his anxieties by leading dissolute lives. In 1788 George had the first outbreak of the madness that was eventually to overwhelm him. Modern research suggests that his 'madness' may have been caused by a rare disorder of the metabolism known as porphyria - though this diagnosis is not universally accepted by medical opinion. The King's illness caused a political crisis. If the Prince of Wales became regent, Pitt would be out and Fox in, so the two rivals for power battled over the extent of the regent's powers. In Ireland, a move to proclaim the Regent without delay and regardless of the outcome in England created a potential constitutional crisis. In the event, George suddenly recovered in 1789 and resumed his powers.

The outbreak of the French Revolution was at first generally welcomed throughout the British Isles, either from liberal conviction or the calculation that France would be seriously weakened as a power. Conservative doubts soon arose, however, and were enunciated brilliantly by Edmund Burke in *Reflections on the Revolution in France* (1790), which in turn stimulated Thomas Paine's famous statement of the democratic case in his *Rights of Man*, Part I (1791). The course of events in France made the British government, aristocracy and upper middle class increasingly fearful and hostile to the Revolution as a threat to monarchy and the established order in general. The execution of Louis XVI in January 1793 was followed shortly by the outbreak of war (declared by France). Most of Fox's followers deserted to Pitt in this national crisis, while the old king became popular as the symbol of the nation's determination to beat the old enemy.

Following the suppression of the rebellion in Ireland in 1798, Pitt moved to unite the British and Irish parliaments, and eventually did so in 1800. But he regarded Catholic emancipation as the necessary accompaniment. George III was persuaded that this proposal would break his coronation oath, and used all his personal prestige to have it defeated. Pitt resigned in 1801. When he returned to office in 1804 he had to promise not to raise the matter again. The Union thus got off to a bad start so far as Irish Catholics were concerned. George's baleful influence in this respect was underlined by his resistance to later proposals for some amelioration for Catholics. So long as he lived the question remained insoluble, despite a good deal of support from liberal opinion from time to time.

From 1811 George was permanently (and often violently) insane. The Prince of Wales was made regent and the old king was given into the custody of his wife. His last years were a kind of living death behind the barred windows of his quarters in Windsor Castle, where those who occasionally glimpsed his wild King Lear-like figure, white-bearded and wearing a purple dressing-gown, never forgot it. He died there in 1820.

Agostino Carlini was born at Genoa about 1718 and settled in England in the middle of the eighteenth century. His marble bust of George III was exhibited at the Royal Academy in 1773 and afterwards presented to the Academy. It was described in 1780 as 'a strong, expressive likeness'. It has an almost pugnacious appearance which accords well with the king's known obstinacy, and has been described by one authority as 'the finest sculptured portrait of that monarch'.

Sources: *Encyclopaedia Britannica* (15th edition).
John Brooke, *King George III* (1972).
Ida McAlpine and Richard Hunter, *George III and the Mad Business* (1969).
Marjorie Trusted, ' "A Man of Talent": Agostino Carlini (c.1718-1790), Parts I & II, Burlington Magazine, December 1992 and March 1993.

2 *Louis XVI (1754-93)*

By Antoine François Callet (1741-1823)
Musée National du Château de Versailles
Reproduction (photo Bridgeman Art Library)

Louis was the third son of the dauphin Louis and his consort Maria Josepha of Saxony. Known in his early years as the duc de Berry, he became heir to the throne on his father's death in 1765 and succeeded his grandfather Louis XV in May 1774. In 1770, aged sixteen, he married Marie-Antoinette, a year younger, daughter of the empress Maria Theresa of Habsburg. The marriage got off to a humiliating start, normal sexual relations proving impossible until Louis had an operation. Their first child - the Dauphin - was not born until 1785.

Louis was well-meaning if rather weak and lethargic, inclined to take refuge in times of crisis in his passion for hunting and his hobbies of clockmaking and masonry. It was his misfortune to come to the throne just when the *ancien régime* was falling apart from internal faction and financial collapse, the latter made worse by the cost of intervening in 1778 to help the American colonists free themselves from British rule. It was French aristocrats themselves who set off the revolution that was to destroy them, when they opposed essential reforms and forced the King to summon the States General (representing the clergy, nobles and commoners) in 1789. The Third Estate, given this opportunity, made the States General into a National Assembly and set about a sweeping programme of reform, in effect creating a limited constitutional monarchy. Incapable of grasping the opportunity of allying with the middle-class reformers, Louis listened to the reactionaries around him and defended the privileges of the upper orders. Instead of burning itself out, as he had hoped, the Revolution became increasingly radical. Louis's reluctance to accept such fundamental things as the Declaration of the Rights of Man and the ending of feudalism was one of the reasons for the royal family's forcible transfer from Versailles to Paris in October 1789. His credibility as a constitutional monarch was largely destroyed when he and his family fled from Paris in June 1791 and made for the frontier, only to be arrested at Varennes. Thereafter they were prisoners of the Revolution and Louis himself was more than ever dominated by Marie Antoinette. From the autumn of 1791 he pinned his hopes of rescue on foreign intervention, at the same time encouraging the dominant group in the Assembly, the Girondins, to make war on Austria, in the belief that France would lose. Though he swore to accept the new constitution of 1791 he secretly opposed it, again rejecting the advice of moderates.

The outbreak of war with Austria in April 1792 and the threat of the Austrian commander, the Duke of Brunswick, to destroy Paris if the royal family were endangered led to the seizure of the palace of the Tuileries by the people of Paris, the imprisonment of its royal occupants and (21 September 1792) to the proclamation of the French Republic. A search of the Tuileries uncovered a secret chest containing proof of counter-revolutionary intrigues. This sealed the king's fate. He was tried for treason before the Convention (as the republican assembly was called) under the name of Citizen Capet in January 1793, condemned to death and guillotined on 21 January. His dignified bearing during the trial and his courage on the scaffold made him a martyr for monarchy. The queen, after many indignities, was tried and executed on 16 October 1793. Their son, the dauphin, contracted tuberculosis of the bones in prison and died there in 1795 at the age of ten.

Antoine François Callet was one of the leading French historical and portrait painters of his day. In 1764 he won the Prix de Rome and in 1780 was elected to the Académie Royal. His portrait of Louis XVI, of which there are several versions, was regarded as his masterpiece. It shows the King in his royal robes with the regalia of kingship and wearing the Order of the Holy Ghost (St Esprit), the highest honour of the *ancien régime*.

Sources: *Encyclopaedia Britannica* (15th edition).
             E. Bénézit, *Dictionnaire des Peintres, Sculpteurs, Dessinateurs et Graveurs* (Paris,1976).

3 *The Death of General Wolfe*

BY EDWARD PENNY
ASHMOLEAN MUSEUM, OXFORD
REPRODUCTION

The painting shows Wolfe expiring in the moment of victory over the French under Montcalm, on the plateau outside Quebec, 13 September 1759. The fall of Quebec was the turning point in the war between Britain and France for control of

North America: at the end of the Seven Years War in 1763, the French ceded the whole of Canada.

James Wolfe (1727-59), though physically frail, was an intrepid soldier, whose death in the arms of victory at the age of thirty-two made him a national hero. His exploit at Quebec was celebrated in art and literature and in generations of school history books, most famously perhaps in the painting by Benjamin West. Penny's picture, painted in 1764, resembles West's in some respects but is probably more realistic.

Edward Penny (1714-91) was a successful painter of portraits and historical subjects. In 1768 he was one of the founding members of the Royal Academy and was appointed its first professor of painting.

4 North American powder horn, 1761

COW HORN, 21.5 CM LONG, INSCRIBED WITH MAPS AND OWNER'S NAME, DONAL MCCALUM, MONTREAL 1761.
ULSTER MUSEUM

In North America the French and British had long been in competition for the lucrative fur trade. During the Seven Years War both sides made use of local volunteers as well as regular troops. The owner of this gunpowder container, Donal McCalum, may have been a member of a local militia group serving in the garrison of Montreal (which had been captured from the French in 1760).

Such horns were used to carry gunpowder for priming flintlock rifles. This one has a wooden base, held in place by wooden pegs, and is closed by a cork and

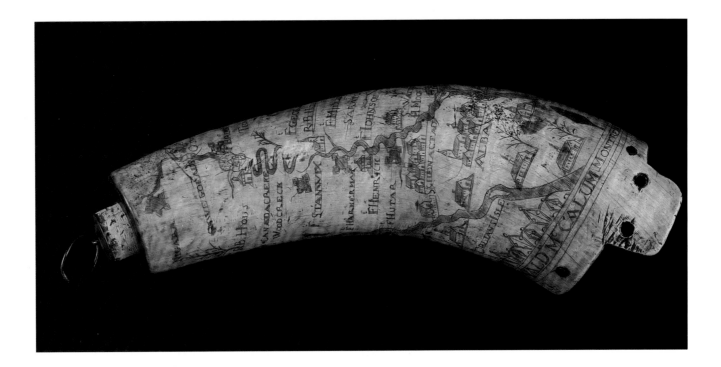

metal stopper. One side of the base has a longer portion which has been pierced with two holes to enable it to be slung from a belt or bandolier. Engraved on the horn is a view of New York and a map of the territory northward to the Canadian border with the forts on the Hudson and Mohawk rivers. As well as showing all the military forts along the route, there are illustrations of large houses with their owners' names alongside, indicating that McCalum was a seasoned traveller. This type of work on bone, horn or whale ivory, called scrimshaw, was the work of the owner. Scrimshaw horns were used throughout the eighteenth century, especially in Colonial America. They served the dual purpose of providing a necessary piece of military equipment along with a useful portable map of the surrounding countryside.

5 *Sir John Caldwell in Red Indian costume, 1780*

BY AN UNKNOWN ARTIST
NATIONAL MUSEUMS & GALLERIES ON MERSEYSIDE (KING'S REGIMENT COLLECTION)

Reproduction

Following the British annexation of Canada in 1763, the frontier region along the St Lawrence River and the Great Lakes was held by a string of forts garrisoned by British regiments. These regular troops, thinly scattered over hundreds of miles of wooded territory, were supplemented in time of war by local settler volunteers and by friendly Indian tribes. During the American War of Independence there was a good deal of fighting in the area, between the British forces and those of the colonists. The 8th (King's) Regiment served in Canada throughout the period from 1768 to 1785.

John Caldwell, from Castlecaldwell in County Fermanagh, was the son of Sir James Caldwell, Bart. Born in 1757, he joined the King's Regiment as an ensign in 1776 at Fort Niagara, where his uncle (also John) was its lieutenant-colonel. Moving on to Detroit, Caldwell became very interested in the adventurous business of liaising with the Indians, living with them for two hunting seasons and taking to

the strenuous open-air life of the frontier with enthusiasm. 'I own I never enjoy myself more nor my health better', he wrote home, 'than when on a voyage with a Bear Skin to sleep on and salt pork for breakfast ... Alliances with the Indians were fragile, however, and Caldwell eventually had to flee for his life, barely surviving after an arduous journey of hundreds of miles. When he finally returned home he took with him the birch-bark canoe he had used in his escape, his Indian costume, tomahawks and other mementoes. When he succeeded his father and settled down at Castlecaldwell, he built a Curiosity Room to house his collection.

Caldwell is shown holding in his left hand a tomahawk-pipe and in his right a wampum belt, consisting of strings of shell beads, bearing the representation of a tomahawk. Wampum was used as currency by the Indians but also had an important symbolic or spiritual significance. The pipe was used to signify peace. During the ceremony of smoking the pipe of peace, hatchets and other weapons were buried in the ground - hence the expression 'burying the hatchet'.

During the 1790s Caldwell played his part as a loyal landowner by taking a commission in the militia and raising a corps of yeomanry, known as the Belleek Yeoman Infantry or Loyal Erne Rangers, which served for a time in Connaught in the aftermath of the 1798 rebellion. He died in 1830.

Sources: David Boston, 'The Three Caldwells', in *The White Horse and Fleur de Lys* [King's Regt journal], vol. 3, no. 6 (June 1964).
John Cunningham, *A History of Castlecaldwell and its Families* (Enniskillen, 1980), ch. 12.

6 *Silver paperweight, incorporating an Irish gun money coin, commemorating the British victory over the French at Wandiwash in India.*

HEIGHT 7 CM, LENGTH 10.5 CM, WIDTH 6.5 CM
NATIONAL ARMY MUSEUM, LONDON

The Jacobite coin, part of the emergency coinage minted for James II in Ireland in 1689, was found on the battlefield of Wandiwash (or Wandewash) after the French and their Indian allies, led by Count Lally, had been defeated by the British and their Indian allies under Eyre Coote on 22 January 1760. The coin had presumably belonged to a soldier in one of the Irish regiments in the French service (Lally's own) which took part in the battle. The victory at Wandewash, following the earlier successes of Clive in Bengal and southern India virtually settled the issue between the two rival powers in India, which henceforth increasingly came under the sway of the British East India Company, backed by the British government.

Thomas Arthur Lally de Tollendal (1702-66), was colonel-proprietor of an Irish regiment in the French army formed in 1742. The son of an exiled Jacobite from County Galway, he made a great name for himself at the battle of Fontenoy in Flanders (1745), during the War of the Austrian Succession. At the outbreak of the Seven Years War in 1756 he was promoted to lieutenant-general and appointed commander of the French expedition which went to India in 1758, and governor of Pondicherry. Unfortunately the forces under his command were entirely inadequate to the task and despite his best efforts defeat was inevitable. He himself was made prisoner a year later when Pondicherry surrendered and was sent to England, where he remained in captivity till the end of the war in 1763.

Lally's imperious manner and lack of tact had alienated the native Indian princes allied to France, while his hatred of corruption had antagonised powerful French officials at home. With no friends at court, he was made the scapegoat for the loss of India and was accused of treason. His regiment in the Irish Brigade was disbanded. Foolishly, he insisted on returning to France in 1764 to clear his name, only to be

11

arrested and thrown into prison. Two years later, in 1766, he was tried, convicted and beheaded. The treatment of Lally - an awkward but entirely loyal and honourable man - was one of the major scandals of the pre-revolutionary regime in France. He was partially vindicated in 1778 through the efforts of his son, an event commemorated by the painter Jacques-Louis David in a picture which shows the Marquis Trophime Gerard de Lally-Tollendal unveiling a bust of his father; one hand holds a document bearing the legend 'Mon Père n'était pas coupable' (My father was not to blame). Not until 1929, however, was his degradation officially erased and his name and rank restored to the rolls of the French army.

Sources: *Encyclopaedia Britannica* (11th edition).

7 *Sword of honour commemorating the siege of Seringapatam, 1799*

MADE BY GREEN & WARD, LONDON
HILT AND GUARD OF GOLD, HALLMARKED, DECORATED WITH ENAMELS AND SET WITH DIAMONDS; TRIANGULAR-SECTION BLADE BLUED AND GILT; SHARKSKIN SCABBARD WITH GOLD FITTINGS; OVERALL LENGTH 99 CM.
MRS N. A. WHITTLEY

The disc guard of this splendid presentation sword is inscribed on the underneath: *FROM THE East India Company TO LIEUT^T COLONEL BARRY CLOSE Adjutant General to the Army under the Command of LIEUT^T GENERAL HARRIS in Testimony of their Sense of the ABILITY ZEAL and ENERGY which he displayed during the Brilliant & Successfull Campaign in MYSORE in 1799.*

The hilt, pommel and disc guard are all decorated with pairs of scenes, devices and inscriptions which are composed of coloured enamels and surrounded by small diamonds. The pommel, which is topped by a large solitaire, has Close's initials and crest opposite to a trophy of arms. On the grip are the arms of Close and those of the East India Company, with sprays of brilliants at the base. The inside of the disc guard has two views of Seringapatam, taken from Home's *Select Views in Mysore, the Country of Tippoo Sahib*, published in London in 1794. On the knuckleguard are the inscriptions *Seringapatam* and *May 4 1799*.

Barry Close, born in 1754 into a family of Yorkshire origin which had settled

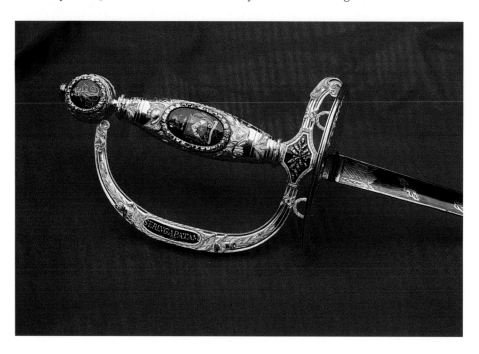

in County Armagh in the seventeenth century, went to India in 1771 as a cadet in the army of the East India Company. In 1780-82 he served as a subaltern at Tellicherry during the long siege of that town by France's ally Hyder Ali, sultan of Mysore. Hyder Ali's son, Tippoo Sultan (or Sahib), who had been instructed by his father's French military advisers, succeeded to the throne of Mysore in 1782. He remained a thorn in the side of the British and intrigued with the French whenever possible. In 1790-92 under Cornwallis, Close took part in the first siege of Seringapatam, Mysore's fortress capital, after which Tippoo was forced to cede half of his territory and pay an enormous fine. At the siege of Seringapatam in 1799, when Tippoo was finally defeated and killed, Close distinguished himself as adjutant-general in the army of General Harris. As well as his share of the prize money, Close received £4,000 for acting on the commission which arranged the annexation of Mysore. The sword presented to him by the court of directors cost £300, a considerable sum at the time. Close was subsequently appointed British Resident at Mysore, then at the court of the ruler of Poona. He returned to England in 1811, after an absence of forty years, a major-general and soon a baronet, but the climate of India had broken his health and he died in 1813.

Sources: *Dictionary of National Biography* (DNB).

8 *Seringapatam medal, 1799*

DESIGNED BY C.H. KÜCHLER, MADE IN BIRMINGHAM BY MATTHEW BOULTON.
GOLD, 48 MM DIAMETER, WITH ORIGINAL BOX.
MR NEVILLE WHITTLEY.

Obverse: The British Lion attacking the Tiger of Mysore; in exergue the date IV MAY MDCCXCIX.
Reverse: The attack on the fortress of Seringapatam, showing a breach in the wall and a scaling party.

Issued in 1808, five types of the medal were produced in England, of which 30 were gold, 185 silver gilt, 850 silver, 5,000 bronze and 45,000 pewter. Another set, slightly smaller (45 mm), was issued in Calcutta in gold (83) and silver (2,786). All the medals were issued unnamed, though some were engraved by the recipients themselves.

The medal was awarded for the siege and capture of Seringapatam, the immensely strong island fortress of Tippoo Sahib, sultan of Mysore, who followed his father Hyder Ali in being an inveterate opponent of British power in India and a friend to the French. (Among the loot from Seringapatam, and now in the Victoria and Albert Museum, was a life-size automaton of a tiger devouring a British soldier with realistic sound effects). Seringapatam had been besieged twice before and Tippoo had been forced to cede nearly half of his territory. In 1799 he was attacked by the army of the East India Company (consisting of European troops and sepoys) because of his hostile movements and his negotiations with the French. The British left wing was commanded by Lt Col. Arthur Wellesley, later Duke of Wellington. The prize-money amounted to the enormous sum of £1,140,000, of which the commander-in-chief got £100,000, generals £10,000 each, colonels £4,300, lieutenant-colonels £2,600, majors £1,700, captains £860, lieutenants £430, warrant officers £105, sergeants £14 and privates £7.

Source: DNB.

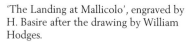

9 *Two volumes illustrating the Pacific voyages of Captain Cook (c.1785)*

PAGE SIZE 58 X 88 CM
ULSTER MUSEUM

These two volumes, consisting of maps and engraved illustrations pasted in, cover the three epic voyages of Captain James Cook in the Pacific between 1769 and 1776 in the *Endeavour, Resolution* and *Discovery*. The volume covering his first two voyages has Hodges's portrait of Cook engraved by Basire as its frontispiece, along with seventy plates which come from the text volumes of *A Voyage to the Pacific*, Vols I and II written by Captain J. Cook, Vol. III by Captain J. King (London, 1784).

The other volume has two charts and sixty-one plates. Both carry the bookplate of William Perceval Esq., who was evidently a member of the prominent Anglo-Irish family of that name from Temple House, County Sligo.

The engravings, produced from first-hand illustrations by the artists John Webber, Sidney Parkinson and William Hodges, who accompanied Cook on his voyages, provide a visual record of the inhabitants of the Pacific islands and their weapons, tools, ornaments and customs. The series of portraits by William Hodges of men and women in the Marquesas, Tongan and New Caledonian islands, in the first atlas, are the most naturalistic; other illustrations were idealised or prettified during the engraving process to conform to the artistic conventions of the time. Cook's interest, as a naval officer, in the boats used by the islanders is reflected in the splendid and accurate illustrations of Marquesan, Tongan and Tahitian canoes.

The second volume contains a chart of the Southern Hemisphere 'showing the tracks of some of the most distinguished Navigators of his Majesty's Navy'. It also contains a chart of the north-west coast of America and the north-east coast of Asia.

At the start of his career Cook took part in the Seven Years War between the French and British, seeing action in the Bay of Biscay and serving in North America, where his chart of the navigable channel in the St Lawrence River downstream

'The Landing at Mallicolo', engraved by H. Basire after the drawing by William Hodges.

from Quebec was instrumental to the success of General Wolfe's landing and the defeat of the French garrison there in 1759.

Despite earlier voyages of discovery by Dutch, Portuguese and French explorers (notably Bougainville) it was really Cook's three voyages that opened up the Pacific Ocean to the outside world. His abilities as a navigator and cartographer were quite exceptional, and acknowledged as such even by his rivals. By the end of his second voyage, he had discovered many new islands and had proved that there was no great continent in the Southern Pacific between Australia and America. In just five and a half months he was able to draw an extremely accurate map of the previously uncharted North and South Islands of New Zealand.

Cook was a humane and kindly man with, for his day, an uncharacteristic appreciation of and sympathetic regard for the native populations he encountered. He was killed in 1779 by natives of the Hawaiian Islands.

10 *Louis XVI giving instructions to La Pérouse, 29 June 1785*

By N.A. MONSIAU (1754-1837)
MUSÉE NATIONAL DU CHÂTEAU DE VERSAILLES
REPRODUCTION (PHOTO BRIDGEMAN ART LIBRARY)

Jean-François de Galaud, comte de La Pérouse (1741-c.1788), was the second great French explorer of the Pacific during the eighteenth century (the first was Bougainville, who in 1768 discovered the largest of the Solomon Islands, named after him, as was the plant bougainvillaea). Like most serving officers of the French royal navy, La Pérouse had experience of fighting the British in the successive wars between the two powers. In the Seven Years War, aged eighteen, he was wounded and captured when the ship in which he was a midshipman was taken by Admiral Hawke; and in 1782, during the American War, he made a name for himself by capturing and destroying two British forts in the Hudson's Bay area of Canada. In

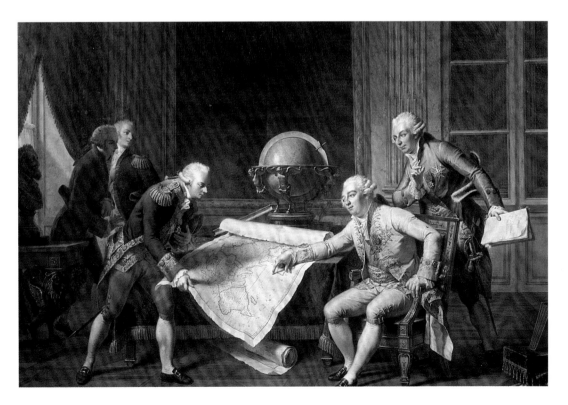

1785 he was given command of an expedition of two ships - his own *La Boussole* and another named *L'Astrolabe* - with the main object of discovering the North-West Passage from the Pacific side, something Captain James Cook had failed to achieve on his last voyage. As well as this he was instructed to explore the north-west coasts of America and the north-east coasts of Asia, the seas off China and Japan, the Solomon Islands and Australia; and he was to collect information about the prospects for fur trading in North America and whale fishing in the South Seas.

Having reached Alaska the following summer, La Pérouse was soon driven from the area by bad weather and had to abandon hope of exploring the elusive (and, without a modern icebreaker, illusive) Passage. Sailing south he visited the Hawaiian Islands, before crossing to Asia, where he visited Macao (Portuguese) and the Philippines (Spanish) and explored the area of modern Vladivostock and Kamchatka (Russian). The strait between Sakhalin and northern Japan is still named after him. Turning south again he arrived at the Samoan Islands, where the captain of the *Astrolabe* and some of his crew were murdered by the warlike natives. The expedition reached the British colony of Botany Bay in Australia in January 1788. His last letter was written from there early the following month, just before he set sail again and disappeared without trace. The mystery of La Pérouse's fate was not solved till nearly forty years later, when the Irish sailor Peter Dillon found the wreckage of the *Boussole* and the *Astrolabe* on the reefs of Vanikoro, to the north of the New Hebrides. Dillon's *Narrative ... of a Voyage in the South Seas for the Discovery of the Fate of La Pérouse* was published in London in 1829, in itself an indication of the fascination and importance Pacific exploration held for both of the great European maritime powers during this period. Fortunately for posterity the records of the earlier part of La Pérouse's great cruise - his achievements in the northern Pacific - had been sent overland from Kamchatka to Paris, while those of the trip from Kamchatka to Australia had been sent home by a British ship. They were published in Paris in four volumes in 1797.

Nicholas André Monsiau (or Monsiaux) was a painter of historical subjects who exhibited at the Paris Salon between 1787 and 1833. This painting, done in 1817 after the Bourbon monarchy had been restored in France, reconstructs the scene at Versailles in 1785 when Louis XVI - accompanied by Marshal de Castries, his Minister of Marine - gave La Pérouse his instructions, shortly before the expedition set out.

Sources: *Encyclopaedia Britannica* (11th edition).
               Bénézit, *Dictionnaire*.

11 *Pair of scrimshaw teeth with royal portraits, late eighteenth or early nineteenth century*

18 CM HIGH
ULSTER MUSEUM

Scrimshaw was a favourite pastime of British and American whalers. The man who did such carving was called a scrimshander. Some practitioners signed their work with their initials. The design was usually inscribed with a sail needle and then darkened by rubbing in a mixture of oil and lampblack. The teeth and jawbones of the sperm whales were the most common material but walrus and narwhal tusk, porpoise jaws and baleen from the mouth of the bowhead, right, humpback and grey whales were also used.

These two sperm whale scrimshaw teeth have full-length portraits of George III (1760-1820) and his wife Queen Charlotte, holding a crown and sceptre. The illustration of the King seems to be based on a print by Metz after Heath dated

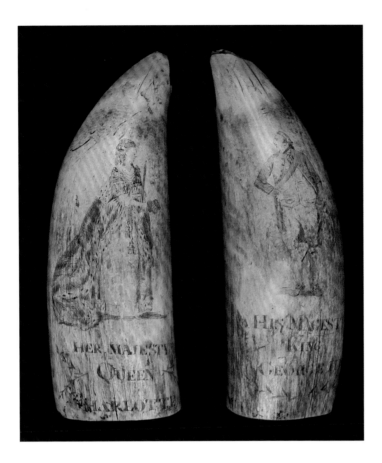

15 March 1783, which was published by J. Cooke in Raymond's *History of England*. If the portraits are contemporary with George III these would be of very early date for sperm whale scrimshaw.

On the reverse side of George's portrait is a drawing of a man gazing at a woman lying on her side, holding a baby, with the inscription *I found her pale and without strength at the side of the spring* and *Cain my first born lying on her bosom*.

On the reverse of Charlotte's portrait is a drawing of one man kneeling in front of another, who stands beside a tree with the inscription *He threw himself on the earth and cryed forgive me forgive me O my father*. Such Biblical references are unusual.

12 *The Jennings Cup, 1760*

SILVER, 34 CM HIGH; MAKER'S MARK R+C [ROBERT CALDERWOOD]
ULSTER MUSEUM

Inscribed: To Lieutenant Colonel JOHN JENNINGS
Of the Sixty Second Regiment of Foot,
In Grateful Remembrance
Of the Gallant Defence he made at CARRICKFERGUS
On the 21st Feb: M, DCC, LX.
When attacked by the FRENCH under General Flobert,
This Cup is presented
By the Inhabitants of the Town of BELFAST

The Jennings Cup commemorates what was not just a notable event in the local history of County Antrim but also an occasion of some significance for later developments in Ireland, as well as illustrating how, in any war of the period, France could threaten to invade Ireland as a means of attacking Great Britain.

Though Flobert, the military commander of the French force which suddenly appeared off Carrickfergus on 21 February 1760, alone is named in the inscription on the cup, the naval commander is much better known to history. François Thurot (1727-60) was born in Nuits St-Georges in Burgundy and first apprenticed to a surgeon. The legend that he was really an Irishman named Farrell is nonsense. In 1774 he took service on a French privateer ship, only to be captured and imprisoned in England. He escaped the following year and managed to cross the Channel in a small boat. This feat brought him to the attention of a powerful patron, the duc de Belle-Isle, who gave him a proper naval education. When war with England broke out again in 1756 Thurot became a highly successful privateer, preying on English shipping (he captured no fewer than sixty prizes in one year) in the Baltic, the North Sea and around the coast of Ireland with his squadron of frigates. These activities made his fame as well as his fortune, and he became a popular hero in France. He was then appointed to lead a commando-style raid on the British coast involving six ships and an army of 1,500 men, a diversion to cover a more serious invasion that was planned. The troops were to be led by Brigadier Flobert, a seasoned soldier in his fifties who had commanded the Genoese army. While at sea everyone was to obey Thurot, who would also decide the time and place of landing, on land Flobert was to be in charge. Unfortunately, from the outset the two men detested each other.

Early in October 1759 the expedition at last slipped out of Dunkirk and

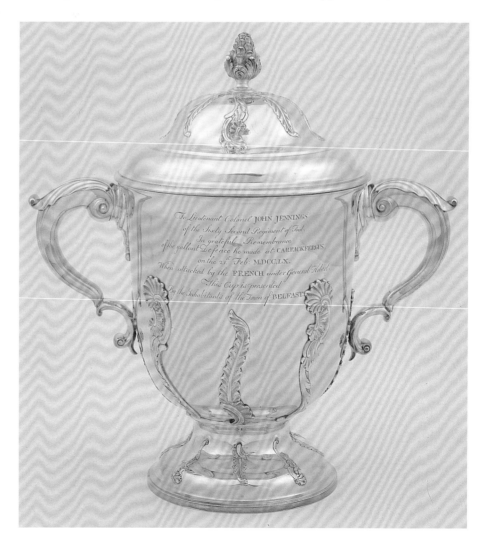

disappeared into the North Sea. Here Thurot's usual luck deserted him. Storms dispersed his fleet, and some ships were damaged and had to return home. By January 1760 he was left with only three ships - his own *Maréchal de Belle-Isle*, a frigate of forty-eight guns, and the two smaller vessels *Blonde* and *Terpsichore* - and 600 soldiers. On 20 February the three French ships entered the North Channel and Thurot told Flobert they would make for Carrickfergus Bay and land at dawn to attack Belfast. Flobert agreed, but only if Carrickfergus was taken first.

Not until the French actually landed did the garrison of Carrickfergus realise who they were. (As usual in such circumstances, in order to achieve surprise, the invading ships flew enemy colours, a tactic regarded as perfectly legitimate by both sides.) Colonel Jennings had only 200 men in the Castle, the rest of the 62nd under Major-General Strode being stationed in Belfast. Furthermore the Castle was partly in ruins and not a single cannon was mounted. The mayor of Carrickfergus, Willoughby Chaplin, insisted nevertheless that the town should be defended and Jennings was reluctantly obliged to agree. The vanguard of the French, led by Flobert, tried to rush the Castle, attempting to smash the gates. Here Flobert got a bullet in the leg. The main French force advanced more slowly. By the time it reached the Castle, Jennings - faced with a threat to destroy the town if he did not surrender - had already capitulated on honourable terms. The garrison would become prisoners of war but could stay in Ireland on parole; the French would not burn or plunder the town; any French wounded left behind would not be treated as prisoners of war but would be returned to France as soon as possible. These conditions were scrupulously observed. The French had lost nineteen men and had thirty wounded; the defenders lost only four with twelve wounded.

Flobert then refused to attack Belfast, as Thurot wanted to do. Instead he proposed to demand provisions from the Belfast authorities, under the threat of destroying the town. This demand was conveyed by a local Presbyterian minister, who was accompanied by a French officer under a flag of truce. Belfast was in a panic, some citizens sending their families to the country and burying their valuables. General Strode called out the militia and sent an urgent message to Dublin, where it was thought that the Carrickfergus landing might be the prelude to a full-scale French invasion. Troop reinforcements were sent north. In the meantime companies of Volunteers had sprung to arms all over Antrim, Down and Armagh and had assembled to bar any French advance on Belfast. Faced with this, and anxious to get away before British warships caught up with him, Thurot re-embarked the French troops and sailed away on 27 February. Shortly afterwards, his ships were engaged by three British frigates off the Isle of Man. After a sharp fight, in which Thurot himself was killed, the French surrendered. Thurot was buried at sea. His body was later washed ashore on the Mull of Galloway, where it was identified by his uniform and a snuff-box with his name engraved on it.

The Volunteer army of 1760, though not in the end needed to do any fighting, was not forgotten. This helps to explain why eighteen years later, when the threat of French invasion recurred, Volunteer companies were raised and organised so quickly.

Sources: A.T.Q. Stewart, *A Deeper Silence: The Hidden Origins of the United Irishmen* (London, 1993), ch.2.

2 THE PROTESTANT ASCENDANCY

Under the Penal Laws enacted by the Irish Parliament in the reigns of William III and Anne, all political power and government appointments - both national and local - were reserved for members of the established church, the Church of Ireland. Both Catholics and Protestant Dissenters (mostly Presbyterians) were excluded and discriminated against by the Test Act of 1704. In addition Catholics were seriously disadvantaged in such vital matters as the ownership and inheritance of landed property, the right to bear arms and the right (if qualified) to vote for MPs and sit in Parliament. Both of the non-Anglican groups were obliged to pay tithes to support the established church.

So far as its constitution was concerned, Ireland was in theory a separate kingdom. It had the same ruler as Great Britain but a Parliament of its own in Dublin. The government was run from Dublin Castle by the King's representative, the lord lieutenant or viceroy, who was appointed by the prime minister at Westminster and who appointed the officials. This remained the case even after 1782, when the Irish Parliament became 'independent' as a result of the American War of Independence and irresistible pressure from the Volunteer movement. Grattan's Parliament, as it became known, after the Irish politician who had played a large part in achieving it, still represented only Protestants and remained a corrupt institution, easily bribable by the Castle administration, and usually opposed to reforming itself. With few exceptions, members of the Ascendancy were content to enjoy their privileged position. The Revolution in France and the spread of radical ideas were to make most of them even more opposed to reform and more inclined to value the British connection.

The Rebellion of 1798 gave them a great fright. When it was over, most of them accepted, if they did not welcome, the Union, even though it heralded the end of the Ascendancy itself.

13 *Simon, first Earl Harcourt (1714-77)*

ATTRIBUTED TO ROBERT HUNTER
OIL ON CANVAS, 280 x 178 CM FRAMED
DUBLIN CORPORATION: DUBLIN CIVIC PORTRAIT COLLECTION

Harcourt was lord lieutenant of Ireland 1772-76, following Lord Townshend. As a young courtier he made a favourable impression on King George II, attending him at the battle of Dettingen (1743), the last occasion when a king of England led his troops in person. In 1751-2 he acted as governor to the young Prince of Wales - the future George III - and later was his envoy in the negotiations with Mecklenburg-Strelitz which led to the king's marriage with Princess Charlotte in 1761. Following a spell in Paris as ambassador (1768-72), he was sent to Dublin as lord lieutenant. His predecessor Townshend had been the first to reside full-time in Dublin, instead of going there only during the parliamentary session, a change of practice insisted on by George III himself. As lord lieutenant Harcourt at first supported a proposal to tax Irish absentee landowners, proposed by the Patriot party in the Irish Parliament, but later -when it became apparent that too many powerful interests in England were opposed - skilfully achieved the rejection of the move in the Irish

Commons. When the outbreak of hostilities in the North American colonies from 1775 caused the withdrawal of troops from Ireland, Harcourt successfully opposed a proposal from Lord North's government to bring in German mercenaries in their place. He also created many new peers to bolster support for his administration in the general election of 1776. In 1777, not long after his retirement, he died at his home in Oxfordshire, Nuneham Park, when trying to rescue his dog from a well.

The lord lieutenant (or viceroy) was the head of the whole Irish administration, with powers - as his patent of appointment put it - 'to do all acts which the king himself might or could do if he were present there in his proper person'. In practice these wide powers were exercised under the close supervision of the prime minister and cabinet at Westminster, who gave him the directions of the king or the government and bombarded him with advice and instructions. Nevertheless, the viceroy was the key figure in Irish politics and society, responsible for the day-to-day administration of the entire country, for managing the Irish Parliament, and for carrying out important ceremonial duties. On state occasions he was escorted by the Battle Axe Guards, the Irish equivalent of the Yeomen of the Guard. The occasions over which he presided - state functions of various kinds, the viceregal court, balls, military reviews - were the most important in the social calendar of the capital, and he was expected to provide lavish hospitality. From the formation of the Order of St Patrick in 1783 the viceroy was also *ex officio* its grand master.

This fine portrait of Harcourt in his robes of office, dated 1777, was for many years ascribed to Thomas Hudson, one of the leading English portrait painters of the mid-eighteenth century. Dublin city records show that a copy of a portrait of Harcourt was commissioned in that year by the lord mayor, William Dunne, to hang in the Mansion House. Hudson had retired from painting in 1767, however, and cannot have been the artist of this portrait. The original, which belonged to the Harcourt family and hung in the dining-room at Nuneham, and of which this picture is a copy, was painted by Robert Hunter (or the head and shoulders by Hunter and the remainder by William Doughty). This copy is also likely to be by Hunter. Other, half-length versions exist in the National Gallery of Ireland and the Ulster Museum.

Hunter, born sometime in the 1720s and still alive in 1803, was 'born in Ulster' according to a contemporary. He flourished as a portrait painter in Ireland from the early 1750s to the early 1780s. The fact that he worked all his life in Ireland limited his fame, but his contemporaries had a high opinion of him and a modern authoritative judgement is that he was 'for 30 years the most important painter of the Irish establishment' *(Painters of Ireland)*.

Sources: Anne Crookshank and The Knight of Glin, *The Painters of Ireland c.1660-1920* (1978)
            DNB.
            R.B. McDowell, 'Ireland in 1800', in *New History of Ireland*, IV (Oxford, 1986),
            ch. XX.
            Eileen Black (private communication).

14 *Court Sword, c.1770*

BY THOMAS GRAY OF LONDON
100 CM OVERALL LENGTH, WITH SCABBARD
MR NEVILLE WHITTLEY

The hilt and guard of this sword are a fine example of decorative cut-steel work of the kind produced by the best London makers for ceremonial swords of the late eighteenth century.

15(a) *Man's suit of satin with floral embroidery, c. 1775-80*

LENGTH FROM NECK TO HEM - 112 CM
ULSTER MUSEUM

This suit, probably worn by the second Earl of Belvedere, is a good example of the fine clothing worn on formal occasions by the Anglo-Irish nobility during the late eighteenth century. The suit comprises coat and breeches. The beautiful and subtle colour of the fabric, probably Lyon silk, is enhanced by the lavish embroidery, which is oriental in inspiration and may even have been worked in China. It was not unusual for cut-out costume pieces to be sent to the East for embroidery and then re-imported for making up.

The coat has a stand collar and a slim-fitting cut. It closes with only two hooks, which are most likely not original. The large embroidered buttons are a purely decorative feature at the front edge and can also be seen at the back vents. The coat is lined in the body with cream satin and interlined with cotton wool. Flannel lines the sleeves. The breeches are of typical cut, with a small fall opening. The knee bands are embroidered, as are the buttons at the leg openings.

An outfit such as this would be worn for formal, court wear, with a powdered wig. The wig was first covered with pomatum paste, to which the powder could stick. Traces of the pomatum can still be seen at the back neck of the coat.

15(b) *Open robe and petticoat of ivory raised and figured silk with brocaded coloured flowers, and ribbons and leaves of gold thread. Fabric and original dress c.1755-58, altered 1770s.*

LENGTH FROM NECK TO HEM 153 CM
ULSTER MUSEUM

The fine silk of this outfit was probably woven in Spitalfields, London. As was the custom when such valuable fabric was involved, the dress was remodelled over the years. It has a sack back, where the fabric falls in folds straight from the back of the neck to the hem, and its last alteration was to a 'polonaise', a fashion of the 1770s. Silk loops on the underside of the skirt fasten to gold lace and sequin buttons at the bottom of the outside of the pocket slits, thereby ruching up the skirt of the robe into bunches.

The cuffs are trimmed with gold lace, and the petticoat with meandering panels of pinked ruched fabric. The bodice is lined with coarse linen, and the hem with cream silk. The sewing of the dress is surprisingly crude - all the easier to unpick, when the time for remodelling came around.

The robe and petticoat were probably worn by Jane, Countess of Lanesborough, born 1737, the only daughter of Robert Rochfort, first Earl of Belvedere. He was notorious for having imprisoned his adulterous wife on his estate near Mullingar for thirty years, till his death in 1774, when her son released her.

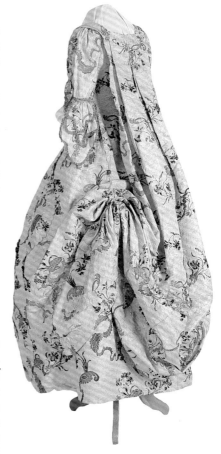

16 *Freedom box of the City of Londonderry, presented to the Bishop of Derry, 1768*

BY BARTHOLOMEW STOKES, DUBLIN 22 CT GOLD, HALLMARKED 1768
DIAMETER 7 CM, HEIGHT 3 CM, WEIGHT 4 OZ.
ULSTER MUSEUM

The box is round, with a slightly domed lid. It is engraved with three scenes in rococo scrolled cartouches - the arms of the City, a bridge and a coal-mining scene. It was presented to Frederick Augustus Hervey, Bishop of Derry and later Earl of Bristol, when he was made a Freeman of the City late in 1768, a year after his appointment as bishop. The engraved bridge and coal-mining scene both refer to projects he had immediately adopted - a bridge across the Foyle to replace the ferry from the Waterside (eventually built in wood in 1790 by the American firm of Lemuel Cox and Thompson of Boston and opened by the Earl Bishop himself) and his search to find and mine coal in his diocese. The box is inscribed on the underside in Latin which translates as follows:

> To that most reverend and very honourable man, Frederick, Bishop
> of Derry, most passionate champion and defender of the common
> good, chiefly in earnestly promoting the commerce and public welfare
> of the city, this box, containing the freedom of the city, is given,
> consigned and dedicated by the Corporation and people of
> Londonderry as a token of gratitude for favours received.

> 4th August 1768.

Hervey, an able and energetic, if vain and eccentric, figure in Irish life and politics during the late eighteenth century, typically came of an English noble family. He was an enthusiastic Volunteer, supported Catholic emancipation, political reform and the abolition of tithes, and was a notable builder of churches and palaces. The great house he built at Ballyscullion is long gone but the ruins of his palace at Downhill can still be seen, along with the charming cliff-top Mussenden Temple in the grounds (National Trust). As well as building the spire of the Protestant cathedral in Derry he contributed toward the cost of the Catholic chapel in Long Tower Street.

Hervey was born in 1730 at Ickworth in Suffolk, the third son of John Lord Hervey. As a younger son he was expected to make his way in the world and trained for the law before taking holy orders in 1754. He failed to find preferment in England but after he became George III's chaplain in 1763 and his brother the Earl of Bristol became lord lieutenant of Ireland, he was appointed Bishop of Cloyne in County Cork in

1767. The following year, he was translated to the much richer diocese of Derry as soon as it became vacant, a rival candidate put forward by a new lord lieutenant being overruled by the king himself. In 1779 he succeeded the second of his elder brothers and became Earl of Bristol. He remained Bishop of Derry for the rest of his life. His last years were largely spent travelling on the Continent and he died in Italy in 1803. His body was brought home and buried at Ickworth. The nineteenth-century historian Lecky summed him up sternly as follows:

> He appears to have been a man of respectable learning and of real talent, sincerely attached to his adopted country, and on questions of religious disqualification greatly in advance of most of his contemporaries; but he was at the same time utterly destitute of the distinctive virtues of a clergyman, and he was one of the most dangerous politicians of his time. Vain, impetuous, and delighting in display, with an insatiable appetite for popularity, and utterly reckless about the consequences of his acts, he exhibited, though an English peer and an Irish bishop, all the characteristics of the most irresponsible adventurer.

Sources: *DNB.*
           Webb, *Compendium of Irish Biography.*
           Peter Rankin, *Irish Building Ventures of the Earl Bishop of Derry* (1972).

17 *Archbishop the Hon. William Stuart (1755-1822)*

ATTRIBUTED TO ADAM BUCK
PASTEL, 25 X 22.5 CMS
ULSTER MUSEUM (ARMAGH MUSEUM COLLECTION)

William Stuart was Archbishop of Armagh and primate of the Church of Ireland from 1800 to 1822. He was typical of eighteenth-century archbishops, who were appointed by the crown, in being English (though in his case with Scottish antecedents) rather than Irish (or Anglo-Irish) and in being well-connected. Stuart was the fifth son of John Stuart, third Earl of Bute, George III's first minister in the early days of his reign. Educated at Winchester and St John's College, Cambridge, he entered the church and was appointed vicar of Luton in 1774. James Boswell,

who introduced Stuart to his friend Samuel Johnson, described him as 'being with the advantages of high birth, learning, travel, and elegant manners, an exemplary parish priest in every respect'. He was in fact a worthy if undistinguished cleric. Good behaviour and good connections led to his appointment as Bishop of St David's in Wales in 1793. From there he was translated to Armagh.

As primate he was also, *ex officio*, prelate of the Order of St Patrick. This attractive portrait shows him wearing his Prelate's badge, the very symbol of Protestant ascendancy in church and state.

He died in London on 6 May 1822 after accidentally poisoning himself by swallowing a draught of embrocation in mistake for medicine. He was buried at Luton park in Bedfordshire.

Adam Buck (1759-1833), to whom the portrait is attributed, was the son of a Cork silversmith. He produced miniatures in Dublin before moving in 1795 to London, where he had a very successful career as a portraitist and genre painter.

Sources: *DNB*.
             Anne Crookshank and the Knight of Glin, *Painters of Ireland*

18 *Regalia of the Most Illustrious Order of St Patrick*

ULSTER MUSEUM

This order of knighthood was established in 1783 as a means by which the Dublin Castle administration could reward and assure the continued support of important members of the Irish nobility, to whose ranks membership was confined through almost all its history. The date of foundation is significant: the Order can be seen

as another indication of the growing administrative independence and national spirit manifested the same year by the Volunteers and the incorporation of the Bank of Ireland. There was always considerable emphasis on the Irish nature of the Order, which was equivalent to the English Most Noble Order of the Garter and the Scottish Most Ancient and Most Noble Order of the Thistle, and third in precedence after them. Knights' robes at first were made from Irish poplin and, initially at least, Irish jewellers were commissioned to make insignia. The first installation was marked by almost hysterical enthusiasm in Dublin. The political complexion of the institution is emphasised by the symbolism of a collar consisting of harps and roses joined by knots of friendship, and the fact that the lord lieutenant was *ex officio* Grand Master and the Protestant Archbishop of Armagh Prelate.

Almost nothing survives of the Order from the eighteenth century, but many items of regalia retained the same approximate style throughout its history. The four shown here are:

Collar of seven roses joined by fourteen knots to six harps. Worn by the Earl of Shaftesbury.

Top, Grand Master's Badge, worn by Earl Talbot, lord lieutenant 1817-19.

Centre left, Gold Knight's Badge, thought to have belonged to the Marquis of Sligo. Later badges were oval and enamelled, but this is the original form, though dating from 1818.

Centre right, Prelate's Badge, 1819.

19 *The Kildare Toilet Service c.1720-26*

BY DAVID WILLAUME
ULSTER MUSEUM

The twenty-eight pieces of this splendid toilet service were commissioned by Robert FitzGerald, nineteenth Earl of Kildare, as a gift to his wife Mary on the birth of their third and surviving son, the future Duke of Leinster. David Willaume was a distinguished Huguenot goldsmith who was made a freeman of the Goldsmiths Company in 1693 and set up his workshops in Pall Mall. From the late 1690s to the first quarter of the 1700s he was much patronised by the rich and titled in society because of the skill and design of his work.

The service was commissioned in 1720 and took over two years to complete. The formal stylised construction of the silver gilt caskets and boxes is sparingly embellished with simple gadrooning and applied motifs. Beautifully engraved arms depict the family crest with the motif of a chained monkey and the motto 'Crom a Boo', the ancient war cry of the FitzGeralds.

The tradition of the levée in the eighteenth century was originally a French fashion and involved the entertainment of guests during the process of dressing the lady of the house. The porringers contained liquid foods such as possets, presented on the salvers, while the boxes and pincushion stored pins and accessories for the costume. Perfumes and lotions were kept in the flanks, and whisks and brushes then removed the powder and cosmetics from the completed ensemble.

The twentieth Earl of Kildare was created Duke of Leinster in 1766. He continued his family's tradition of grand patronage by commissioning the silver gilt Leinster Dinner Service, which consisted of 240 pieces.

20 *Arthur, 5th Earl of Donegall (1739-99)*

BY THOMAS GAINSBOROUGH
OIL ON CANVAS, 232 x 152 CM
ULSTER MUSEUM

Arthur Chichester, who inherited the estates and titles of his uncle, the fourth earl, in 1757 while still a minor, was the greatest landowner in Ireland, with estates totalling not less than a quarter of a million acres in Antrim, Donegal and Wexford, as well as some property in England. His Antrim estate included the entire town of Belfast, which he did much to improve by town planning in the Georgian style, by building an Exchange, Assembly Rooms and new parish church at his own expense, and by completing the Lagan Canal. He was, however, an absentee from the country that was the source of his wealth. Born and educated in England, he lived there too, in London or at the great house he built at Fisherwick in Staffordshire in the 1770s, paying occasional visits to Belfast. He took his seat as an Irish peer in the House of Lords in Dublin but never attended, preferring to sit in the Commons at Westminster until the grant of an English barony enabled him to sit in the Lords.

As a great Irish landowner, however, he exercised considerable influence in the Irish Parliament. Belfast's two MPs were invariably relatives or friends of the Chichesters, since the only electors were the dozen members of the corporation, all of whom were the landlord's nominees. One of the reasons why Belfast became a hotbed of radical politics in the late eighteenth century was the tension between its owner - the very epitome of the Protestant ascendancy, and a notorious absentee to boot - and most of the town's leading citizens who, as Presbyterians, were excluded from power both nationally and locally. Donegall, not altogether fairly, also got much of the blame for a serious outbreak of agrarian discontent in County Antrim in the 1770s. The activities of the Hearts of Steel were ascribed to a heart

of flint in the landlord; his income was so seriously affected that he never managed to complete the building of Fisherwick Park. Many of the United Irishmen in County Antrim were to come from areas most affected by the Steelboy disturbances.

Donegall (the spelling of his title was a seventeenth-century form of the county where he owned his largest acreage) was raised to the rank of marquess in the peerage of Ireland in 1791. He married, as his first wife, a daughter of the Duke of Hamilton. Thomas Gainsborough (1727-88), one of the greatest English artists of his century, painted portraits of both of them for the house at Fisherwick. This fine example of his work dates from c.1780.

Sources: W.A. Maguire, 'Lord Donegall and the Hearts of Steel', in *Irish Historical Studies*, vol. 21, no. 84 (1981); 'Absentees, Architects and Agitators' in *Proceedings of Belfast Natural History and Philosophical Society*, second series, vol. 10.

21 *Robert Stewart, Viscount Castlereagh as a young man*

BY AN UNKNOWN ARTIST, C. LATE 1780S
DETAIL
LADY MAIRI BURY
REPRODUCTION

This charming primitive painting, perhaps done by a travelling painter, shows the young Robert Stewart holding a golf club. In view of his later unpopularity it is an unexpected picture of innocence. In fact he was very fond of field sports, including golf. The game at that time was played mainly in Scotland but, from the evidence of this picture, perhaps also among families of Scottish descent in the north of Ireland. In any case, this is probably the earliest golfing picture of an Irishman. The date is uncertain, but appears likely to be before 1788, when Stewart set off on a two-year Grand Tour, following which he became absorbed in politics.

22 *Views of Dublin, c.1790*

BY JAMES MALTON (C.1766-1803)
COLOURED AQUATINTS, EACH APPROXIMATELY 40 X 50 CM
NATIONAL LIBRARY OF IRELAND, DUBLIN
REPRODUCTION

(a)   Parliament House, College Green
(b)   Great Court Yard, Dublin Castle
(c)   New Custom House
(d)   Law Courts, looking up the Liffey

With a population of around 200,000, late eighteenth-century Dublin was the second city of the British Isles (and Empire), twice as big as its nearest rivals Edinburgh and Manchester and, in the opinion of one enthusiast, 'if not the first ... the completest city in Europe, if not the world'. The city was not only extraordinarily large, it was also the centre of national life - seat of the viceregal court, meeting place of the Irish parliament, legal and administrative capital, site of the country's only university, headquarters of the army and an important garrison town, the greatest Irish port and industrial centre. The work of the Wide Streets Commissioners (established in 1757) had done much to plan the development of the city's main streets and public places, with the result that visitors were impressed by its beauty as much as its size and bustle.

James Malton, the most important and famous recorder of what Georgian

31

Dublin looked like, came to the city from England in 1785 with his father Thomas. To begin with, the younger Malton worked as a draughtsman for James Gandon when the latter was building the Custom House. Between 1792 and 1799 he produced his great series of engraved aquatints - twenty-five in all - delineating the city's architecture and street life. His picture of Dublin in its heyday is of course an idealised one. However fine its public buildings and urban prospects, Dublin was also in some of its older quarters, such as the Liberties, a warren of slums and low life,

> 'The graceful with the gross combined,
> The stately with the stinking'.

Sources: Anne Crookshank and The Knight of Glin, *The Watercolours of Ireland* (London, 1994).
             R.B. McDowell, *Ireland in the Age of Imperialism and Revolution, 1760-1801 (Oxford, 1979)*.
             The Knight of Glin, Introduction to Malton's *Dublin Views in Colour* (reprint, Dublin, 1981).

23 *James Stewart of Killymoon*

BY POMPEO BATONI (1708-87)
OIL ON CANVAS, 137.2 x 99.1 CM
ULSTER MUSEUM.

James Stewart was the eldest son of William Stewart of Killymoon, County Tyrone and Eleanor King of Rockingham, County Roscommon. He succeeded his father as one of the MPs for County Tyrone in the Irish Parliament in 1768, retaining the seat continuously and without a contest for the next thirty-two years in Dublin and a further twelve after 1800 at Westminster. It was said of him that 'without place or pension, one shilling of public money has never found its way into his pocket ... during a period of 44 years'. Most county seats in the Irish Parliament, like most of the boroughs, were dominated by great landowning families. Tyrone was unusual at this period in having a large number of independently-minded Presbyterian voters, and its great landowners happened to be at loggerheads. Only when faced by a combination in 1812 was Stewart obliged to retire. Though he himself was a member of the Protestant Ascendancy, as it came to be called, his father was (and remained) a Presbyterian and Stewart was one of the leading spokesmen in the Irish Parliament for the northern Presbyterians and instrumental in promoting legislation to mitigate or remove the penal laws which affected them. In particular, he supported the Act (19 & 20 Geo. III, c.6) that repealed the Test Act for Protestant Dissenters, proposed the Act (21 & 22 Geo. III, c.25) declaring marriages by Presbyterian ministers valid and helped to secure an increase in the *regium donum*, the annual grant to approved Presbyterian clergy. Their regard for him was shown not only by electoral support but also, in the usual fashion of the time, by numerous presentations of silver plate.

Stewart was prominent in the Volunteer movement, from its foundation in the late 1770s to its suppression in 1793. He was the close ally of the Volunteer commander-in-chief Lord Charlemont, active at Volunteer meetings and parades, and a spokesman for Charlemont in the Commons after Grattan fell out with his patron in 1783. In September 1783 he took the chair at the second great convention of northern Volunteer companies in Dungannon, in preparation for the national meeting in Dublin. Like Charlemont, and unlike Grattan, Stewart thereafter opposed political concessions to the Catholics; not till after the Union did he come round to supporting Catholic emancipation. Then too he became friendly with the Prince of Wales, a friendship somewhat exaggerated in family folklore. The two men did patronise the same architect, however: John Nash rebuilt

Killymoon in the early 1800s, at an estimated cost of £100,000.

In 1772 Stewart married Elizabeth Molesworth, daughter of the third Viscount Molesworth. She was one of the survivors of a tragic fire in London in 1763, when living with her widowed mother. Lady Molesworth herself and two of her daughters were killed, along with six of the servants. Two of the daughters were badly injured when they jumped from upper windows - one had to have a leg cut off after landing on the railings below - and a third was severly burned.

Shortly before embarking on his long parliamentary career, young James Stewart had done the Grand Tour in Europe. This splendid portrait of him was painted in Italy sometime in 1767 by Pompeo Batoni, a highly fashionable painter of foreign visitors to Italy and then at the height of his considerable powers. Early the following year Stewart was reported to have left Turin on his way home. The future Duke of Leinster (the eldest brother of Lord Edward FitzGerald) wrote to his mother in March 1768 describing him as 'a gentlemanlike young man, and also very amiable. I know no gentleman better liked than he has been in every town he has passed through ... He lived a great deal with Charles Fox, Lord Fitzwilliam and me at Florence, and they'll both say as much for him as I do'.

Sources: *Public Record Office of Northern Ireland : Deputy Keeper's Report, 1976-9.*
Mina Lenox-Conyngham, *An Old Ulster House* (1946).
A.M. Clark, *Pompeo Batoni: A Complete Catalogue of his Works* (1985).
Edith M. Johnston, History of the Irish Parliament Project.

24 *John Reilly of Scarvagh, MP*

BY THOMAS POPE STEVENS
OIL ON CANVAS, 123 X 99 CM
ULSTER MUSEUM

John Reilly was born in 1745, the son of John Reilly of Scarva, County Down, a minor landowner, and Lucy, daughter of Francis Savage of Ardkeen. He married in 1773 Jane Lushington, daughter and co-heiress of Colonel William Lushington of Kent.

Reilly was returned to Parliament by Lord Hillsborough in 1779 for the borough of Blessington, County Wicklow and held his seat till 1800, when the borough was extinguished as part of the arrangements for the Union. His ambition was a position in the Revenue, preferably that of Collector of Newry. Instead, he was made a Commissioner of Accounts, a post worth £800 a year. This was a recognition of the influence of his patron. In the 1790s the Hill family, whose head from 1793 was the second Marquess of Downshire, controlled nine seats in the Irish House of Commons. Reilly was the leader and manager of this group, though not a particularly energetic or active one. The marquess treated his lack of energy as a joke, writing in September 1793, 'I have not heard of your being dead, but you might as well have been so with regard to friends, especially with respect to the militia ...' And in 1795 he was writing, 'If you did not spend so much time, twice a day at your toilette and put your cravatt into so elegant a form, you would find time perhaps to give a line more frequently to your faithful and affectionate friend Downshire'. Led by Reilly, the Downshire MPs were a group of 'uninspiring modest country gentlemen'. They voted against the Union in the debates of 1799 and 1800; Reilly turned down an offer of a baronetcy and £1,000 a year to vote the other way, in deference to his patron's wishes. One of his sons, William Edmond Reilly, became chief agent of all the Downshire estates in Ireland under the third marquess.

Thomas Pope Stevens was one of a number of painters named Pope Stevens, who as individuals are difficult to identify precisely. This portrait of Reilly was done when the sitter was aged thirty. One of the books on which Reilly rests his

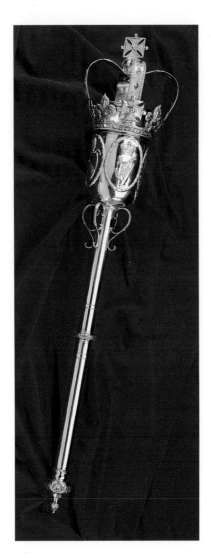

arm is a life of King William III.

Sources: A.P.W. Malcomson, 'The Gentle Leviathan', in P. Roebuck (ed.), *Plantation to Partition* (Belfast, 1981).
Edith M. Johnston, History of the Irish Parliament Project

25 *Mace of the Corporation of Blessington, County Wicklow*

MADE BY CHARLES ALDRIDGE, LONDON 1786
SILVER, LENGTH 104 CM, WIDTH 20 CM, WEIGHT 100 OR 13 DWT
MARQUESS OF DOWNSHIRE, ON LOAN TO ULSTER MUSEUM

The head bears the arms of the Corporation, with its motto *Da Gloriam Deo* and the arms of Archbishop Michael Boyle - a crowned harp and a crowned rose and thistle intertwined within oval wreaths. The end plate has the royal coat of arms. Around the decorated end is inscribed *The Gift of Wills Earl of Hillsborough*. The stem is plain, the head supported on four scrolls and crowned, complete with cross and orb and the date 1786.

The lordship of Blesinton or Blessington had been acquired by Michael Boyle, Archbishop of Armagh, in the Restoration land settlement. It consisted of an estate of some 15,000 acres and included the borough of Blessington, which though a mere village sent two members to the Irish House of Commons.

Boyle's eldest daughter Eleanor married, as his first wife, William Hill of Hillsborough, County Down, a union which eventually led to Wills Hill, Earl of Hillsborough, inheriting the property in 1786. He evidently marked his succession by presenting a new mace to the Corporation. The election of Blessington's MPs was the merest formality, carried out by the burgesses (the only voters, and themselves appointed by the lord of the manor) in the great hall of the house Archbishop Boyle had built. The owner in 1798, Arthur second Marquess of Downshire, was a leading opponent of the United Irishmen and his family's MPs consistently voted against Catholic relief bills in the Dublin Parliament. Not surprisingly, the Wicklow rebels burned Blessington House in 1798. Since the Downshires never lived there, the house was never rebuilt.

Sources: W.A. Maguire, *The Downshire Estates in Ireland* (Oxford, 1972).
E. Porritt, *The Unreformed House of Commons.* (1963) vol. 2.

26 *Suit and Rod of Black Rod of Ireland, 1751*

LENGTH, NECK TO HEM OF COAT, 99 CM
ULSTER MUSEUM

The Gentleman Usher of the Black Rod was originally an official of the English House of Lords, instituted in 1350. 'Black Rod', as he was commonly called from his staff of office - an ebony stick surmounted by a golden lion - was appointed by royal letters patent. He was a personal attendant of the Sovereign in the House of Lords and responsible for the maintenance of order there. His most public role nowadays is his summoning of the Commons and their Speaker to the upper house to hear the speech from the throne at the opening of Parliament or to hear the royal assent given to bills. This curious formality, with its ceremony of shutting the doors of the Commons and requiring Black Rod to knock three times, dates from the reign of Charles I, when the King tried unsuccessfully to arrest five MPs.

The suit comprises coat and breeches of dark brown and cream cut-velvet with an unusual pattern of flower heads and flashes of a type which seems to have been briefly in vogue about 1750. The coat has typical features of its date - elaborately pleated and stiffened full skirt, pockets with deep scalloped flaps, no collar. The front edges of the coat curve away from each other slightly below the waist, a fashionable development. Other elements seem to indicate that, due to the owner's taste or the formal event for which the suit was worn, a conservative appearance was desired. The back vent of the coat is of a cut more usual in the 1730s, the buttons which extend from neck to hem were fashionable until c.1735 and then worn only by the less fashionable until c. 1760; and open sleeves, i.e. cuffs open behind, went out of fashion by 1750. These striking cuffs of silver brocade are particularly interesting because they are of a type often portrayed in contemporary paintings but very rarely seen on surviving specimens.

The buttons and buttonholes are a further focus for decoration. The buttons are of a silver wire and sequins on a wooden base. The buttonholes, outlined by strips of silver, are mostly sham, open just enough to admit a button at the outer edge. The back vent and pockets are also decorated with this metal strip. The coat is lined with silk and interlined with linen and sheepswool where extra thickness is required. The cut of the breeches is of a type which was going out of fashion by 1750. They button down the front without a fly. Gartered stockings were pulled up over the breeches at the knee.

The wig, sword, cravat, sleeve ruffles, waistcoat, stockings and shoes are non-contemporary replicas. The original waistcoat worn with the suit would probably have been of the same silver brocade as the cuffs.

27 *The Irish House of Commons (1780)*

BY FRANCIS WHEATLEY
LEEDS CITY ART GALLERY (LOTHERTON HALL)
REPRODUCTION

The scene shows Henry Grattan (third from right in the front row) addressing a packed House and public gallery on 19 April 1780, when he moved the following resolution to repeal Poynings' Law: 'That the people of Ireland are of right an independent nation and ought only to be bound by laws made by the King, Lords and Commons of Ireland'.

Francis Wheatley was a leading English painter who, fleeing from his creditors

and accompanied by a mistress, arrived in Dublin about 1779 and worked in Ireland for the next few years, returning to England early in 1783. During that period he produced a number of notable group portraits, of which this one and his Dublin Volunteers meeting on College Green are the most famous. He also painted individual portraits, topographical works and numerous lively sketches depicting ordinary people at gatherings such as fairs and gypsy encampments.

Sources: Anne Crookshank and The Knight of Glin, *Painters of Ireland, c.1660-1920.*

28 *The Penal Laws*

TITLE PAGES OF SOME OF THE ACTS OF THE IRISH PARLIAMENT DISCRIMINATING AGAINST CATHOLICS AND PROTESTANT DISSENTERS
ULSTER MUSEUM PHOTOGRAPHS

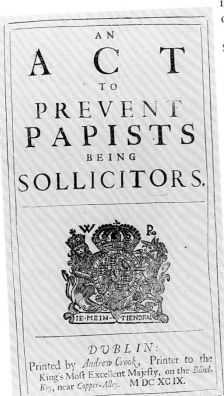

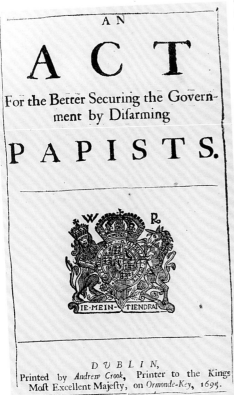

The Penal Laws which operated in Ireland for most of the eighteenth century were an accumulation of discriminatory Acts passed by the Irish Parliament between 1695 and 1727. (The 1691 law excluding Catholics from sitting in Parliament was passed at Westminster). At the time, the motive behind most of these Acts, even those aimed directly at the Catholic clergy, was a political one, concerned with preventing a Jacobite restoration. After early attempts to enforce the legislation against the clergy, the laws were for the most part invoked only spasmodically by local magistrates. Nevertheless they remained on the statute book, and as late as 1756 the Catholic archbishop of Armagh and a group of his clergy, meeting on diocesan business, were detected by a zealous Protestant, arrested and lodged in Dundalk gaol. It was a sign of more tolerant times that they were immediately released, through the influence of a local peer, who treated them with the greatest politeness. Catholic ecclesiastical buildings were generally plain and inconspicuous in order to avoid giving offence, though - like almost every aspect of life - much depended on local conditions; as early as 1730 the mass house at Mullingar was described by a scandalised Protestant clergyman as having 'an aisle, three galleries and a spacious altar piece; painted and set off with images, flower pots and gilded candle sticks', while St Patrick's Church in Waterford (1764) had a very stylish interior, reflecting the taste of its wealthy Catholic congregation.

The penal laws affecting Catholic ownership of land, the basis of power, wealth and social status, were on the other hand rigorously and successfully enforced. By the 'Act to prevent the Further Growth of Popery' (2 Anne, c.7), no Catholic could buy land or lease land for more than thirty-one years, or acquire land from a Protestant by inheritance or marriage. Furthermore, a Catholic landowner could not leave his land by will; on his death it had to be divided equally among all his sons, unless the eldest became a Protestant, in which case he inherited the lot. By the same Act, Catholics were forbidden to act as guardians for minors, and were effectively deprived of the vote in parliamentary elections (this last was specifically confirmed later, in 1727). A sacramental test for all public office or employment, by which appointees had to take holy communion at least twice a year in the Church of Ireland, closed off all civil and military appointments to them. The Test was also applied to Protestant Dissenters, thus excluding conscientious Presbyterians as well. Though numbers of Catholic estates were preserved by friendly collusion with Protestant relations or neighbours, the proportion of Irish land officially in Catholic ownership fell between 1703 and the 1770s from approximately fourteen per cent to about five per cent.

Under the 'Act for the better securing the Government by Disarming Papists' (7 Will. III, c.5) Catholics, with a few special exceptions, had been forbidden to have arms, armour and ammunition. To be unable to carry arms when to do so was the mark of a gentleman and when the roads were infested with highwaymen was a severe thing and, as time passed, was widely disregarded, to judge by the number of duels involving Catholics that were fought. The Disarmament Act also laid down that no Catholic was to own a horse worth more than £5 (in effect, one good enough to make a cavalry mount). A later amendment exempted stud animals and their progeny up to five years old. In practice, such a law must have been widely evaded; Catholic country gentlemen were certainly every bit as prominent in the hunting field as their Protestant neighbours.

An 'Act to prevent Papists being Sollicitors' (10 Will., III, c.13), passed in 1699, was in 1727 extended to include barristers as well, thus closing off the whole legal profession to Catholics and depriving them of one of the chief ways of rising in society as well as of safeguarding their rights.

The essential purpose of the penal laws was not to destroy Catholicism in Ireland but to make sure that its adherents were kept in a position of social, economic and political inferiority by monopolising power in the hands of members of the Established Church. Protestant Dissenters were also affected, though to a considerably lesser extent. Both groups felt themselves to be excluded and discriminated against, a feeling not much diminished by the declining effect of the legislation in practice. The fact remained that in the early 1770s these laws were still on the statute book. The farmers of both excluded communities shared the additional grievance of being liable to pay the tithes that supported a church and clergy other than - and hostile to - their own.

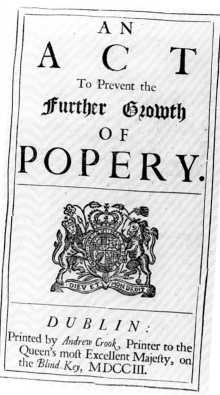

Sources: M. Wall, *The Penal Laws, 1691-1760* (Dundalk, 1976).
S.J. Connolly, 'The Penal Laws' in W.A. Maguire (ed.), *Kings in Conflict: The Revolutionary War in Ireland and its Aftermath, 1689-1760* (Belfast, 1990).
Charles Chenevix Trench, *Grace's Card: Irish Catholic Landlords 1690-1800* (Cork, 1997).

29 *Pair of flintlock duelling pistols, late eighteenth century*

BY MCCORMICK, BELFAST
ULSTER MUSEUM

The practice of defending one's honour by risking one's life in fighting anyone who was thought to have impugned it was by the latter part of the eighteenth century deeply embedded in Irish life. So far as the social rank of participants was concerned, affairs of honour were particularly numerous among the aristocracy and gentry, while among the professions the military naturally figured prominently, along with politicians and lawyers, both of whom were in the way of insulting publicly men they came across professionally. Fortunately, duels did not always need to result in injury for honour to be satisfied: incompetence sometimes came to the rescue. In 1772 two Dublin attornies exchanged forty shots without one hitting its target. By the 1770s, duelling was not only common in polite society; it was also, though officially illegal, accepted as an essential component of gentility and winked at by the courts - not surprisingly, when the lord lieutenant himself and leading politicians and lawyers indulged in it. Lord Townshend's meeting with Lord Bellamont in 1773, which ended in victory for the viceroy, caused a great sensation. Another in the same year, between a new chief secretary for Ireland, Sir John Blaquiere, and a Carlow MP, Beauchamp Bagenal, also attracted great interest. Grattan himself was prevented from fighting his great Patriot rival Flood, but later did exchange shots with Isaac Corry, chancellor of the exchequer.

The 1770s and 1780s were the peak period for duelling in Ireland, the era of the 'Fire-Eaters' such as George Robert FitzGerald. Duels were so frequent that a semi-official code of rules for conducting them - sometimes called the 'Thirty-Six

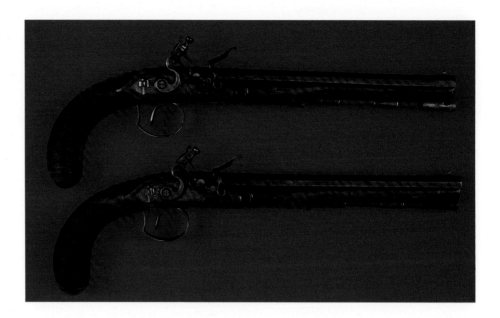

Commandments' - was drawn up by leading aficionados in 1777. This was the heyday of Sir Jonah Barrington, who was

'so good a *marksman* that he can repeatedly strike out a mark upon the ace of spades at twelve paces distance; he has frequently fought and never missed his men'.

No wonder that Leonard MacNally, having by mere chance survived an encounter with Barrington, never had any difficulty with his fellow lawyers afterwards. Barrington's racy account of duelling in Ireland, though based upon his own experiences, probably gives an exaggerated idea of the prevalence of the practice; the likelihood is that most gentleman of the time, though owning pistols, went through life without feeling that they needed to defend their honour by using them.

The whole subject has been thoroughly explored in James Kelly's recent book *'That Damn'd Thing Called Honour': Duelling in Ireland 1570-1860* (Cork, 1995).

30 *Resolutions of meetings held in the Presbyterian Meeting -house at Rathfriland, County Down on 18 and 24 August 1783, defending the conduct of the Rev. Samuel Barber and censuring that of Lord Kilwarlin, who had reportedly said he 'would rather give money to pull down Rathfriland Meeting-house than to rebuild it'.*

PRINTED PAPER, 29 X 16 CM
ULSTER MUSEUM (BARBER MSS)

The Rev. Samuel Barber was the minister of the Rathfriland Presbyterian congregation. Lord Kilwarlin was the son and heir of Wills Hill, Earl of Hillsborough and later Marquess of Downshire, and succeeded his father as second marquess in 1793. The Hill family had large estates in County Down, including one at Hilltown, near Rathfriland, and would indeed have been approached to subscribe to any churchbuilding in the neighbourhood.

This document illustrates the animosity that could (and frequently did) exist between landowners of the Established Church and their Presbyterian tenants.

On this occasion Kilwarlin appears to have acted in a gratuitously insulting and high-handed manner, while the congregation (or at least part of it) was clearly far from deferential to those who expected deference from their inferiors.

31 *Letters about tithes*

MS CORRESPONDENCE
PUBLIC RECORD OFFICE OF NORTHERN IRELAND

(a)   Letter concerning tithe payments in Counties Tyrone and Donegal
      Nisbitt to Abercorn, 1 January 1751
      (Abercorn Papers)

(b)   Letter concerning tithes in some parishes in North Down
      Cooper to Hillsborough, 23 September 1792
      (Downshire Papers)

(c)   Tithe demand in the parish of Newtownards, County Down
      Cleland to Cooper, 18 September 1792, enclosed with (b) above

Tithes, representing gifts to God for the use of the church and notionally equal to one-tenth of every man's yield of the annual increase of the earth - crops and new-born animals - were paid to the Established Church, the Church of Ireland. In practice the clergy of the Church depended on tithes for the greater part of their income, and could enforce payment of them, either in kind or - more usually by the late-eighteenth century - by means of a cash payment.

Tithe owners usually collected the tithe by means of middlemen called tithe-proctors, who took a percentage of what they collected, or by letting the right to collect the tithe to tithe-farmers, who gave the owners a lump sum and then collected all they could in addition in order to make their profit. The burden of tithes, and the way they were collected, was unpopular even with members of the Established Church; it was much more so with Catholics and Dissenters, who were thus obliged to help support a church they did not belong to, as well as their own. Nisbitt's estimate in (a) that the tithe owner's demand was equal to one-fifth of the rent payable to the landlord is a surprisingly high one and may be an exaggeration. There is no doubt, however, that tithes were a heavy burden, and any attempt to extend them, as Lord Londonderry was said to be doing in (b), was strongly resented and resisted. Londonderry's agent in (c) was the Rev. John Cleland, who was also vicar of Newtownards. Andrew Cooper of Milecross appealed to Lord Hillsborough against the action of his own landlord because Hillsborough's father, the Marquess of Downshire, was governor of the county and a political opponent of Londonderry's family, the Stewarts.

Lord Londonderry himself was, and remained till his dying day, a member of the Presbyterian Church, though his son Lord Castlereagh changed to the Established Church. Yet he was a tithe-owner. This was because the tithe due to a rector - amounting to two-thirds of the yield, as compared with the one-third due to a vicar, the original distinction in status between the two - was sometimes owned by laymen as their private property. In this case, part of Londonderry's estate had once belonged to abbeys, dissolved at the Reformation, which had owned the rectorial tithe of the parishes concerned. If it was true, as Cooper claimed, that the tenants had indeed not paid any tithe since the time of Henry VIII, Londonderry's attempt to impose it was bound to be bitterly resented. It may be no coincidence that many of the Presbyterians who joined the United Irishmen in North Down came from this area.

Sources: W.H. Crawford and B. Trainor (eds), *Aspects of Irish Social History, 1750-1800* (HMSO, Belfast, 1969).

3 The American Revolution and Ireland

The deteriorating relationship between the British government and the British colonies on the eastern seaboard of North America was watched with great interest by people in Ireland. As a kingdom with its own legislature but subject to oversight, limitation and interference from the imperial power Ireland found itself in much the same situation as the colonies and had similar grievances about trading and manufacturing restrictions. Had the colonists been successfully suppressed, a precedent would have been set for Ireland. The many personal and commercial ties between Irish people and the colonists created keen sympathy in Ireland for the latter's dilemma. Franklin and Washington became heroes.

Living closer to Europe, however, Irish patriots had no desire to encourage French intervention as a means of getting what they wanted. On the contrary, they detested the French and all they at that time stood for - arbitrary government, persecuting Catholicism, lack of personal liberty. The government could safely withdraw large numbers of troops from the Irish garrison to serve in America.

The vacuum was filled by the Volunteers, enthusiastic to defend their country against any invasion from France but - armed and equipped at their own expense and officered by local people - not entirely under the control of government. As it happened, the British were beaten in America, the French never came, and the opportunity arose to back demands for constitutional reform and free trade by a powerful citizen army which had became a political pressure group. The experience of volunteering, and the evident success of Volunteer agitation, was to politicise many Irishmen for the first time and prepare the ground for the message of the French Revolution.

32 *Wills Hill, Earl of Hillsborough and Marquess of Downshire (1718-93)*

By Joseph Nollekens (1737-1823)
Marble bust, 80 cm high
Representative Church Body, Dublin

Wills Hill was born in 1718, the year after his father Trevor was raised to the peerage of Ireland as Baron Hill of Kilwarlin and Viscount Hillsborough. At that time the family's estates and influence were confined to County Down, where they were major landowners in the area around Hillsborough. In 1742 Wills succeeded his father. During his time the family property was substantially increased, particularly by the inheritance of a substantial estate at Blessington, County Wicklow. He succeeded his father as lord lieutenant of County Down and in 1746 he was appointed to the Irish privy council. His first marriage, to Margaretta FitzGerald, only surviving daughter of the nineteenth Earl of Kildare and sister of the twentieth earl (who became first Duke of Leinster), connected him to the most distinguished family in Ireland and helped him to become a figure at court and in English politics (he was already MP for Warwick, a seat he held until 1756). In 1751 he was advanced in the peerage of Ireland as Earl of Hillsborough. He served George III as comptroller and treasurer from 1754 to 1756, when he was rewarded by a barony in the peerage of Great Britain (as Baron Harwich) which enabled him thereafter to sit in the House of Lords.

Under George III he held a number of political posts, notably as President of the Board of Trade and Plantations 1763-65 and Secretary of State for the Colonies

1768-72. In 1772 he was created Viscount Fairford and Earl of Hillsborough in the peerage of Great Britain, and his remarkable collection of titles (as many as Wellington got, and twice as many as Nelson) was crowned in 1789 when he became Marquess of Downshire in the Irish peerage. Contemporaries noted Lord Hillsborough's ambition and his elegant manners, but doubted that his abilities deserved so much recognition - 'a man of more pomp than solidity', said Horace Walpole, none too solid himself but never easy to please.

As a statesman, Wills Hill's reputation rested on his performance as colonial secretary during a crucial phase of relations with the Americans. The general verdict was that his unyielding manner had made matters worse rather than better; he was forced to resign in 1772. Certainly his meeting in 1771 with Franklin, whom he invited to Hillsborough, did more harm than good. As an Irish landowner, on the other hand, he set a good example, despite long absences in England: he did much to encourage the linen industry, both nationally through his influence on the Linen Board in Dublin and locally on his own estates; and the village of Hillsborough is still largely a monument to his interest and good taste.

Not surprisingly in view of his own career, Downshire was a firm supporter of the administration in Dublin and of the British connection, so much so that he was an early advocate of the union of the two kingdoms. He lived long enough to see the beginnings of the United Irishmen, and hated what he saw. He died at Hillsborough in 1793.

Joseph Nollekens was the son of Joseph Francis Nollekens, an Antwerp-born artist who settled in London in 1733 and painted conversation pieces. Young Joseph was placed by his father in the studio of the sculptor Peter Scheemakers, also from Antwerp, who worked in London between 1735 and 1769. There he won prizes for his modelling, before departing for Rome. He became one of the most successful sculptors of his day, exhibiting at the Royal Academy 1771-1816 and numbering among his sitters all the important people of the time. He also produced sculptural monuments, and was famous for his Venuses. He died a rich man, having also made a fortune on the Stock Exchange, but was senile in his later years. This fine bust of Lord Hillsborough, one of his early works, was done in 1771-72.

Sources: *DNB*
             W.A. Maguire, 'Owners and Occupants', in *Hillsborough Castle* (Belfast, 1993);
             The Downshire Estates in Ireland (Oxford, 1972).
             John Barry, *Hillsborough: A Parish in the Ulster Plantation* (Belfast, 1982).

33 *Benjamin Franklin (1706-90)*

ATTRIBUTED TO BENJAMIN WEST OR DAVID MARTIN
OIL ON CANVAS, 48.2 x 39.4CM
PRIVATE COLLECTOR

Next to George Washington, Benjamin Franklin was the most famous eighteenth-century American, admired at home and abroad for eminence in an amazing range of activities, from printing and public service to practical invention. Born in Boston, Massachusetts in January 1706, the tenth son among the seventeen children of a soapmaker and candlemaker, he learned to read early but received no formal education beyond the age of ten. At the age of twelve he was apprenticed to his brother James as a printer. In the years that followed he taught himself to write effectively by using Addison and Steele's *Spectator* essays as his model. Having fallen out with his brother he moved to Philadelphia, where he found employment as a printer. On the promise of help from the governor of Pennsylvania, Sir William Keith, Franklin went to London to buy type to establish his own business. When the expected funds failed to materialise, he worked at his trade in the capital for a couple of years before returning to Philadelphia, where he set up first in partnership

and then (1730) on his own. His previous master's daughter, Deborah Read, to whom he had been unofficially engaged, had in the meantime married a man who had deserted her and disappeared. In 1730 Franklin contracted a common-law marriage with her which lasted till her death in 1774; they had two children, one of whom died young, and the household also included an illegitimate son of Franklin's who was born about 1730.

In 1729 Franklin published a pamphlet entitled *A Modest Enquiry into the Nature and Necessity of a Paper Currency*. This led to his firm getting the contract to print Pennsylvania's paper money; for many years he was to be the public printer also for New Jersey, Delaware and Maryland. Another successful venture was the *Pennsylvania Gazette*, published from 1729. A third was *Poor Richard's Almanack*, published annually between 1732 and 1757 under the pseudonym Richard Saunders. This was an oracle on how to get on in the world and contained much practical, not to say cynical, advice such as the following gem: 'Keep your eyes wide open before marriage, half shut afterwards'. Though some other schemes failed, such as that for a German-language newspaper, Franklin on the whole made money, which he invested in real estate and printing partnerships. As well as making money, he was instrumental in establishing the first public library, a city watch or police force, a volunteer fire company, the American Philosophical Society and the Academy of Philadelphia, forerunner of the University of Pennsylvania. In local politics, he was clerk of the state legislature from 1736 to 1751 and postmaster of Philadelphia from 1737 to 1753. He organised a militia to defend the colony against French and Spanish privateers, which operated in the Delaware River. In the late 1740s he and his friends carried out experiments into the nature of electricity. These were communicated to the Royal Society in London and subsequently (1751) collected and published as *Experiments and Observations on Electricity*. Translations into French, German and Italian followed, making Franklin internationally known. Though he was perhaps not quite so original as his admirers thought, and may have got more than his fair share of credit for what were collaborative experiments, he did invent many of the terms still used in discussing the subject - positive, negative, battery, conductor and so on - and, always practical, suggested the metal lightning conductor as a way of protecting buildings.

Franklin's appointment as deputy postmaster general in 1753, in charge of the mails in all the northern colonies, made him an early advocate of co-operation, for common defence against the encroaching French on the western frontier and for some way of supervising relations between new settlements and the native Red Indians. Between 1757 and 1762, and again from 1764, he was in London on state business and became well known and much admired (among many other distinctions he was elected to the Royal Society). He stayed on to represent the interests of Pennsylvania and other states when the Stamp Act caused a storm in America. With the support of the Whigs, he did his best to present the American case to the British public as relations between George III's Tory ministry and the colonies steadily worsened, publishing no fewer than 126 newspaper articles. One stage in the process by which he came to realise that the views of the colonists and those of the administration were irreconcilable was a personal meeting with the Colonial Secretary, Lord Hillsborough. They met, by chance, at a levée in Dublin Castle in 1771, when Franklin visited Ireland and attended the opening of Parliament as an honoured guest. Franklin's unfavourable opinion of the minister, as expressed in a private letter to a friend, was as follows: 'His character is Conceit, Wrongheadedness, Obstinacy and Passion. Those who speak most favourable of him allow all this; they only urge that he is an honest man and means well. If this be true, as perhaps it may, I wish him a better place where only Honesty and Well-meaning are required'. On this occasion, however, Hillsborough went out of his way to be civil to Franklin and, when the American travelled north, insisted on entertaining him at Hillsborough Castle.

Franklin enjoyed all this but was not moved by it. If the government's policy towards the grievances of the colonists was not changed, he reckoned, such plausible behaviour meant only 'by patting and stroaking the Horse to make him more patient while the Reins are drawn tighter and the Spurs set deeper into his Sides'. The 'Hillsborough Conference' did no good; Franklin later said the minister had treated him like 'an orange that would yield no more juice and [was] therefore not worth more squeezing'. He gradually came to realise that his dream of a British Empire of self-governing nations would not come true. By 1773 Franklin was writing 'Rules by Which a Great Empire May be Reduced to a Small One'. In March 1775, with war looming, he left England. On arrival in Philadelphia he immediately became a delegate to the Second Continental Congress and subsequently helped to draft the Declaration of Independence.

When the rebellious colonists sought economic and military assistance from France, Franklin was sent as one of the three delegates, arriving in Paris just before Christmas 1776. He soon became a cult figure in France, with his fur hat and bifocal spectacles (his own invention) and graceful manners the very embodiment of the simple nobility of the New World. Everybody - diplomats, scientists, literary figures, Freemasons, fashionable ladies - wanted to meet him. His portrait appeared everywhere, on everything from snuffboxes to chamber pots. The help Franklin and his colleagues sought was obtained in 1778, after the British general Burgoyne and his army of 6,000 had been forced to surrender to the Americans, at Saratoga in upstate New York, and it had become clear to the French that the colonists might actually win. By the time victory came at Yorktown in 1781, some 12,000 French soldiers and 32,000 sailors had been sent to America. Franklin stayed on in France until 1785, to negotiate trade treaties, and was thus able to observe the first balloon ascent by the Montgolfier brothers and to investigate Mesmer's wonderful new cure-all, mesmerism or hypnotism. Back in America, and now ill with a large stone in his bladder, he gave his last important service as a member of the Convention of 1787, which drew up the Constitution. Bedridden for the last year of his life and dependent on opium to ease his pain, he died in Philadelphia on 17 April 1790 at the age of eighty-four.

Franklin's long life and fame ensured that his likeness was taken many times. In fact a substantial volume has been devoted to representations of him. One of the most appealing portraits, by the Scottish painter David Martin, was done in the 1760s before the loss of his teeth altered Franklin's appearance. It shows the great man reading' at a table, glasses on nose, scholarly and active-looking. The picture exists in several versions, one of which now hangs in the White House in Washington. The label on the frame of the version shown here attributes it to Benjamin West. If West did indeed paint it he was copying Martin's work.

David Martin (1737-98) studied painting under Allan Ramsay and had a successful practice as a portrait painter in late eighteenth-century Edinburgh, painting in the style of Ramsay; he also produced engravings. Benjamin West (1738-1820) though American by birth, made his career in England, where he was patronised by George III and became president of the Royal Academy. His most famous painting was 'The Death of Wolfe' (1771).

Sources: *Encyclopaedia Britannica* (15th edition).
            W.B. Wilcox (ed.), *The Papers of Benjamin Franklin* (Yale UP, 1975), vol. 19.
            John Barry, *Hillsborough: A Parish in the Ulster Plantation*.
            Charles Sellers, *Benjamin Franklin in Portraiture* (Yale, 1962).

34 *George Washington (1732-99)*

AFTER GILBERT STUART
OIL ON CANVAS, 71 X 50 CM
NATIONAL PORTRAIT GALLERY, LONDON

George Washington, general, statesman and first president of the United States of America, was born in Westmoreland County, Virginia on 22 February 1732 into a landowning family. He received little enough formal education but acquired practical skill in tobacco farming, stock raising and surveying which stood him in good stead when he inherited the Mount Vernon estate in 1752. Though disapproving of slavery as an institution, he eventually owned nearly fifty slaves. Tall and imposing, he was an excellent horseman and enjoyed outdoor country pursuits such as hunting and fishing as well as dancing, billiards and cards.

During the 1750s Washington gained military experience against the French and their Indian allies along the frontier, notably as an officer of the Virginia militia in support of General Braddock's ill-fated attack on Fort Duquesne in 1755, when Braddock himself was killed and Washington had two horses shot under him and narrowly escaped serious injury. In a letter to his brother he remarked: 'I have heard the bullets whistle; and believe me, there is something charming in the sound'. In 1755, aged only twenty-three, he was appointed commander of all the Virginian troops. He found his colonial troops ill-disciplined and frustrating to

command, however, and resented the refusal of the commander of the British regular army to do anything about fulfilling a promise, made by Braddock, of a king's commission. In 1758 he resigned his command with the honorary rank of brigadier-general and retired to his estates, which were shortly afterwards greatly increased by marriage to a wealthy widow. The Washingtons lived, and entertained, in aristocratic style, buying their clothes in London. As a slaveowner he set a good example, refusing on principle ever to sell slaves and ensuring that they were fed and well clothed and had proper medical attention.

Washington would no doubt have spent the rest of his life as an enlightened but obscure colonial landowner if relations between the government of George III and the American colonies had not become increasingly hostile following the end of the Seven Years War. On the one hand, the British defeat of the French had largely removed the colonists' need for military protection; on the other, the imperial power was left with a heavy post-war debt and high taxation at home. In 1764 the government decided to make the colonies contribute towards the cost of their own defence by means of a Stamp Tax. As a member of the state assembly, the House of Burgesses, Washington became involved in the growing resistance to rule from London in the interests of England, though, like most Americans, he believed at first that opposition need not lead to rebellion. By 1774, however, he had become a strong supporter of the proposal for a Continental Congress and when the first Congress met in Philadelphia in September of that year he took his seat as one of the delegates from Virginia, wearing his full military uniform. At that stage he was still opposed to the idea of independence, but was determined never to submit to the loss of the colonists' rights and privileges and warned that if the ministry in London pushed matters to extremes 'more blood will be spilled on this occasion than ever before in American history'. Virginia appointed him to command its troops, and in 1775, following the clash between British troops and local militia at Lexington and Concord in Massachusetts, the second Congress unanimously chose him as commander-in-chief. He accepted the command without any payment beyond his expenses, an account he kept with scrupulous exactness in his own hand and presented to Congress at the end of the war (it came to £24,700).

After many vicissitudes, throughout which Washington's force of personality, powers of leadership and greatness of character were often displayed, the war was won. Apart from Washington's generalship, which was on the whole superior to that of the British commanders sent to defeat him, the crucial factor that decided the outcome was the intervention of France on the American side; it was French control of the sea at Yorktown in September and the presence of 5,000 French troops that sealed the fate of Cornwallis and his army and virtually ended the fighting.

Washington subsequently served two terms as the first president of the United States, retiring finally in 1797.

Events in America had profound effects in Ireland. Irish public opinion in general took the side of the colonists, and the parallel between the situation of the king's subjects in Ireland and in America was too obvious to be overlooked. It was pointed out that if America was taxed without consent Ireland might be next. Apart from such constitutional comparisons, there were strong ties of kinship between the Americans and the northern Irish in particular, because of emigration during the previous two generations. 'The presbyterians in the north are in their hearts Americans', wrote Harcourt, the lord lieutenant. More generally, Irish newspapers reported in some detail the development of the quarrel and the progress of the war of independence that followed, usually in a way that was sympathetic to the colonists, and Dublin booksellers did a brisk trade in reprints of English and American pamphlets. On a more practical level, the closing of the American markets in the spring of 1775 added to an existing crisis in the Irish textile industry and threatened the treasury with bankruptcy. The British prime minister, Lord North, could not afford to have another America on his doorstep and began to make concessions to encourage Irish prosperity in trade and manufacture - an important change of attitude which, however, fell well short of Irish expectations. Harcourt did manage to get a majority in the Irish parliament to endorse North's American policy and to allow troops to be withdrawn from Ireland for service in America, but only with difficulty. The entry of France into the war in America in 1778 marked an important change of attitude, for while Irish Dissenters in particular sympathised with the Americans, they hated and feared the French. Out of all this emerged the Volunteers, to defend the country against the French on the one hand and to assert the rights of Ireland on the other.

There are numerous portraits of Washington by painters and sculptors, starting in 1772 with the painting by Peale. Later likenesses suffer from the fact that the artificial teeth the great man was obliged to wear altered the expression of his face. Gilbert Stuart (1755-1828) was born in America, in Rhode Island, and came to England in 1775 to work with Benjamin West, returning home in 1792. His great canvas of Washington, though idealised as a portrait, expresses both the achievement of the man and the dignity he brought to the presidency of the new republic. This version from the National Portrait Gallery is a reduced copy.

Sources: *Encyclopaedia Britannica* (15th edition).
            J.C. Beckett, *Making of Modern Ireland* (London, 1966).
            DNB.

35 *Lafayette (Prise d'Iorktown 19 Oct. 1781)*

ENGRAVING
BIBLIOTHÈQUE NATIONALE, PARIS

This engraving shows the youthful Lafayette (then aged twenty-four) at the taking of Yorktown, the decisive engagement of the American War of Independence. He is shown wearing the uniform of a major-general in the American army, the rank awarded to him by Congress on his arrival from France as a nineteen-year-old volunteer in 1777. Subsequently, on the recommendation of Washington himself, Lafayette was given command of a division and played an honourable if undistinguished part in the fighting. His importance to the Americans, however, was not his military talents, which were modest, but his example and connections.

Marie Joseph Paul Yves Roch Gilbert du Motier, Marquis de La Fayette (1757-1834) was born in the Auvergne on 6 September 1757. His father was killed at the battle of Minden in 1759, and his mother and his grandfather died in 1770, leaving him an immensely wealthy orphan. He married at the age of sixteen and entered the French army. He was nineteen and a captain of dragoons in 1776 when the Americans declared their independence from Great Britain. Fired with enthusiasm for the cause of liberty, Lafayette offered his services and fitted out a ship to take him and some like-minded companions to America. He persevered, against the advice of friends and even of the new American envoy, Franklin, and in the face of royal disapproval. The ship was moved from Bordeaux to a Spanish port and, when arrested and lodged in prison, Lafayette escaped and joined it along with a handful of the others. They managed to avoid two British ships sent in pursuit and landed in South Carolina after a voyage of nearly two months. When this lad of nineteen, with scarcely a word of English, appeared before the Congress in Philadelphia to claim the rank in the American army that the agent in Paris had originally promised him, his reception was at first a cool one. When such a well-connected Frenchman offered to serve as a volunteer without pay, however, Congress, which wanted to gain the support of France in its struggle, resolved on 31 July 1777 'that his services be accepted', and that 'in consideration of his zeal, illustrious family and connections, he have the rank and commission of major-general of the United States'. Next day he met Washington, who was to be a lifelong friend; Lafayette's son and heir was given the names George Washington.

After the French alliance was secured, in February 1778, and England declared war on France, Lafayette was given permission to return to France, where he found himself a hero. He returned in time to take part in the closing stages of the war. After Yorktown he returned again to France, to help in the negotiations for a general peace, and was promoted to the rank of *maréchal de camp* (major-general) in the French army. In 1784 he visited the United States as the guest of the nation.

Lafayette was subsequently to play a leading role in the early stages of the French Revolution, as commander of the National Guard, supporter of constitutional monarchy and opponent of the excesses of the Jacobins. In August 1792 he was declared a traitor, and escaped the guillotine only by fleeing across the frontier. He spent the next five years imprisoned in Prussian and Austrian gaols. Released in 1797, he returned to France two years later. In 1824-25 he visited America again, receiving a rapturous welcome everywhere as well as Congressional gifts of money ($200,000) and land. He made a brief return to national prominence in his own country in 1830, when he was called out of retirement to take command of the National Guard during the revolution that overthrew the last of the Bourbon kings, Charles X. He died in 1834 at the age of seventy-six.

Sources: *Encyclopaedia Britannica* (11th edition).

36 *James Caulfield, Earl of Charlemont*

ENGRAVED PORTRAIT BY L. SCHIAVONETTI AFTER HONE, FROM *MEMOIRS* BY F. HARDY
ULSTER MUSEUM

James Caulfield (sometimes spelt Caulfeild), fourth Viscount and first Earl of Charlemont in the peerage of Ireland, was born in Dublin 18 August 1728 and succeeded as Viscount in 1734. A cultivated man with strong literary and artistic tastes, he travelled extensively in Italy, the Balkans and the Near East between 1746 and 1754 before returning to Ireland, where he was appointed governor of County Armagh and given a seat on the Irish privy council. Charlemont held liberal views. Though his health was always delicate and he was painfully shy in public and no orator, he became highly respected as a patriotic statesman, particularly through his long association with and influence in the Volunteer movement. The association with volunteering began in 1760, when he organised and commanded the Volunteers raised in several northern counties to defend Belfast against Thurot's threatened attack. In 1763 he was created Earl of Charlemont.

Between 1764 and 1773 Charlemont lived in London, where he frequented the literary salons and was the friend of many of the leading literary and artistic figures of the day, such as Johnson, Hume, Burke, Goldsmith, Reynolds and Hogarth. In 1768 he seconded the bill to limit future Irish parliaments to a term of eight years (before this Octennial Act they lasted for a whole reign). With the completion of his town house in Rutland Square, Dublin in 1773 Charlemont lived more frequently in Ireland, taking part in the stirring events of the late 1770s and early 1780s as the friend of Grattan (whom he put into Parliament for his own borough of Charlemont) and Flood. In 1780 he was elected commander-in-chief of the Volunteers, and presided over the moves by which their power helped to secure legislative independence two years later. Charlemont's liberalism had its limits, however, and in 1783, at the Rotunda Convention in Dublin, he exercised a moderating influence. The subsequent failure of Flood's bill to reform Parliament marked the high water mark of Volunteer influence; Charlemont dissolved the Convention. Thereafter he presided over the movement's decline.

In 1788, at the time of the Regency question, which arose from the temporary madness of George III, Charlemont supported Grattan and the Patriots who wanted to offer the regency in Ireland to the Prince of Wales regardless of what happened in England, moving the address himself. Another aspect of his patriotism was his interest in the recently-founded Royal Irish Academy; he was its first president, and its meetings often took place at Charlemont House. The outbreak of the French Revolution revived the hopes of reformers, even moderate ones. Charlemont was a founder member of the Dublin Whig Club, which had the young Wolfe Tone as a member for a time. The progress of the Revolution, however, soon began to alarm moderates, and the reform movement in Ireland became increasingly unattractive to Charlemont. His support for Catholic emancipation, always limited, now fell off entirely, though such was his personal standing and integrity that he retained much of his previous popularity. The Rebellion of 1798 was a bitter blow to his patriotic feelings, while the proposals for union that followed it were deeply repugnant to him. Perhaps fortunately, he died in August 1799, before the bill was passed. He was buried in Armagh Cathedral.

The engraver Luigi Schiavonetti (1765-1810) was born at Bassano in Italy and came to England with his younger brother Niccolo in 1790. Both merited entries in the *Dictionary of National Biography*.

Sources: *DNB*.
             Webb, *Compendium of Irish Biography*.

37 *Portrait of a Lurgan Volunteer, c.1780*

By Strickland Lowry (1737-c.1785)
Oil on canvas, 92.5 x 72.5 cm
Ulster Museum

The Lurgan Volunteers were formed in 1779, under the command of the town's landlord William Brownlow, MP as captain and two lieutenants named Thomas Druitt and [?] Godfrey. The subject of this portrait is probably either Druitt or Godfrey. The Lurgan company, whose total strength in 1780 was just over eighty, formed part of the northern battalion of the Armagh or First Ulster Regiment of the Volunteers. The regiment's colonel was the movement's commander-in-chief, Lord Charlemont; the lieutenant-colonel of the northern battalion was Brownlow.

The artist Lowry was an Englishman, born at Whitehaven in Cumberland, who worked in Shropshire, Staffordshire and Worcestershire before coming to Ireland in the 1760s. Details of his career are obscure, but he is believed to have stayed in Ireland at least until 1780, when this portrait was painted. He then returned to England, probably to Worcester, and was dead by 1785. There was a connection of some sort between Lowry and his chief competitor Joseph Wilson,

for Lowry's son - the engraver Wilson Lowry - was named after his rival and his grandson was christened Joseph Wilson Lowry.

Sources: Eileen Black, *Irish Oil Paintings, 1572-c.1830;* Ulster Museum Catalogue (1991); 'Volunteer Portraits in the Ulster Museum, Belfast', in *Irish Sword*, vol. 13, no. 52.

38 *Waddell Cunningham (1729-97)*

BY ROBERT HOME
OIL ON CANVAS, 61 X 50.5 CM
ULSTER MUSEUM

Waddell Cunningham was the youngest son of a Couny Antrim farmer. He went to New York about 1750, to assist a relative in the flaxseed trade with North America, and by 1752 had opened a store and become part-owner of a small ship engaged in trading with Ireland. Two years later, he was a leading figure in the Belfast and Newry group in New York's Irish merchant community. By the time he was thirty-four he was the largest shipowner in New York, partly through his ventures in Dutch contraband, an illegal but profitable trade. He established an extensive trade in the Caribbean and acquired a large estate in Dominica, prospering in partnership with Thomas Greg of Belfast. In 1765 he returned to Belfast a very wealthy man and soon became a leading citizen as first president of the Chamber of Commerce, a member of the Ballast Board (set up to improve the harbour), chairman of the committee that built the new Linen Hall, trustee of the Second Presbyterian Congregation and so on.

A supporter of reform and a Volunteer, Cunningham was one of the Belfast delegates at the Dungannon Convention of 1782. When Lord Donegall, landlord of the town and owner of the borough, refused a request to make him one of Belfast's MPs in 1784, Cunningham stood against the Donegall candidate in the neighbouring borough of Carrickfergus and was elected, only to be unseated on petition. In a fresh election the following year he was defeated by an 'independent' candidate. The incident illustrates his hostile attitude to the ruling Protestant (i.e. Anglican) ascendancy. In the 1790s he was a moderate reformer but opposed full

Catholic emancipation and the programme of the United Irishmen. In 1797 he joined the yeomanry, serving as captain of the 4th Company of Belfast Yeoman Infantry. He died in December of the same year, leaving estate valued at the enormous sum of £70,000. There was something enigmatic in his character; Mrs McTier describes him as 'dark-souled'. As her brother William Drennan reported to her, an attempt by Cunningham in 1786 to form a consortium of Belfast merchants to take shares in a slave ship had foundered on the principled opposition of Thomas McCabe, watchmaker and leading radical, who had written in the proposal book, 'May G.. eternally damn the soul of the man who subscribes the first guinea'.

This portrait by Home (who also painted him in civilian dress) shows Cunningham in uniform as Captain of the Belfast 1st Volunteer Company, the rank he held from 1780 to 1793.

Sources: Eileen Black, *Irish Oil Paintings, 1572-c.1830*.
              George Chambers, *Faces of Change* (Belfast, 1984).

39 *The Volunteer Quilt, made from curtains of 'Volunteer Furniture' printed fabric, 1782*

221 x 221 CM
ULSTER MUSEUM

In the mid-1750s important developments in fabric printing were made in the

Dublin area. A short-lived linen printing works in Drumcondra developed a new method of copperplate printing which produced more fast and varied colours than was previously possible. The greatest success enjoyed by the several printworks that set up after this development was during Thomas Harpur's ownership from 1768 to 1786 of the printworks at Leixlip, County Kildare. The best-known product of this firm was the 'Volunteer Furniture' furnishing print, probably designed by the artist Gabriel Béranger. It was advertised in the *Dublin Evening Post* of 14 September 1782 as follows -

'Mr Harpur, of Leixlip, linen printer, has now nearly finished on cotton from copperplate, for Mr. Clarke, proprietor of the Irish Furniture Cotton Ware-house in Werburgh Street, a Volunteer Furniture, *in chintz colours*, which is an exact representation of the last Provincial Review in the Phoenix Park'.

The review mentioned, held on 3 June 1782, was of the Irish Volunteers of the province of Leinster. The reviewing general was Lord Charlemont. He is depicted on horseback in the print, bareheaded and holding his hat. The coaches have 'C' or 'M' on the doors, the cyphers of the Earls of Charlemont and Moira. The Phoenix Column, built by Lord Chesterfield in 1744, and the Chief Secretary's Lodge, still existing and now the residence of the American ambassador, are recognizable eighteenth-century landmarks. Among the many other fascinating vignettes in this charming print are a child falling out of a tree on top of a laden picnic table, a gentleman with a parasol being moved along by a soldier's bayonet, a dining tent set up with food and drink, dogs, fashionable onlookers, drummer boys, as well as the rows of troops presenting arms with fixed bayonets.

There are perhaps seven or eight surviving examples of the Volunteer print.

Fortunately for this particular specimen it was quilted, probably in the nineteenth century, and the backing material has helped keep the fabric in remarkably good condition.

40 *Flag of First Armagh Volunteers, 1778*

SILK, 152.5 × 141 CM
ULSTER MUSEUM (ARMAGH MUSEUM COLLECTION)

County Armagh was an early and enthusiastic centre of volunteering. Its leading figure, Lord Charlemont, was the movement's national commander-in-chief, a position he retained throughout the period of its existence until its demise in 1793. This is the flag of the First [City of] Armagh Volunteers, established in 1778. It bears a device consisting of an embroidered angel harp, with crown above, in black, brown and cream wool on a brown (originally red) silk oval plaque with a cream and brown border entwined with shamrock sprays; on ribbons above and below are ARMAGH FIRST VOLUNTEERS and PRO PATRIA NON TIMIDUS MORI/ [I am not afraid to die for my country]/1778.

41 *Henry Joy McCracken's Volunteer coat*

ULSTER MUSEUM

McCracken became an officer of the Green Company of the Belfast Regiment of Volunteers, a newly-formed radical group, in 1792. The coat was preserved by his family and donated to the Belfast Museum and Art Gallery by their descendants.

42 *Sword presented to James Napper Tandy, c.1780*

INSCRIBED: *THE GIFT OF THE LIBERTY VOLUNTEERS TO JAMES NAPPER TANDY ESQ* ON THE LOCKET.
ULSTER MUSEUM

The sword is a typical light weapon of the late-eighteenth century. Tandy was immensely popular with the more radical citizens of Dublin when volunteering was at its height, so much so that he was regarded as a dangerous influence and in 1780 was expelled from the movement.

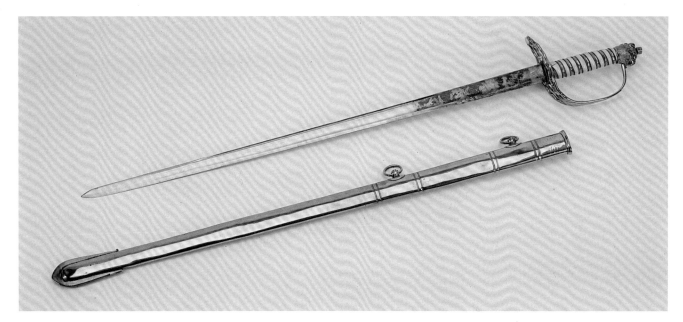

43 *Flute case, Richhill Volunteers, c.1780*

<small>ULSTER MUSEUM</small>

Volunteering was especially strong in County Armagh, the county of Lord Charlemont, the movement's commander-in-chief. The more cautious stance Charlemont adopted towards the question of Catholic emancipation in the later 1780s reflected the realities of life in Armagh, however. The county became the cockpit of serious agrarian strife, which increasingly took on a sectarian character. The fact was that whereas opposition to British control had united almost all shades of opinion, the possible arming and enfranchising of Catholics had the contrary effect, making the decline of Volunteer influence on national politics almost inevitable.

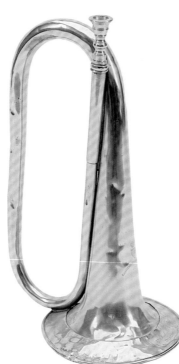

44 *Volunteer trumpet*

<small>INSCRIBED: KILLYLEAGH VOLUNTEER COMPANY 1778 UNDER A CROWNED HARP; MAKER'S NAME
T.B. LOGIER/27 SACKVILLE ST/DUBLIN AT BOTTOM.
ULSTER MUSEUM</small>

45 *Dublin Volunteers meeting on College Green*

<small>BY FRANCIS WHEATLEY (1747-1801)
NATIONAL GALLERY OF IRELAND, DUBLIN
REPRODUCTION</small>

Wheatley's great picture depicting the Dublin Volunteers assembling on College

Green, captures the spirit of the heyday of volunteering, when anyone who was anyone put on regimentals and paraded to the admiration of society at large. It contains many portraits of actual people, such as the Duke of Leinster and Napper Tandy. The painting, the first of Wheatley's major Volunteer groups, was raffled in 1781.

46 *Henry Grattan (1746-1820)*

BY GILBERT STUART
OIL ON CANVAS, 75 x 63 CM
NATIONAL GALLERY OF IRELAND, DUBLIN

Grattan was the son of James Grattan, Recorder of Dublin and MP for the city in the 1760s. Young Henry was educated at Dublin schools, where his fellow pupils included many who later became his political friends or foes (John Fitzgibbon was notable among the latter). He went on to Trinity College and then to study law in London at the Middle Temple. In London he practised oratory and attended parliamentary debates, where he was thrilled by the speeches of William Pitt, Earl

of Chatham in particular. Returning to Dublin he was called to the Irish Bar in 1772. His father, who had died in 1766, had left the family mansion to someone else because of a disagreement with his son, and his mother by dying intestate had deprived Grattan of most of her own property. Impecunious, and ill-adapted to earning much of a living as a barrister, Grattan owed his entry into Irish politics to the patronage of the Earl of Charlemont, who in 1775 put him in for the borough of Charlemont, County Armagh.

The leader of the Patriot opposition in the Irish House of Commons up to the autumn of 1775 was Henry Flood (1732-91), whom Grattan knew and admired. By 1775, however, Flood had become convinced that nothing could be gained if he remained in opposition. The lord lieutenant, Lord Harcourt, and his astute chief secretary, Blaquiere, worked to bring Flood into the administration and in October 1775 he accepted the post of Vice-Treasurer. Grattan condemned Flood as a turncoat, 'with a metaphor in his mouth and a bribe in his pocket', and by his own eloquent and determined opposition soon filled the vacant place. The outbreak of hostilities in America and the rise of the Volunteers provided a unique opportunity for mobilising public opinion in Ireland in favour of greater independence from England for the Dublin parliament. This was at last conceded in 1782; free trade had already been granted. The first action of 'Grattan's Parliament', as it became known, was to vote £50,000 to Grattan himself, with which to purchase an estate in Queen's County (Laois). He intended this gift eventually to revert to the nation to be used for charitable purposes, but his descendants challenged the will successfully and held on to the property. He also acquired the house at Tinnehinch in County Wicklow that became his favourite residence.

Chagrined by Grattan's popularity and convinced that Ireland's legislative independence would never be safe until the Westminster parliament specifically renounced all claim to legislate for Ireland, Flood declared himself far from satisfied with what Grattan had achieved and - supported by many Volunteers - agitated for the Renunciation Act which was conceded early in 1783. This created personal animosity between the two men, whose careers continued to be intertwined.

Despite offers, Grattan never accepted government office, either in the Irish Parliament or later when he sat at Westminster. After 1783 he supported a moderate reform of the Irish Parliament and tithe reform, and constantly advocated admitting Catholics to the franchise and to Parliament. In the 1790s he opposed repressive measures such as the Convention Act, the suspension of Habeas Corpus, the Insurrection Act and the imposition of martial law in Ulster, while supporting the war against France. Along with other liberals, he found himself uncomfortably caught between a repressive government on the one hand and republican conspirators on the other. As a result, in 1797 he and his friends withdrew from Parliament. 'The reason why we seceded', he wrote later, 'was that we did not approve of the conduct of the united men, and we could not approve of the conduct of the government. We were afraid of encouraging the former by making speeches against the latter'. Grattan also resigned his commission in the yeomanry, who got their revenge during the Rebellion by sacking his house at Tinnehinch. Seeing any opposition as Jacobin, the government dismissed Grattan from the privy council, on what was believed to be the evidence of an unreliable informer that he was a sworn member of the United Irishmen; one must mention, however, the fact that the upright James Hope told Madden that Grattan had indeed been sworn. In fact he spent the summer of 1798 in England, returning the following year to re-enter Parliament in order to oppose the Union Bill, which he did with great fervour and eloquence despite being very ill at the time, but in the end unsuccessfully. So bitter was the debate about the union that both parties established duelling clubs to challenge opponents. Grattan himself fought a duel with Isaac Corry, chancellor of the exchequer, who had charged him with encouraging the rebellion. The two met at Ballsbridge, with Sir James Blackwood (afterwards Lord Dufferin) as Grattan's second and Major General Cradock as Corry's. Corry was wounded in the arm. When a sheriff's officer arrived to intervene, the burly Cradock lifted him bodily and he was held face down in a ditch until the affair was over.

After the Union, Grattan retired from politics for a while. In 1801 he refused Lord Fitzwilliam's offer of a seat in the united parliament for Peterborough, but four years later, persuaded by Fox and Fitzwilliam, he stood for the borough of Malton and was elected, making his maiden speech in support of a motion by Fox in favour of a petition by the Catholics. It was said to be one of the most brilliant speeches ever heard in parliament and drew the admiration of Pitt himself. The new ministry in 1806 restored Grattan to the Irish privy council and offered him the post of Irish chancellor of the exchequer, which he refused. At the general election of 1806 he was elected one of the members for Dublin and thereafter continued to represent the city till the day he died. He unsuccessfully raised the Catholic question in 1808, 1810, 1811 and 1812, and was nearly successful with his Roman Catholic Relief Bill in 1813, when the second reading was carried by 245 votes to 205 only to fail by four votes at a later stage. He failed again in 1816 and 1817 and on several occasions in 1819. In May 1819, when his health was failing, he promised a deputation from the Catholic Association, led by O'Connell, to make one last effort. He became so ill that he could not go on by road from Liverpool and had to make the rest of the journey very slowly by canal boat. He died shortly after reaching London. At the request of the leading Whigs he was buried in Westminster Abbey, close to the graves of Chatham and Fox.

Grattan was one of the greatest orators of his day, yet had none of the natural gifts of an orator. He was described as

> short in stature, and unprepossessing in appearance. His arms were disproportionally long: his walk was a stride. With a person swaying like a pendulum, and an abstracted air, he seemed always in thought, and each thought provoked an attendant gesticulation. How strange it seems that a mind so replete with grace and symmetry, and power and splendour, should have been allotted such a dwelling for its residence. Yet so it was, and so also was it one of his highest attributes, that his genius by its excessive light, blinded the hearer to his physical infirmities. It was the victory of mind over matter - the man was forgotten in the orator'.

Daniel O'Connell remarked that he nearly swept the ground with his gestures, and the motion of his arms could be compared to the rolling of a ship in a heavy swell. As for the matter of his speeches, they lacked wit and lightness but they fired educated audiences with enthusiasm and, like Burke's, were full of political aphorisms and memorable phrases. Though always in favour of maintaining the connection with England, he was a great Irish patriot.

Sources: *DNB.*
             Webb, *Compendium of Irish Biography.*
             J.C. Beckett, *The Making of Modern Ireland, 1603-1923.*
             R.B. McDowell, *Ireland in the Age of Imperialism and Revolution 1760-1801.*

47 *Resolutions of the Volunteers, Grand Juries, &c. of Ireland...*

TITLE PAGE OF VOL. 1, WITH ENGRAVED PORTRAIT OF GRATTAN (DUBLIN, 1782)
ULSTER MUSEUM

The Volunteers, originally raised to safeguard the country against possible invasion by the French, never saw action against the enemy but instead became a powerful political pressure group and the extra-parliamentary engine of the Patriot party. This 'compleat Collection' of the resolutions adopted by meetings throughout the country is an impressive record of organised agitation for reform.

HENRY GRATTAN Esq.

A compleat Collection of the

RESOLUTIONS

OF THE

Volunteers, Grand Juries, &c. of Ireland,

Which followed the celebrated Resolves of the

FIRST DUNGANNON DIET.

To which is prefixed

A train of HISTORICAL FACTS relative to the Kingdom, from the Invasion of Henry II. down,

WITH THE

HISTORY OF VOLUNTEERING, &c.

" We know our Duty to our Sovereign, and are *loyal*; we know our Duty to *ourselves*, and are resolved to be FREE."
The PEOPLE.

BY C. H. WILSON.

VOL. I.

DUBLIN:

PRINTED BY *JOSEPH HILL.*
M DCC LXXXII.

4 THE FRENCH REVOLUTION AND GREAT BRITAIN

France paid a high price for helping the Americans break free from her old enemy Great Britain. The cost of the American war was the last straw so far as the French treasury was concerned. It was the resulting financial crisis that led directly to the summoning of the long-disused Estates - General by the King in 1789, thus setting in train the chain of events known as the French Revolution. The rest of Europe looked on in fascination mixed with alarm as arbitrary rule was replaced first by constitutional monarchy, then by republican democracy, as the feudal system was ended, as abstract rights of citizenship were proclaimed only to be ignored in a system of rule by terror, as proclamations of universal peace gave way to the prospect of universal war and conquest.

Great Britain's reaction to events in France was at first one of either enthusiasm or indifference. Many people welcomed France's apparent adoption of an English-style constitutional monarchy as the dawn of a new age. For those uninterested in ideas, the changes could be welcomed because they appeared likely to weaken the old enemy. Long before the overthrow of the monarchy and the spectacle, shocking to conservatives and moderate reformers alike, of a martyred king and queen, more thoughtful minds were expressing doubts. Burke's *Reflections on the Revolution*, the source-book of all subsequent critiques, was published in 1790. The reply to it, Part 1 of Paine's *Rights of Man*, defended the Revolution and a great public debate ensued.

When Great Britain's vital interests in the Low Countries were threatened in 1792 by French revolutionary expansion, however, war was virtually inevitable. Once war broke out, the forces of reaction in Britain began to be mobilised against 'Jacobin' contagion in all its forms; reforms of any kind became anathema. Pitt's government increasingly encouraged popular anti-French manifestations such as Church and King Clubs. Against the phenomenal success of Paine's *Rights of Man* could be set Hannah More's *Village Politics* (1792) and her *Cheap Repository Tracts*, which by 1798 had sold nearly two million copies. The government also made effective use of caricaturists such as Gillray to influence the public mood, creating a propaganda view of France that bore little or no resemblance to the place itself. At the sharp end, though clever liberal lawyers and independent-minded juries foiled most prosecutions of reformers for high treason, severely repressive measures were taken against radicals in London and in Scotland.

48 *The Taking of the Bastille, 14 July 1789*

BY JEAN-PIERRE HOUEL
MUSÉE CARNAVALET, PARIS
REPRODUCTION (BRIDGEMAN ART LIBRARY)

The Bastille was a fortress-prison in Paris, originally constructed in 1370 to defend the entrance to the city. In the eighteenth century it was intended for use in repressing possible uprisings by the Parisians; cannons on its four towers could in fact be trained on the city. Furthermore, since the reign of Louis XIV it was a state prison, where any royal subject could be put away, without trial and for an indefinite period, on the authority of the King as expressed in a *lettre de cachet*. The Bastille was therefore a symbol of arbitrary royal power. Rumour exaggerated the number of prisoners it was supposed to contain. In fact, when it was stormed in 1789 it was found to contain only seven. Nevertheless, its destruction was rightly seen as a great event, and was afterwards celebrated as the national holiday. Abolished under later monarchical regimes, the holiday was restored in 1880.

At the time of the assault, the Bastille's garrison consisted of only thirty Swiss guards and eighty veterans, under the governor de Launay. The fighting resulted in the death of ninety-eight citizens and the wounding of another seventy-three; de Launay was subsequently torn to pieces by the infuriated mob. Six of the garrison were also killed. Afterwards, the fortress was totally demolished, the unscrupulous contractor doing a brisk trade in souvenirs. At Versailles, the King had assembled several regiments and for a day or two thought about suppressing the revolt in Paris, but the morale of the troops was not encouraging and they were sent back to their garrisons. Bowing to the inevitable, Louix XVI then went to Paris, where he recognised the new municipal authorities and accepted from the hands of the mayor the tricolour cockade adopted by the National Guard, consisting of the blue and red of the city of Paris surmounted by the white of the Bourbons - the invention of their commander, Lafayette.

Jean-Pierre Houel was born in 1735 and died in 1813. Bénézit describes him as an interesting minor master who deserves to be better known and remarks that several of his compositions have been attributed to more famous painters. His image of the fall of the Bastille corresponds closely to that of other artists as the one quickly established as acceptable. It shows three phases of the action: the assault by the National Guards (left), the attack on the inner courtyard (right) and the arrest of the governor (middle distance).

Sources: Scott and Rothaus (eds), *Historical Dictionary of the French Revolution.*
Bénézit, *Dictionnaire.*
David Bindman, *The Shadow of the Guillotine: Britain and the French Revolution*
(British Museum Catalogue, 1989).

49 *Droits de l'Homme et du Citoyen*

COLOURED ENGRAVING WITH TEXT
MUSÉE CARNAVALET, PARIS
REPRODUCTION

The 'Declaration of the Rights of Man and of the Citizen' arose out of the debates in the French National Assembly in 1789, when the deputies were starting to devise a new constitution for France. In all its essentials, the text was settled in one week, 20-26 August 1789; there was a minor correction in October 1789 when the document was prepared for presentation to the King, and amendments to four of the articles were adopted in August 1791, shortly before the promulgation of the constitution, when the Declaration was published as its preface.

There was some debate in 1789 as to whether such a manifesto should be adopted at all. Many deputies were opposed, and a motion that there should be a declaration of citizens' duties as well was put forward but rejected by 570 votes to 433. The Declaration combined two things: a bill of rights for French citizens who had suffered from the defects of the *ancien régime* and a sketch of a future ideal society. It was the latter that gave it universal appeal. In the Europe of the day, many of the ideas expressed in the Declaration were either directly or potentially subversive of the very basis of government and society as hitherto known and accepted. This was why it was hailed with horror by people like Burke and with joy by Paine and other radicals. The seventeen articles of the Declaration, in summary, state that all citizens are born equal and are equal in the eyes of the law, with rights to liberty, property, security and the right to resist tyranny; the sovereign authority is the nation and laws are the expression of the general will; every citizen has the right to freedom of opinion, speech, writing etc. The general background was that of the Enlightenment; particular strands identified by scholars may be ascribed to Jean-Jacques Rousseau, the English philosopher Locke and the French thinkers known collectively as the Physiocrats.

Sources: Scott and Rothaus (eds), *Historical Dictionary of the French Revolution.*

50 *Arrestation du Roi et sa Famille désertant du Royaume*

Handcoloured etching by an anonymous artist
Paris? c.1791; 25 x 38 cm
National Library of Ireland, Dublin

This etching, one of many prints prompted by the episode, depicts the moment

ARRESTATION DU ROI ET SA FAMILLE DÉSERTANT DU ROYAUME ..

when Louis XVI, Marie Antoinette, their two children and the King's sister were stopped at Varennes (here spelt Varrennes) during their flight to the German border, on 21 June 1791. Their escape, in which the King was disguised as the steward of a noblewoman and the Queen as the governess of her children, was organised by a Swedish nobleman, Count Axel von Fersen, who was an admirer of Marie Antoinette. The escape from Paris worked perfectly, but the coach travelled slowly and the party missed the planned rendezvous with troops loyal to the King. Nearing Varennes, at the village of Sainte Ménéhould, the suspicions of a local postmaster, Jean Baptiste Drouet, were aroused. He thought he recognised the Queen from his days as a soldier in Paris, and the King from the portrait on a banknote. Drouet warned the authorities at Varennes, who stopped the coach and made the occupants descend and enter the house of the mayor. Here their identity was confirmed.

The fugitives were escorted all the way back to Paris, 'sans honneurs' as the caption says, where an immense crowd of revolutionary soldiers and citizens - 'plus de 50 mille Citoyens et Soldats' - had assembled to receive them. The episode had important repercussions, destroying any credibility Louis may have had as a constitutional monarch, and leading directly to the imprisonment of the royal family and the proclamation of a republic the following year.

Sources: Christopher Hibbert, *The French Revolution* (London, 1980).

51 *The Execution of Louis XVI, 21 January 1793*

COLOURED ENGRAVING
BIBLIOTHÈQUE NATIONALE, PARIS
REPRODUCTION (BRIDGEMAN ART LIBRARY)

Having imprisoned the King in the autumn of 1792, the revolutionaries had to decide what to do with him. A motion to try him was finally made in the Convention, which referred this tricky matter to a committee. The possible charges had to be considered, as had the impact of a trial and its outcome on the rest of Europe. There were questions of procedure as well: whether to use a regular court or a special tribunal. The committee reported back on 7 November. On the claim that the King's person was inviolable under the constitution, it was argued that he had sacrificed his immunity by his personal actions against the nation and could therefore be tried. Trial by the Convention itself, rather than by the ordinary courts, was recommended, since the Convention represented the people. For the same reason, the verdict should not be submitted to the people in a plebiscite - the proposal of some moderates. The doctrinaire Saint-Just proposed that Louis be judged as an enemy alien and tried for being a king, the worst crime of all, while Robespierre said he should be executed without a trial.

On 3 December the Convention decided it was competent to try the King, and the trial began eight days later. The discovery of a secret iron chest in the Tuileries, which contained evidence of his intrigues with foreign powers, sealed Louis's fate. The trial itself ended on 7 January. Thereafter, between 15 and 17 January, three questions were put to a roll call of the Convention. In the first, Louis was found guilty of conspiracy against the nation, by 716 of the 745 members present. On the question of submitting the judgement to the people, 424 voted against, 283 for. On the death penalty without reprieve, the vote for was 361, against 360, too small a margin to be acceptable. Three days later, however, the reprieve was rejected by 380 to 310 and the execution was set for the following day.

This print shows the state executioner, Charles Sanson (1740-93), holding the head of Louis XVI (reduced to plain 'Citizen Capet') up to the crowd immediately after his execution by guillotine. Sanson's assistants are putting the victim's bound body into the long wicker basket that was used on such occasions. Sanson's trade ran in the family: his son Henri (1767-1840) was also an official executioner and assisted him in beheading Marie Antoinette later in the same year. The famous Madame Tussaud later acquired from the Sanson family, along with other gruesome mementoes, a guillotine blade that may have been the one used on both occasions.

Sources: Scott and Rothaus, *Historical Dictionary of the French Revolution.*
David Bindman, *The Shadow of the Guillotine.*

52 *William Pitt (1789)*

BY JAMES GILLRAY
WATERCOLOUR, 22.9 X 17.1 CM
NATIONAL PORTRAIT GALLERY, LONDON

William Pitt the Younger (1759-1806) was the second son of William Pitt, Earl of Chatham. Educated at Cambridge, he was called to the bar in 1780 and entered Parliament in the following year aged twenty-one, joining Lord Shelburne, the leader of the party that had followed his father. Despite his youth, he resolved to accept no minor office and turned down offers from Lord Rockingham, but was briefly chancellor of the exchequer under Shelburne 1782-83. He refused to serve in the next ministry, that of Fox and North, despite George III's anxiety that he should do so and Shelburne's approval. When the ministry was dismissed in 1783, the King appointed Pitt prime minister despite his youth (he was only twenty-four) and his lack of a majority in the House of Commons, which burst into laughter when it heard the news. Though repeatedly defeated in votes he held on, with the

backing of the King and the Lords, until 1784. In the general election of that year he won a resounding victory. He was to remain prime minister for the rest of his life, with only one interval, 1801-04, throughout the whole period of the French Revolution and much of the long war with France. His ministry was first notable for its financial reforms - funding and reducing the national debt and altering a wide range of Customs and Excise duties in order to make the national pastime of smuggling less attractive and thus raise revenue.

Pitt's position was seriously threatened in November 1789 by the insanity of George III, for if the Prince of Wales had become regent he would have replaced Pitt by his own friend Fox and the Whigs. Pitt maintained that the regent ought to be appointed by Parliament and that his powers ought to be limited; a bill to that effect was being debated when the King's sudden recovery removed the need for it. In Ireland, Grattan and the Whigs had threatened to create a constitutional crisis by proposing to proclaim the Prince regent regardless of the outcome in England - one of the things that the future union was intended to prevent.

When the Revolution broke out in France, Pitt at first regarded it as a domestic matter which did not much concern Great Britain, except in so far as it weakened the power of the old rival. The way the Revolution developed, however, the overthrow of the monarchy and the execution of Louis XVI, the aggressive foreign policy of the Republic in the Low Countries and the spread of republican principles in Great Britain led to the outbreak of war with France in February 1793. The war was to dominate every aspect of policy and politics thereafter. In 1794 most of the Whig opposition turned to supporting Pitt, leaving only Fox and his small band as persistent critics. Pitt now abandoned earlier thoughts of parliamentary reform and (May 1793) suspended the Act of Habeas Corpus (which prevented the keeping of arrested suspects in prison without trial). The government's policy for pursuing the war in Europe was to create coalitions with the anti-Revolution powers, to which Britain provided finance rather than troops. She herself concentrated on naval and colonial activity against France and the powers, such as Holland, that came within the French orbit. This necessitated the raising of huge loans and a vast increase in the national debt.

The policy was both expensive and ineffective, for the professional armies of Britain's allies proved to be no match for Revolutionary armies led by brilliant young generals such as Bonaparte and Hoche, and the coalition members were one by one obliged to make peace with France. In England, financial distress and bad harvests made both the monarch and his minister unpopular, to the point where George III, when opening Parliament in October 1795, was met with cries of 'Bread' , 'Peace' and 'No Pitt', and Pitt was obliged to seek terms with the French Directory in March 1796. The negotiations broke down. Matters got worse in 1797, when Britain, alone still at war with the French, was in a desperate financial plight; to crown it all, there were mutinies in the fleet. By the end of that year Pitt was being insulted and threatened by the mob and had to be given a cavalry escort. In April 1798 he made the land tax - the main direct tax - perpetual; in December 1798 he introduced, as a temporary measure, an income tax.

This was the background to events in Ireland which culminated in the rebellion of 1798, and which made the Union, in Pitt's view, essential to the survival of Great Britain.

James Gillray (1757-1815) was the greatest English caricaturist of his age. Of humble background, he was apprenticed to a letter-engraver and later studied at the Royal Academy. Starting with anonymous caricatures of social subjects, he turned to political themes after 1780. Most of his 1,500 productions were published by Hannah Humphrey at 29 St James's Street, Piccadilly, where he lived. Many of his earlier ones ridiculed the royal family, but in the later 1790s his talents were harnessed in the government's drive against the radicals and the French, in savage attacks on Fox and foreigners. A number of his works in 1798 deal with the Irish Rebellion. His conventional work included two portraits of Pitt; this one was done in 1789.

Sources: *DNB.*

53 *Thomas Muir (1765-98)*

BY DAVID MARTIN
CHALK DRAWING 29.8 x 18.6 CM
SCOTTISH NATIONAL PORTRAIT GALLERY, EDINBURGH

The Scottish reformer and radical Thomas Muir was born in Glasgow in 1765, the only son of a well-to-do merchant, and educated at Glasgow Grammar School and Glasgow University before completing his law studies in Edinburgh, where he was admitted to the Faculty of Advocates (the Scottish Bar) in 1787. He was an elder of the kirk at Cadder in Lanarkshire and sat in the General Assembly of the established Presbyterian church. As an advocate he sometimes gave his services free for defendants he thought oppressed. As a liberal in politics he favoured parliamentary reform and welcomed the French Revolution. When the formation of the London Society of the Friends of the People led to a meeting in Glasgow in 1792 to create something similar, Muir took part in it and subsequently became one of the leaders of the movement in Scotland. At a national convention of delegates, held in Edinburgh, he read out a fraternal address from the United Irishmen, composed by William Drennan and transmitted by Archibald Hamilton Rowan. This was regarded as a seditious document and Muir was arrested on 2 January 1793 and accused of sedition.

Liberated on bail, Muir at once went off to France by way of London, where he was entertained by the London Corresponding Society and commissioned by its then predominantly moderate membership to remonstrate against the proposed execution of Louis XVI (he arrived too late to do anything about it). Remaining in Paris, he was outlawed in Edinburgh, had his bail confiscated and was struck off the roll of advocates. Foolishly, he returned to Scotland, where he was immediately arrested and on 30 August 1793 was tried before the high court in Edinburgh on charges of exciting a spirit of disloyalty and disaffection, recommending Paine's *Rights of Man*, distributing seditious writings and reading aloud a seditious writing. He defended himself, in a trial before a highly prejudiced jury which went on until 2 a.m. the following day. He was found guilty and, to the consternation of even the jury, was given the savage sentence of transportation for fourteen years. Despite a debate in both houses of parliament on its legality, the sentence was allowed to stand and in March 1794 Muir and three other defendants were despatched to Botany Bay. There he purchased a small farm, which he called Hunter's Hill after his house in Scotland and which is now a suburb of Sydney.

Liberal sympathisers everywhere were outraged by the nature and outcome of the Scottish trials. Muir's case excited so much sympathy in the United States in particular that a ship was engaged at New York to sail to Australia to rescue him. The *Otter* arrived in Australia early in 1796 and on 11 February Captain Dawes sailed homeward with Muir on board. They never reached New York. After crossing the Pacific, the *Otter* was shipwrecked in Nootka Sound. The survivors, Muir among them, were made captive by the local Red Indians before reaching Mexico, where they were treated hospitably. Imprisonment by the Spanish authorities in Havana in Cuba followed. From there Muir was sent in a Spanish frigate to Spain. Off Cadiz the Spanish vessel was attacked by two British warships. In the bloody engagement Muir was badly wounded (one eye and part of his cheek was shot off) and left for dead on the deck. An old schoolfellow of his, who was among the boarding party, is said to have identified him by the inscription in the Bible he was holding and sent him ashore with the rest of the wounded. His troubles were far from over. Despite the fact that he had fought for Spain, the authorities in Cadiz detained him as a British subject and kept him as a prisoner of war. His fate became known to the Directory in France, however, which secured his release and offered hospitality and French citizenship to this famous Scotsman.

Muir reached Paris on 4 February 1798. There he made a considerable nuisance of himself to Wolfe Tone, allying himself with the unreliable Napper Tandy, claiming to speak for Ireland as well as Scotland and England, and bombarding the Directors with misleading memorials. In a three-hour interview Tone found the Scotsman incredibly vain and obstinate. 'I could scarcely conceive such a degree of self-sufficiency to exist', he wrote afterwards, 'he told us roundly that he knew as much of our country as we did, and ... had as much of the confidence of the United Irishmen as we had...'. In fact, Muir's mental and physical state had been severely affected by his experiences and his Spanish wound had never healed properly. He died at Chantilly on 27 September 1798, a month after his thirty-third birthday.

This sketch of Muir was done by the Scottish artist David Martin during the trial in 1793.

Sources: *DNB*.
            Tone, *Autobiography*, ed. B. O'Brien, vol. 2.
            C. Bewley, *Muir of Huntershill* (Oxford, 1981).

54 *Robert Burns (1759-96)*

By George Anderson Lawson (1832-1904)
Whole-length bronze, height 95 cm
Ulster Museum

Signed and dated 1891, this is a bronze model for the larger-than-life statue of Burns by Lawson which was erected in 1891 in front of the railway station at Ayr.

It was acquired by the Burns Admirers of Belfast and presented by them, along with other Burns memorabilia, to the municipal museum in Belfast on 21 September 1892. Though done long after Burns's death it is a good likeness, the head being based on Nasmyth's portrait of the poet (now in the Scottish National Portrait Gallery, Edinburgh). It shows him whole-length wearing coat, waistcoat, knee-breeches and woollen stockings, with his arms held over his chest.

The sculptor Lawson was born in Edinburgh in 1832 and died at Richmond, Surrey in 1904. After studying in Edinburgh and Rome he settled in London in 1866, exhibiting in the Royal Scottish Academy from 1860 and in the Royal Academy between 1866 and 1893. His greatest work, in all respects, is the colossal statue of the Duke of Wellington on the memorial column in Liverpool.

Burns was no political activist, especially during his later years when he held a government post as exciseman at Dumfries, but the tone of some of his verses and his evident sympathy with the democratic trend of events in France nearly led to his dismissal in 1792, at a time when the conservative establishment in Scotland was beginning to come down hard on radicalism of any kind. Burns's verses were greatly admired among Presbyterian radicals in the north of Ireland (and continued to be, long after their descendants had abandoned Irish nationalism). Like him, they had little respect for rank and would have approved of his Painite sentiment, 'a man's a man for a' that'.

55 *Reflections on the Revolution in France*

BY EDMUND BURKE, LONDON, 1790
P. AND B. ROWAN

Edmund Burke's *Reflections on the Revolution in France*, as its full title indicates, began as a personal reply to a private letter and ended as a public examination and refutation of the claims of the Revolution's supporters. Late in 1789 a young acquaintance in Paris, C. De Pont, had asked Burke for his views on events in France. Burke's hostility to the Revolution, already stirring, had been further stimulated by a sermon given by a leading Dissenting minister, Dr R. Price, to the Revolution Society in London on 4 November 1789. Price's 'Discourse on the Love of Country' saw the Revolution as the beginning of a golden age of reform throughout Europe which would in England complete the work of the Glorious Revolution of 1688, including the reform of Parliament and the disestablishment of the Church of England. The address had been well received by the Revolution Society, which had sent congratulations to the French National Assembly for its defence of human rights and its reorganisation of government. Burke worked for nearly a year on his project, while Thomas Paine - hearing of it - impatiently awaited its publication so that he could fashion his own reply, *The Rights of Man*. Burke's book was finally published in November 1790, to great acclaim from conservative circles and condemnation from liberals and radicals.

In the first part, Burke set out to show that the Revolution was both unnecessary (because the old regime was gradually reforming itself, absolute monarchy was on the way out and liberty was increasingly secure) and also dangerous. An unholy alliance of moneyed interests and atheistic thinkers had fomented a revolutionary movement that would uproot the natural, traditional order of society in the name of abstract doctrines which were meaningless because unrelated to the real needs of people. 'The age of chivalry is gone', he lamented in a famous phrase, 'That of sophisters, economists, and calculators has succeeded, and the glory of Europe is extinguished forever'.

In the concluding part of his work, Burke reviewed the reforms of the National Assembly and found them on the whole to be an unmitigated disaster. The confiscation of property violated fundamental human rights, discipline in the armed

REFLECTIONS

ON THE

REVOLUTION IN FRANCE,

AND ON THE

PROCEEDINGS IN CERTAIN SOCIETIES
IN LONDON

RELATIVE TO THAT EVENT.

IN A

LETTER

INTENDED TO HAVE BEEN SENT TO A GENTLEMAN
IN PARIS.

BY THE RIGHT HONOURABLE

EDMUND BURKE.

LONDON:
PRINTED FOR J. DODSLEY, IN PALL-MALL.
M.DCC.XC.

forces has been subverted by the challenge to all authority. In the end, Burke predicted - and he was right in this at least - that the Republic would fall into the hands of a military dictator.

Sources: Scott and Rothaus (eds), *Historical Dictionary of the French Revolution.*

56 *Contemporary Portrait of Thomas Paine (1737-1809)*

Attributed to George Romney (1734-1802)
Oil on canvas, 43.2 x 36.5 cm
Mr Neil Clayton

Thomas Paine, the apostle of democracy, republicanism and secularism, was born at Thetford in Norfolk. His father Joseph, a Quaker, was a staymaker and small farmer. After an education at the local grammar school, Tom was apprenticed to his father's trade, but at the age of nineteen ran away to sea, where he joined the crew of a privateer. Returning to Norfolk he became a junior excise officer at Thetford in 1761, then at Grantham and Alford in Lincolnshire, where he was sacked in 1765. For a time he taught and preached and worked as a staymaker before securing another excise appointment, at Lewes in Sussex, where he married for the second time. At Lewes he led an agitation to have the pay and conditions of excisemen improved. This led to his dismissal. Having separated from his wife, in 1774 Paine went to London, where he secured an interview with the American envoy Benjamin Franklin, who gave him letters of introduction. Armed with these, Paine took ship for America.

There, in the rapidly worsening relations between the colonists and George III's government in London, Paine made a great impression with his pen. His pamphlet *Common Sense*, published in 1776, was largely responsible for the colonists' Declaration of Independence, and his subsequent series of tracts entitled *The Crisis*, under the pseudonym 'Common Sense', did much to encourage the American troops in the War of Independence. The opening words, 'These are the times that try men's souls' became famous. In 1777 he was appointed secretary to the Congressional committee on foreign affairs, but was dismissed in 1779 for indiscreet revelations about the colonists' alliance with France. In 1781 he visited France for the first time, as secretary to the American envoy, Laurens, returning in August of that year to Boston. Such was his fame in America that he was allowed a salary of 800 dollars at the end of the war to enable him to continue writing. Paine became concerned about the danger of despotism in the name of the people in the new republic and when he expressed his misgivings in print was bitterly attacked himself. Also, he had become involved in a project for a cast-iron bridge. When this did not prosper, he decided to see what could be done with it in Europe.

Armed with more letters of introduction from Franklin, Paine went to France in 1787 with a model of his bridge, which he presented to the French Academy of Sciences in Paris in July. His bridge created great interest but failed to find backers, so he soon returned to politics. The approach of the Revolution in France provided absorbing politics in abundance. Paine of course welcomed the changes. His famous reply to Burke - Part 1 of *The Rights of Man* - was published in March 1791. It created a great sensation and had an enormous circulation before the government tried to suppress it, which made it more popular still. The publication of Part 2 in 1792 led to Paine's indictment for treason by a London jury and he was followed everywhere by government agents. Before his trial came up he was elected to the new French Convention by the department of Calais and escaped to France. In his absence he was made an outlaw, which probably suited the government better than having him tried in person, such was his fame. No book had ever sold like *The Rights of Man*. No fewer than six editions were published in the first couple of months, 50,000 copies sold. Paine himself later estimated that the complete work had sold 400,000 to half a million by 1802. This was despite its high price of three shillings (the same as Burke's *Reflections*). Cheap editions galore followed, authorised or not.

In France, where he was to live for the next ten years as a French citizen, Paine had a chequered career. In the Convention debates his speeches had to be translated and read for him, since he had little or no French. He created suspicion and enmity among the Jacobins in the assembly by speaking and voting for the detention and banishment of Louis XVI rather than his death, and when Robespierre instituted the Terror was thrown into prison, where he remained for nearly a year, half-starved and in daily fear of his life. Only the fall of Robespierre saved him from the guillotine.

Just before his arrest in December 1773 Paine had composed Part 1 of his next great work, which he entitled *The Age of Reason*. He completed most of the rest of it in prison, and the entire book was published in 1795. A swingeing attack, in his best controversial style, on revealed religion in general and Christianity in particular, it caused delight in some quarters but revulsion in others, not only increasing the hatred with which Paine was regarded in England but also leading to condemnation by many of his American admirers. He was labelled an atheist, though his views were rather those of a deist.

Paine returned to America in 1802 after falling out with Napoleon, then First Consul of the Republic. In America, however, he found himself more or less ostracised, either because of general hostility to *The Age of Reason* or because he had attacked George Washington bitterly in print. He died in New York in 1809 and was buried at New Rochelle. Ten years later, in 1819, the English radical William Cobbett, one of Paine's most enthusiastic converts, exhumed his bones and transported them in a box to Liverpool, where he hoped to raise the money to erect a monument to 'the common sense of the great man'. The money was never raised, and after Cobbett's death the bones were passed about and disappeared completely. A statue of Paine was eventually erected at Thetford in 1964.

In Ireland, the success of *The Rights of Man* was phenomenal, sales of Part 1, at an estimated 40,000, far exceeding those in Great Britain during the first eight months or so. It was published in Dublin within days of its appearance in London, at the substantial price of 2s. 2d. a copy. This edition quickly sold out and was followed by a larger printing. In all, there were seven editions in 1791, six in Dublin and the seventh in Derry, oddly enough none in Belfast, despite Wolfe Tone's remark that 'Paine's book' had become 'the Koran' there. In addition, lengthy extracts were printed in three Dublin newspapers and in the *Belfast Newsletter*. The Dublin 6d. edition - 'six-penny pacquets of sedition' - ran to 20,000 or so. James Napper Tandy, the leading Dublin radical, was a chief promoter in all this. It was not so much Paine's critique of monarchy as his direct style and memorably fresh imagery that struck his Irish readers and thus prepared the ground for the United Irishmen. Part 2 of *The Rights of Man*, published in London early in February 1792, was published in Dublin almost immediately. Rival sixpenny editions in Dublin and Belfast followed in April. Paine's insistence on a republican form of government, without a kingly figurehead, and his advocacy of a wide-ranging social programme - progressive taxation, state pensions, dole for the poor, universal education - provoked less enthusiastic reactions. Moderate Whigs such as Lord Charlemont repudiated Paine, radical printers were indicted, Tandy - accused of having taken the oath of the Defenders - fled the country, even the *Northern Star*, the new radical newspaper in Belfast, was cautious in publishing extracts.

Until his phenomenal success in Ireland, Paine had shown little interest in the country. Thereafter, in France, where he met with his keen disciple Lord Edward (or Citizen) FitzGerald in November 1792, he became converted to the idea of French military intervention and consistently used his influence to promote schemes of invasion.

The publication of *The Age of Reason* in 1795 embarrassed and divided Paine's radical admirers in Ireland as elsewhere. Tone thought it 'damned trash', the devout Russell published a pamphlet against it, as did the Rev. William Jackson and both Catholic and Presbyterian radical clergy. On the other hand, the Shearses and Arthur O'Connor welcomed Paine's uncompromising secularism. According to the loyalist historian of the rebellion, Sir Richard Musgrave, *The Age of Reason* had its most favourable reception in the north, where a large impression 'was struck off in Belfast, and distributed gratis among the united societies. Bundles of them were thrown into meeting-house yards on Sundays, before the congregations assembled; and small parcels were left on the sides of publick roads, to contaminate the minds of those who found them'. He went on to note: 'The popish priests carefully guarded their flocks from the contagion of them...'.

Finally, it is worth noting that in his last years in the United States, when many

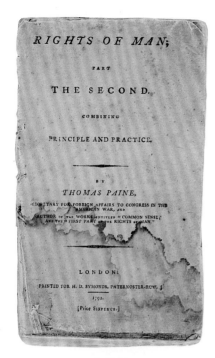

of his old friends there virtually ostracised him, Paine was supported by former United Irishmen; one of them - Thomas Addis Emmet - became his executor.

Sources: John Keane, *Tom Paine: A Political Life* (London, 1995).
            David Dickson, 'Paine and Ireland', in D. Dickson, D. Keogh and K. Whelan (eds), *The United Irishmen* (Dublin, 1993).

57 *Rights of Man: Part The Second*

BY THOMAS PAINE (LONDON, 1792)
P. AND B. ROWAN

This sixpenny edition is prefaced by a copy of Paine's letter to his friend Lafayette, dated 9 February 1792, which accompanied the presentation of a copy of *Rights of Man* Part 1.

58 *Spence tokens*

ULSTER MUSEUM

At the end of the eighteenth century there was a great wave of token issuing - unofficial halfpennies substituting for the scarce, much forged and poor quality official coins. Quite soon, however, some recognised that the tokens could be a valuable means of advertising or supplying a nascent collector's market and among the most important of these was Thomas Spence, radical, eccentric, bookseller and coin dealer. Spence held a number of revolutionary ideas, especially about land tenure, and many of his tokens refer to these and advertise his pamphlets.

(a) *Rouse Britannia*. A seated Britannia, similar in pose to that used on regal coins, holds a Staff of Maintenance with a Cap of Liberty in front.
The reverse shows a manacled prisoner with the legend *Before the Revolution* and the date 1795. Spence complained that year that since 1792 he had been dragged from his shop four times and indicted, but never convicted.

(b) *Pig's Meat*. A Cap of Liberty over a pig trampling on the symbols of monarchy, church and aristocracy.
In 1793 Spence wrote and published *Pig's Meat: or Lessons from the Swinish Multitude Collected by the Poor Man's Advocate*, leading to a seven month imprisonment in Newgate. He also wrote a verse edition of the *Rights of Man* and his identification with Tom Paine and Sir Thomas More is referred to on the reverse.

(a) Obverse

(a) Reverse

(b) Obverse

(b) Reverse

76

(c) *Portrait of Lord George Gordon.* Gordon was an agitator, principally famous for inciting a series of anti-Catholic riots in 1780, which led to his trial for high treason, on which charge he was acquitted. A subsequent visit to France added a further revolutionary tinge to his views. In spite of living quietly in Birmingham, where he adopted Jewish customs (hence the dress shown on this token), he was indicted for libel in 1788 and imprisoned in Newgate, where he died of a fever in 1793.

Reverse shows a caduceus (symbol of the god Mercury) with a Cap of Liberty at top and a crown at the bottom. The edge reads *Spence Dealer in Coins London.*

(d) A native American with legend *If rents I once consent to pay my liberty is past away.* Reverse: a donkey loaded with double panniers labelled (bottom pair) *Rents* and (upper pair) *Taxes;* legend *I was an ass to bear the first pair.* The native American symbolises the noble savage of Rousseau's philosophy, living in a world of innocence, freedom and plenty. Spence was obsessed by issues of land tenure and perceived the ownership of land to be the keystone of political liberty.

(d) Obverse   (d) Reverse

(c) Obverse

(c) Reverse

59 *Anti-Paine copper token*

ANONYMOUS
ULSTER MUSEUM

Many of the eighteenth-century tokens have no identifiable issuer, defeating the purpose of a redeemable token but making additional profit for those involved in the fraud. There is a small group of tokens with anti-Paine types, sometimes combined with anti-Jacobin sentiments. This is a variety of the usual obverse, implying that Thomas Paine's fate ought to be hanging. The other side reverses the title of his book to *The Wrong's of Man,* with the date of publication, given here wrongly as 21 January 1793.

60 *A Right Honorable alias a Sans Culotte*

BY I[SAAC] C[RUIKSHANK]
COLOURED ENGRAVING, 32.4 X 29 CM, PUBLISHED IN LONDON 20 DEC. 1792 BY S. FORES
BRITISH MUSEUM, LONDON

Charles James Fox, the leading liberal Whig in Britain and a supporter of the Revolution in France even after most of his followers had deserted to Pitt, is shown here as a dangerously divided character, on the one hand as an English patriot and

statesman, civilised and decently dressed, on the other a ragged French sans-culotte, ferociously armed with spiked club and singing the revolutionary song *Ça Ira* instead of *God Save Great George our King*. The image of a split personality was - and still is - commonly used by caricaturists to attack politicians.

Isaac Cruikshank (c.1756-1811), caricaturist and watercolourist, exhibited at the Royal Academy in the early 1790s and produced a number of effective caricatures in the government interest during that troubled decade. His two sons, Isaac Robert and George, both became notable as caricaturists, particularly the latter.

Sources: *British Museum Catalogue of Political and Personal Satires*, VI, no. 8142.
            DNB.

61 *The Hopes of the Party! Or The Darling Children of Democracy!*

COLOURED AQUATINT, 33.8 X 27.8 CM, PUBLISHED IN LONDON 28 FEB. 1798 BY W. HOLLAND
BRITISH MUSEUM, LONDON

This extremely effective propaganda print shows a monstrous creature with a manikin on each knee: Fox on the left and Horne Tooke on the right, both wearing a cap of liberty or bonnet-rouge. The figure of Democracy is naked except for a bonnet with tricolour cockade and tricolour sash with dagger. Her chin is bearded, she has shaggy hair and pendant breasts, and her hands and feet end in long talons. She glares delightedly at Tooke. The whole thing indicates that 'democracy' has highly sinister connotations.

John Horne Tooke (1736-1812) was a radical politician and one-time clergyman who defended the radical John Wilkes, met Voltaire, organised a 'Society for

The Hopes of the Party! or the Darling Children of Democracy!

supporting the Bill of Rights' and the Constitutional Society (1771), was fined and imprisoned for organising a subscription for the American colonists, and was tried for high treason in 1794 but acquitted. He was by no means always a supporter of Fox, but was frequently demonised by conservatives along with him because of his radical views.

Sources: *BM Catalogue*, IV, no. 9178.
             DNB.

62 *A Republican Beau. A Picture of Paris for 1794*

BY I[SAAC] CRUIKSHANK
COLOURED ENGRAVING, 27.3 X 19.2 CM, PUBLISHED IN LONDON, 10 MARCH 1795 BY S.W. FORES
BRITISH MUSEUM, LONDON

This print shows a ferocious French ruffian, clad in a ragged tricolour suit. His right hand holds a bludgeon with spikes and a dagger blade, his left a dagger dripping blood. His coat is fastened with another dagger. A dead infant, labelled *for a stew*, protrudes from his pocket. Two pistols are stuck in his belt. Behind him, to left, is an altar with a crucifix thrown down and inscribed *This is our God*. On it is a guillotine. Bodies hang from a gibbet in the background.

The Reign of Terror in France was at its height from September 1793 to July 1794. Events in the Terror, here demonised and much exaggerated, seemed to justify the warnings issued by Edmund Burke in his *Reflections on the French Revolution* and the fears expressed by British reactionaries.

Sources: *BM Catalogue*, IV, no. 8435.

A REPUBLICAN BEAU.
A Picture of Paris for 1794.

63 *A Republican Belle. A Picture of Paris for 1794*

<small>BY I[SAAC C[RUIKSHANK]
COLOURED ENGRAVING, 26.4 X 19.2 CM, PUBLISHED IN LONDON, 10 MARCH 1794 BY S.W. FORES
BRITISH MUSEUM, LONDON</small>

This companion print to Cruikshank's *Republican Beau* shows a Parisian virago, also in rags, with a mouthful of fangs. The pistol in her left hand carelessly fires point-blank at a poor man lying on the ground; her right hand holds a dagger. A ribbon in her wild hair is inscribed *War War Eternal War,* a model guillotine hangs from her neck and another, tiny guillotine is worn as an earring. Her skirt consists of a piece of fringed cloth decorated with skulls and crossbones, perhaps part of a church pall. The sign of the inn in the background is the bleeding head of Louis XVI; a naked corpse hangs from it. Outside the inn a game of bowls is being played with skulls.

During the Terror the guillotine motif was actually used in decoration, and women in some parts of the country where support for the Revolution was particularly strong did indeed hang little gold guillotines from their ears.

64 *London Corresponding Society, alarm'd, Vide. Guilty Consciences*

<small>BY J[AME]S G[ILLRA]Y
COLOURED AQUATINT, 23.5 X 18.3 CM, PUBLISHED IN LONDON 20 APRIL 1798 BY H. HUMPHREY
BRITISH MUSEUM, LONDON</small>

Six brutish-looking conspirators are shown sitting around a table in a cellar listening to their equally brutish chairman reading a paper marked *State Arrests - O'Connor*

London Corresponding Society, alarm'd, Vide. Guilty Consciences

Binns Evans Quigley. The chairman's tankard is inscribed, *Tom Treason Hell-Fire Cellar Chick Lane.* Beside his chair leans a book, *Proceedings of the London Corresponding Society,* with the names of delegates such as Forging Sam, Barber Joe and so on. Portraits of *Horne Tooke* and *Tom Payne* hang on the wall.

These grotesque figures were not typical members of the London Corresponding Society. Some of its wilder spirits, however, including the secretary Evans and Benjamin Binns, did favour revolution with the help of France and tried to form a society of United Englishmen. The Corresponding Society ceased to meet soon after its Committee was arrested, and it was suppressed by name in the 1799 Act (29 Geo. III, c.79) against seditious and treasonable societies.

Sources: *BM Catalogue,* VII, no. 9202.

65 *SEARCH-NIGHT; OR State-Watchmen, mistaking Honest-Men for Conspirators - Vide State Arrests.*

BY J[AME]S G[ILLRA]Y
COLOURED ENGRAVING, 24.2 x 34.2 CM, PUBLISHED IN LONDON 20 MARCH 1798 BY H. HUMPHREY
BRITISH MUSEUM, LONDON

One of many prints of the period depicting all opponents of the government, whatever their politics, as dangerous revolutionaries, this one shows Pitt and Dundas, attired as watchmen, battering down the strongly barricaded door of a hovel. The occupants are shown hiding or fleeing, all except Lord Moira (to left) in uniform

SEARCH-NIGHT; — or — State-Watchmen, mistaking Honest-Men for Conspirators. Vide State Arrests.

and cocked hat, who stands stiffly to one side. The table in the middle of the room is covered with incriminating papers: a *Plan of Invasion* with maps of France and Ireland, a paper signed *O'Connor*, the open pages of the *Proceedings of the London Corresponding Society*. Hiding under the table are the British opposition figures Horne Tooke, Nicoll and Tierney. Fox and his friend Sheridan escape up a ladder to a trap-door in the roof. On the floor below the ladder is a chest full of daggers, with more scattered about. Under these are two papers - a copy of *The Press* (the Dublin paper of the United Irishmen, run by O'Connor) with the headline *Bloody News from Ireland Bloody News Bloody News* and a paper signed *Munchausen*. The liberal Duke of Bedford, followed by the Duke of Norfolk, is halfway up the chimney, which is decorated with French motifs and bears portraits of *Buonapart* and *Robertspier*. In the corner of the room to right is a pile of caps of liberty or bonnets-rouges. Rats make for a hole in the floor; nearby are papers marked *Assignats* and *Plan for raising United Irishmen*.

The background to the publication of this Gillray print was the recent arrest at Margate, en route to France to arrange for the invasion of Ireland, of Arthur O'Connor, James O'Coigley (Quigley), John Binns and two others. Binns was a leading member of the London Corresponding Society, other members of which were arrested and examined by the Privy Council. Baron Munchausen was the fictional hero of an eighteenth-century collection of tall tales; assignats were French revolutionary banknotes.

Sources: *BM Catalogue*, VII, no. 9189.

66 *EXHIBITION of a DEMOCRATIC-TRANSPARENCY, - with its Effect upon Patriotic Feelings: Representing the Secret Committee throwing a Light upon the Dark Sketches of a Revolution found among the Papers of the Jacobin Societies lately apprehended. NB. The Truth of the Picture is reffered to the Consciences of the Swearers to the Innocence of O'Connor; And is dedicated to the bosom-Friends of Fitzgerald; Quigley, Shears, Tone, Holt, & all other well wishers to their Country -*

BY J[AME]S GILLRAY
COLOURED AQUATINT, 34 X 42 CM, PUBLISHED IN LONDON 15 APRIL 1799 BY H. HUMPHREY
BRITISH MUSEUM, LONDON

This powerful piece of propaganda shows the members of the Secret Committee of the House of Commons examining incriminating documents relating to the United Irishmen and other revolutionary societies. The lamp on the table illuminates, from behind, a large transparency divided into four sections illustrating the supposed intentions of the conspirators: 'Plundering the Bank', 'Assassinating the Parliament', 'Seizing the Crown', and 'Establishing the French Government'. The Report of the Committee was presented to Parliament by Dundas on 15 March 1799.

In the sections of the transparency, leading members of the Opposition are shown plundering the bank (Tierney, Moira, Sheridan are prominent), murdering fellow MPs (Erskine, Fox, Sheridan), seizing the crown (Bedford, Fox, Grattan) and welcoming the French (Grattan, Norfolk, Moira). Faced with this evidence of their guilt, they are shown hastening from the room in terror. The nearest figures are those of Erskine (in lawyer's wig etc.), Fox, Taylor and the Duke of Norfolk;

behind are Tierney, Sheridan and Nicholls; at the back are Sir John Sinclair, Sir Francis Burdett, Lord Moira and the Duke of Bedford.

Sources: *BM Catalogue*, VII, no. 9369.

5 THE UNITED IRISHMEN: RADICAL POLITICS 1791-95

The political influence of the Volunteers, which had achieved so much in the early 1780s, waned after 1783. The Volunteers continued to exist, however, and when revolution broke out in France in 1789, and agitation for reform in Ireland revived, they received a new lease of life as the means by which it might be advanced. In 1791 a group of Presbyterian radicals within the Belfast Volunteers formed a secret committee to take advantage of the new situation. Out of this arose the first Society of United Irishmen, formed in Belfast in October 1791. The idea of such a body to organise and direct agitation for reform came from a Belfast-born Presbyterian doctor practising in Dublin, William Drennan, but the name adopted was suggested by a young Dublin lawyer, Wolfe Tone, and he and his friend Thomas Russell helped to establish the Society in the north before doing so in Dublin, where membership included adherents of the established church and Catholics as well as Presbyterians. While the Dublin Society soon became the movement's leading political club, its leading organ was the *Northern Star*, published in Belfast.

At first the United Irishmen were open in their aims - parliamentary reform and full Catholic emancipation - and largely constitutional in their methods. The turn of events in France, however, and the outbreak of war between the revolutionary government of the French Republic and Great Britain, changed matters. Under pressure from Pitt's administration, the Irish government adopted a policy of considerable (but grudging) concessions to Catholics mixed with legal moves to attack the reformers in the courts as advocates of sedition. Some of the more moderate began to draw back. The more advanced, however, became more determined and prepared to reorganise themselves along revolutionary and military lines. The Fitzwilliam episode in early 1795 was an important step in this disillusionment of radicals and Catholics with hopes of real reform by political agitation alone. Following Fitzwilliam's dismissal as lord lieutenant, a New System was adopted in Belfast in May of that year which began to transform the movement into a secret army, swelled by alliance with the Catholic Defenders and looking for French aid to establish a French-style republic. The chief agent of this new policy was Wolfe Tone, who accepted banishment to America in the summer of 1795 as the alternative to trial on a capital charge.

67 *New Map of Ireland*

BY ALEXANDER TAYLOR [1793]
DEDICATED TO JOHN EARL OF WESTMORELAND
70 x 60 CM; OUTLINE COLOURING
ULSTER MUSEUM

Alexander Taylor and his brother George were Scottish surveyors who made their careers in Ireland. George came to Ireland first, to work as a road surveyor. In 1778, with Andrew Skinner, he published a well-known book of Irish roads. Alexander Taylor began in Scotland as an estate surveyor, then came to Ireland where he joined the army in 1781 as a lieutenant in the 81st Regiment of Foot, transferring later to the Corps of Engineers. During the 1780s and 1790s he assisted in the completion of Vallancy's military survey of Ireland (published 1811), at the same time trying his hand at county maps (Kildare 1793, Longford and others); from about 1800 he surveyed roads. The Taylor brothers and their one-time partner Skinner were credited with training an Irish school of road surveyors to use the modern theodolite instead of the obsolete circumferentor in their work.

Though undated, Taylor's map of Ireland was published in 1793. Lord Westmoreland, to whom it was dedicated, was lord lieutenant of Ireland from 1789 to 1794. Tone gave a copy to General Desaix in Paris.

Sources: J.H. Andrews, *Plantation Acres* (Belfast, 1985).

68 *Jug celebrating the fall of the Bastille*

CREAMWARE, 25CM HIGH, TRANSFER PRINTS ON EITHER SIDE ENTITLED (LEFT) DESTRUCTION OF THE BASTILLE AND (RIGHT) THE FARMER'S JUG; OWNER'S NAME ON FRONT, JAMES MCKINNEY, BURNT HILL.
NEWTOWNABBEY BOROUGH COUNCIL

The French Revolution, at least in its early stages, was welcomed with enthusiasm by many Irish people, and by none more than the Presbyterians of Belfast and its neighbourhood. The local newspapers reported in considerable detail the progress of events in France, and the local Volunteers in the early 1790s organised Bastille Day celebrations as a way of demonstrating their support for radical reform in Ireland. Bastille commemorative jugs were sold in large numbers, often - as here - inscribed with the purchaser's name.

James McKinney was a Presbyterian tenant farmer in the parish of Carnmoney, County Antrim, just outside Belfast. He appears to have held the farm at Burnt Hill jointly with his father until 1792, and continued to live there until his death in 1808. His younger brother John became tenant of Sentry Hill, a neighbouring farm, sometime in the 1780s. John McKinney was a United Irishman and played a

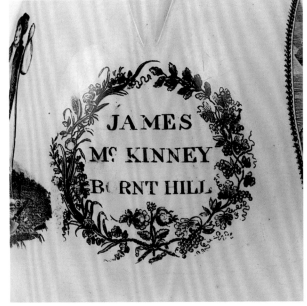

role in the events of 1798. His future brother-in-law was killed at the battle of Antrim, and the leading radical Samuel Neilson was his second cousin. His grandson, William F. McKinney, later collected information and memorabilia about the history of the area. He and his descendants preserved the past, making Sentry Hill almost a local museum; appropriately, the house with all its contents has recently been purchased by the local borough council for that purpose.

Sources: Brian M. Walker, *Sentry Hill: An Ulster Farm and Family* (Belfast, 1981, reprinted 1991).

69 *William Drennan, MD (1754-1820)*

ATTRIBUTED TO ROBERT HOME
OIL ON CANVAS, 75.2 x 62.5 CM (SIGHT)
ULSTER MUSEUM

William Drennan was the son of the Rev. Thomas Drennan, minister of the First Presbyterian congregation, Rosemary Street, Belfast. After taking his MA degree at Glasgow, Drennan studied medicine and took his MD degree in 1778 in Edinburgh where, according to his own words, 'A student of medicine is a term of contempt, but an Irish student of medicine is the very highest compilation of disgrace'. Specialising in obstetrics, he practised first in Belfast, then in Newry, before moving to Dublin. His liberal Presbyterian background and wide reading made him a political radical, an advocate of parliamentary reform and - with some reservations - Catholic emancipation. *Orellana or An Irish Helot* (1785), which was first published anonymously as a series of letters in the *Belfast Newsletter*, made Drennan's name well-known. *Orellana* preached the unity of all Irishmen in a common patriotism, separate from England. His scheme for a secret inner circle of dedicated reformers, within the Volunteer movement, to reform Parliament and break the power of the Protestant Ascendancy, foreshadowed by six years the formation of the Society of United Irishmen. In the meantime, however, the Volunteers as a political pressure group, and interest in reform itself, continued to decline, causing Drennan to exclaim in 1788, 'I almost wish there was a hearty rebellion'.

The French Revolution revived reform and reformers. At the same time, Drennan's move from Newry to Dublin put him close to the centre of Irish politics and he made the acquaintance of many of the leading political figures of the day. He himself was by that time a republican as well as a separatist, and very critical of mere Whigs such as Charlemont and Grattan. Drennan always regarded himself as the father of the Society of United Irishmen, which met first in Belfast under the auspices of the Green Company of the Belfast Volunteers, though the catalyst for its formation was the publication of Wolfe Tone's pamphlet *An Argument on Behalf of the Catholics of Ireland* and Tone was also responsible for suggesting the name (Drennan had proposed to call it the Irish Brotherhood). Drennan became secretary and then chairman of the Dublin Society, and it was he who devised the secret oath each member took, promising to do 'whatever lies in my power to forward a brotherhood of affection, an identity of interests, a communion of rights, and an union of power among Irishmen of all religious persuasions...'. Contrary to popular belief, the United Irish movement did not immediately sweep the country. In fact it never swept the country at all. The establishment of the first society in Belfast was followed soon by the founding of others in County Antrim, County Down and more in Belfast but, apart from Dublin, that early, constitutional phase of the movement produced none of any importance anywhere else in Ireland.

The crisis of the Volunteers in Dublin came late in 1792, when the Privy Council issued a proclamation forbidding the parading in arms of a new Volunteer organisation formed by radicals led by Napper Tandy. This body called itself, in the

French style, the First National Battalion and had a French-style uniform. The Dublin Society of United Irishmen produced a counter-proclamation, signed by Drennan as chairman, calling on the citizen soldiers to stand to their arms. The Volunteers backed down, however, and Drennan was subsequently, in 1794, tried on a charge of seditious libel. Curran's brilliant defence secured his acquittal, but he had had a bad fright and never again occupied centre stage in politics. Instead, tired of 'striving to live like a gentleman on £150 per annum in the centre of a splendid city', he concentrated on trying to make a decent professional living. At the same time he began to lose touch with the more advanced radicals and to feel a general disgust for politics - both for 'the cruel system adopted by the upper ranks' and 'the stupidity, ingratitude and barbarity of the lower orders'. Nor did he like the plots and conspiracies that characterised the popular cause during the years before 1798. He did not abandon politics entirely, of course, but his interest was expressed in pamphlets and verse rather than political activity of a more direct sort. His role in the 1798 rebellion was that of an observer only.

In 1807 he gave up his Dublin practice and returned to Belfast, where he devoted himself to education (the establishment of the Academical Institution), radical journalism (the *Belfast Monthly Magazine*) and literature (*Fugitive Pieces*, 1815, and a translation of Sophocles's *Electra*). His considerable literary talents had already left some enduring mark: he coined the epithet 'Emerald Isle' for Ireland, his poem 'The Wake of William Orr' became immediately famous, and some of his hymns were highly regarded by connoisseurs. He died in 1820. An ironic footnote to the career of this founder of the United Irishmen is that many years later, during the first Home Rule crisis, when a local Republican Club asked for a copy of his likeness to put on its banner, his son refused, saying that Drennan, had he been alive, would have been a unionist as he himself was.

This portrait of Drennan, painted about 1786 and the only known likeness of him, was donated to the Ulster Museum by a direct descendant.

Sources: Webb, *Compendium of Irish Biography.*
             A.T.Q. Stewart, *A Deeper Silence* (London, 1993).
             D.A. Chart (ed.), *The Drennan Letters*, (Belfast, 1931).

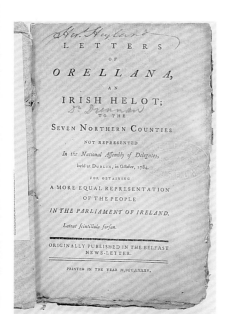

70 *Orellana, or An Irish Helot*

BY [WILLIAM DRENNAN]
PRINTED BOOK, DUBLIN 1785
ULSTER MUSEUM

Orellana began as a series of three letters by Drennan which were published anonymously in the *Belfast Newsletter* in November and December 1784. They were immediately reprinted as a pamphlet by the Constitution Society of Dublin under the title *Orellana, or An Irish Helot*. Drennan eventually wrote four additional letters. In vivid language, Drennan deplored the retreat of the Volunteers from radical reform, a retreat he blamed largely on Charlemont, their commander; urged the reform of Parliament by overawing it by the power of the Volunteers in the name of the people; preached the unity of all Irishmen in a common patriotism; pleaded for the unity of the sects - Catholics and Dissenters - to break the power of the Protestant Ascendancy; and castigated those who mixed religion with politics.

As for the title, a helot was one of the slave class in ancient Sparta, and *Orellana, or An Irish Helot* was a play on the title of *Oroonoka, or the Royal Slave*, by Mrs Aphra Benn.

Sources: A.T.Q. Stewart, *A Deeper Silence.*

71 *Martha McTier*

COPY BY EILEEN AYRTON OF AN ORIGINAL PASTEL
PASTEL OVAL, SIGHT 29.8 X 24.3 CM
ULSTER MUSEUM

Martha (Matty) McTier was the eldest of the three surviving children (there were eleven in all) of the Rev. Thomas Drennan, minister of Belfast First Presbyterian congregation, and his wife Anne Lennox, and the sister of Dr William Drennan, one of the founders of the United Irishmen. Like her brother she held radical views, as did the widower she married, Samuel McTier (d. 1795). McTier, a merchant and member of her father's congregation, became president of the first Belfast Society of United Irishman.

Martha took a deep interest in her famous brother's career, and in the political radicalism that absorbed the attention of all three of them. She was also in her copious correspondence a shrewd - and sometimes shrewish, though essentially good-hearted - commentator on the social scene in Belfast. During Drennan's long absence, first in Newry and later in Dublin, he and she corresponded regularly and frankly. The Drennan letters, preserved by William Drennan's granddaughter and now in the Public Record Office of Northern Ireland, are a uniquely important source for historians of the radical movement and of Belfast life in the late-eighteenth century. A selection of them, severely edited, was published in 1931.

As a keen card-player and gambler, Martha had an intimate knowledge of the social scene in Belfast and of the denizens of that comparatively small but lively place. 'I play as well as any of them', she wrote, 'and when I lose too much, will quit it'. Her description of the effect of a performance by the actress Sarah Siddons on the hardened hearts of the local bourgeoisie is a good example of her style at its sharpest and most entertaining:

'Mrs Siddons is now here working wonders ... The effects of her Belvidera have done credit to the feelings of the audience ... Haliday swelled, Mattear snivelled, Major Leslie cried and damned the play, W. Cunningham rubbed his legs and changed his posture, a Miss Alderton was taken out in convulsions, and Miss Lewis, that was, Mrs. Britt, left the house and is at present in danger of a miscarriage ...'.

Sources: Introduction to D.A. Chart (ed.), *The Drennan Letters*.
             Kate Newmann, *Dictionary of Ulster Biography* (Belfast, 1993).

72 *Cherry Crawford (c. 1768-1845)*

BY JOSEPH WILSON
OIL ON CANVAS, 76 X 63 CM, SIGNED AND DATED 1789
THE BELL GALLERY, BELFAST

Cherry Crawford, daughter of George Crawford, was born in County Down and brought up in County Monaghan. She married one of the Hyndmans, a prominent family of Belfast merchants, and was the mother of George Crawford Hyndman, a well-known auctioneer and amateur scientist. Her sister Elizabeth, who married another respectable Belfast man, David McTear of Hazelbank, Whitehouse, was also painted by Wilson in 1789; that painting was acquired from a direct descendant by the Belfast Museum and Art Gallery in 1927. This portrait of Cherry Crawford, according to an old inscription on the back of the original lining, was taken when she was twenty-one.

According to Hyndman family tradition, Cherry Crawford was a radical young woman who took a keen interest in politics. She was reputedly the only woman ever admitted as a member of the Society of United Irishmen.

Sources: Eileen Black, *Irish Oil Paintings, 1572-c.1830*.
             W. G. Strickland, *A Dictionary of Irish Art and Artists*, 2 vols. (Dublin, 1913).
             Owner's correspondence.

73 *Samuel Neilson (1761-1803)*

BY AN UNKNOWN ARTIST
OIL ON CARDBOARD, 17.5 X 14.8 CM
ULSTER MUSEUM

Samuel Neilson was born in September 1761 at Ballyroney, County Down, where his father Alexander was Presbyterian minister. At the age of sixteen he was apprenticed to his elder brother John, a woollen draper in Belfast. He set up in business on his own in High Street, Belfast in 1785, the year of his marriage, so successfully that by 1790 he had made the considerable fortune of £8,000. Like most radicals, he started his political career as a Volunteer. In 1790 he acted as election agent for Robert Stewart - then standing as a reform candidate in the contest for County Down, against Lord Hillsborough - and helped to secure his election. Neilson is credited with suggesting to his friend Henry Joy McCracken, in the summer of 1791, the idea of forming a society of Irishmen based on religious equality to work for parliamentary reform and Catholic emancipation. He was certainly among the most active of the Belfast radicals in the formation of the first Society of United Irishmen by Wolfe Tone (in whose journals he is 'the Jacobin')

later that year. When the *Northern Star* newspaper was established in January 1792 he was the principal shareholder and was unanimously chosen as manager and editor (he subsequently became sole proprietor). Along with others, Neilson was arrested in September 1796 and sent to gaol in Dublin.

In prison, Neilson's health deteriorated badly and he began to drink heavily. In February 1798 he was released, through Castlereagh's intervention, on condition that he did not join any treasonable committee. He kept the letter but not the spirit of this agreement, for, staying in Dublin, he immediately became associated with Lord Edward FitzGerald in preparation for an armed rising; it was his idea to give the signal for revolt by stopping the mail coaches. With the arrest of the Leinster Directory, FitzGerald and he were the two main figures in the movement still at large, till the latter's arrest on 18 May left Neilson alone. There is absolutely no evidence to support the story that Neilson betrayed Lord Edward's hiding place in Thomas Street, but he did visit him twice on the day of the arrest and, fearless himself, may have been careless. On 23 May, the day the rebellion was to begin, he was reconnoitring Newgate, where FitzGerald was held, when the gaoler recognised his large shambling figure (he was drunk and shouting in the street, according to one version). After a struggle, in which he received severe wounds, he was arrested and imprisoned. When brought up for trial on 26 June along with Bond, Bryne, McCann and the two Sheares brothers, Neilson refused to plead or to name his counsel, and protested at being loaded with fetters 'so heavy that three ordinary men could scarcely carry them'. The others were tried, found guilty, sentenced to death and, except for Bond, executed. Neilson's life was saved by the compact made between some of the leading state prisoners and the government, by which the lives of all remaining prisoners still in custody were spared in return for information about the origins and activities of the United Irish movement. Neilson was one of those who were examined by the Secret Committees of the Lords and the Commons.

Neilson was sent, along with some of the leading prisoners, to Fort George in Scotland, where he was to remain imprisoned without trial from 9 April 1799 to 30 June 1802, by which time the war in Europe was over for the time being. His son William, a boy of eight, was allowed to join him at Fort George for the latter part of his stay there, benefiting educationally from the varied talents of the prisoners; Emmet taught him History, Russell Mathematics, Dr Dickson Latin and his father English. On Neilson's release, on condition that he emigrated to America, the boy returned to Belfast. Neilson went to Hamburg but, unable to get a direct passage, decided with characteristic intrepidity to risk a last visit to his friends and family in Ireland. Arriving in Dublin, where he was met by James Hope, he disguised himself with a wig and spectacles and they went north. Neilson stayed in Belfast three days, before returning to Dublin to board the American vessel that took him to New York; it is believed that his presence in Belfast somehow came to the notice of the Rev. Dr Bristow, sovereign (mayor) of the town, but that he turned a blind eye.

In America, Neilson's health declined; he suffered particularly from rheumatism, a legacy of his long imprisonment. In 1803 he contracted yellow fever and died on 29 August at Poughkepsie, upriver from New York.

This portrait of Neilson, painted about 1795, is after a miniature by Charles Byrne (1757-1810) which was engraved by T.W. Huffam and reproduced in R.R. Madden, *The United Irishmen, their Lives and Times*.

Sources: Madden, *The United Irishmen*, second series, vol. 1 (1843).
W.T. Latimer, *Ulster Biographies, Relating Chiefly to the Rebellion of 1798* (Belfast, 1897).
Eileen Black, *Irish Oil Paintings, 1572-c.1830*.

74 *John Magee (d.1811)*

BY JOSEPH WILSON
OIL ON PANEL, 24.2 x 19.6 CM, OVAL
ULSTER MUSEUM

John Magee was a member of a notable eighteenth-century family of Belfast printers. The business was founded by James Magee, whose premises were at the Crown and Bible in Bridge Street, and lasted until 1803. His son John settled in Dublin, where he established *Magee's Weekly Packet* in 1777. From then until 1790 he conducted a fearless campaign against corruption in high places - notably against Francis Higgins (the 'Sham Squire') and Lord Clonmel, lord chief justice of the Court of King's Bench - which ruined him. He was arrested and imprisoned in Newgate, where his health was permanently undermined. The family ran his paper until his death in 1811, when his son John took it over.

Sources: Eileen Black, *Irish Oil Paintings, 1572-c.1830.*

75 *The Hon.*^ble *Simon Butler*

IRISH SCHOOL
STIPPLE ENGRAVING, 20 x 12 CM, OVAL IMAGE
NATIONAL GALLERY OF IRELAND, DUBLIN

Simon Butler was a radical aristocrat - he was a brother of Lord Mountgarret - who was the first president of the Dublin United Irishmen and for a time in the early 1790s played a leading role in radical politics. Following the formation of the new radical club in Belfast in October 1791, Wolfe Tone and Thomas Russell returned to the capital and made contact with Napper Tandy and others to tell them about this interesting development. Tandy convened a meeting of eighteen Catholics and Protestants which met on 9 November 1791. With Butler - 'the

only man of fashion among us' - in the chair, the declaration devised for the Belfast Society was adopted and the Dublin Society established. It was a fairly exclusive body: candidates had to be proposed, seconded and balloted for (one black bean in five meant rejection), and every member had to pay one guinea on admission as well as an annual subscription. Altogether, about 400 members were admitted during the life of the Society, between its foundation and its dissolution in May 1794. Only half of them attended at all regularly, and the average attendance at meetings ranged from 40 to 90. No fewer than 26 members, one of whom was Butler, were barristers; more than twice that number were attornies; 24 were medical men; 14 were booksellers and printers; half a dozen were army officers; one was a Fellow of Trinity College; most of the rest were businessmen, including over a hundred merchants, and manufacturers. From the start the government was well informed about the Society's views and activities, from its own publications and from regular reports by Thomas Collins, a linen merchant member who had gone bankrupt.

In March 1793, following the outbreak of war with France, Butler (president) and Oliver Bond (secretary) were arrested, imprisoned for six months and fined £500 for publicly challenging the right of the House of Lords to summon and question witnesses. In Newgate, the two prisoners lived so lavishly at the Society's expense that the members revolted - Martha McTier, then on a visit to Dublin, reported that Butler's mistress had been seen carrying home large baskets of fruit. Butler's influence in the Society began to wane. His participation in radical politics largely ceased with the Society's dissolution in 1794; he was no conspirator, and had already rejected the idea of seeking help from revolutionary France.

Sources: R.B. McDowell, 'The personnel of the Dublin Society of United Irishmen 1791-4', in *Irish Historical Studies*, vol. 2 (1940-41).

76 *James Napper Tandy*

BY JAMES PETRIE
STIPPLE ENGRAVING, 24 x 14.5 CM
NATIONAL GALLERY OF IRELAND, DUBLIN

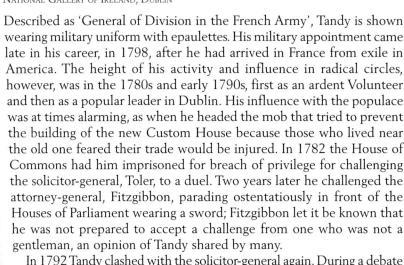

JAMES NAPPER TANDY,
General of Division
in the French Army.

Described as 'General of Division in the French Army', Tandy is shown wearing military uniform with epaulettes. His military appointment came late in his career, in 1798, after he had arrived in France from exile in America. The height of his activity and influence in radical circles, however, was in the 1780s and early 1790s, first as an ardent Volunteer and then as a popular leader in Dublin. His influence with the populace was at times alarming, as when he headed the mob that tried to prevent the building of the new Custom House because those who lived near the old one feared their trade would be injured. In 1782 the House of Commons had him imprisoned for breach of privilege for challenging the solicitor-general, Toler, to a duel. Two years later he challenged the attorney-general, Fitzgibbon, parading ostentatiously in front of the Houses of Parliament wearing a sword; Fitzgibbon let it be known that he was not prepared to accept a challenge from one who was not a gentleman, an opinion of Tandy shared by many.

In 1792 Tandy clashed with the solicitor-general again. During a debate Toler had made fun of Tandy's famously ugly face: 'I have seen', he said, 'papers signed by Tobias McKenna with Simon Butler in the chair, and Napper Tandy lending his countenance'. To roars of laughter he added 'It is rather odd that they could not contrive to set a better face on the matter'. This time Tandy hesitated to call his man out and feared another action for breach of privilege. He ended by hiding from the authorities, which destroyed his reputation not only in society at large but also with his colleagues in the Society of United Irishmen, of which he was a founding member. As Drennan said, 'Poor Tandy, after eighteen years' struggle against his own interests in the public cause, has nearly lost his reputation as a gentleman in a quarter of an hour'. Tandy tried to repair the damage by taking the lord lieutenant and leading officials to court for abusing their power, but it was no use. When prosecuted later for distributing a seditious pamphlet and communicating with the Defenders, he fled to America.

Sources: *DNB.*
            James Kelly, *'That Damn'd Thing Called Honour'.*

77 *Thomas Addis Emmet (1764-1827)*

IRISH SCHOOL, LATE EIGHTEENTH CENTURY
PASTEL ON PAPER, 25.5 X 20 CM
NATIONAL GALLERY OF IRELAND, DUBLIN

Thomas Addis Emmet, one of the most prominent of the Dublin United Irishmen, was born in Cork on 24 April 1764. He was the second son of Dr Robert Emmet, a leading member of the medical establishment and state physician of Ireland, and the elder brother of Robert Emmet the revolutionary. Emmet attended Trinity College, Dublin, before going on to Edinburgh to study medicine. A gifted scholar and a sociable young man, he was president of no fewer than five undergraduate societies (medical, literary, scientific) during his time there. After graduating MD in 1787 he spent time visiting medical schools in Great Britain and then travelled in Germany, France and Italy. On the way home he heard of the sudden death of his elder brother, Temple, who was a barrister. At his father's request he gave up medicine and instead took up law, studying for two years at the Temple in London before being admitted to the Irish Bar in 1790.

Though the Emmets were a well-to-do Protestant family, with a fine house in the fashionable St Stephen's Green and another in the country, Thomas had imbibed ideas subversive of the Protestant ascendancy. As a lawyer, he made a name for defending radicals, most notably in 1792 Napper Tandy, in a case involving the lord lieutenant, Lord Westmoreland. His speech on that occasion attracted much attention, and was published by the Society of United Irishmen. In 1795 he defended a number of people charged with administering the United Irishmen's oath, taking it himself in court to demonstrate its legality. From 1796 he began to play a leading part in the movement. As for the Catholics, in Tone's opinion he was 'the best of all the friends of Catholic Emancipation' next to himself.

On the Directory of the United Irishmen in 1797-98, Emmet was one of the more cautious leaders, arguing in favour of delay till the French appeared, against Lord Edward FitzGerald and others who urged an immediate rising. In March 1798, following the arrests at Oliver Bond's house in Dublin, Emmet was also arrested at his home and lodged in Newgate. His wife somehow got permission to join him in prison, and remained with him when he was moved to Kilmainham - a period of a year. He and other state prisoners were thus removed from the scene when the rebellion itself broke out. In order to stop the executions that followed its suppression, Emmet, O'Connor, McNeven and Neilson entered into an agreement with the authorities to disclose the history of the United Irishmen. In his own examination Emmet argued that revolution became inevitable only when moderate demands were rejected - an interpretation that played down the separatist and republican intentions of the movement's earlier history.

With the USA refusing to accept the prisoners if deported, and the government fearing to let them loose in Europe while the war with France continued, Emmet and the other leading figures were sent to Fort George in Scotland. Here Mrs Emmet followed him in 1800 along with their three boys, and here their youngest child, a daughter, was born. Released in 1802, the Emmet family went to Holland, then Hamburg and Brussels, before reaching Paris, where in September 1803 news reached them of Robert Emmet's execution. In December 1803 Emmet met Napoleon Bonaparte and there were hopes of another expedition to Ireland, but these hopes collapsed the following April when Bonaparte changed his plans. Emmet decided then to go to New York, where the Irish exiles were by that time welcome. He died in 1827 and was buried at St Mark's Church, Broadway, where a monument to him was erected, with inscriptions in English, Latin and Irish. His faithful wife survived him by nineteen years, dying in 1846.

Sources: Madden, *The United Irishmen*, second series (1843), vol. 2.
              Webb, *Compendium of Irish Biography*.

78 *Archibald Hamilton Rowan Esqr, 'Late President of the Society of United Irishmen of Dublin', c.1794*

LINE ENGRAVING, 19.2 x 12.5 CM
NATIONAL GALLERY OF IRELAND, DUBLIN

Archibald Hamilton Rowan was one of the most prominent leaders of the early Society of United Irishmen. Born Archibald Hamilton in London in 1757, he was the son of James Hamilton of Killyleagh Castle, County Down. He was educated at Westminster School and Cambridge University, where he made aristocratic acquaintances and acquired expensive tastes. He adopted the surname of his maternal grandfather on inheriting his property in 1767. As a young man he visited America as private secretary to the governor of South Carolina. There he acquired a small menagerie of animals. In his autobiography, which was published in 1840 after his death, he wrote of his return from Carolina : 'after a very rough passage, I landed at Portsmouth - my racoon dead, my bear washed overboard, and my possum lost in the cable tier ..' After Cambridge he lived for three years with his mother in France (where he was presented to Marie Antoinette) and married there.

He settled in Ireland, in County Kildare, in 1784 and became active in the Volunteer movement. He first came to public notice in 1788 when he published his *Investigation of the Sufferings of Mary Neal*. The case of this poor girl in Dublin, who had been seduced and badly treated with impunity by a person of quality, roused the strong sense of social justice that was the motive force of Rowan's life. His powerful personality and formidable appearance added to his reputation in Dublin Society; few people cared to cross him and he feared no one. Jonah Barrington relates how on one occasion he cowed a whole roomful of drunken lawyers.

In 1790 Rowan was a founder member of the Northern Whig Club in Belfast. In 1792 he joined the Society of United Irishmen in Dublin, and succeeded Simon Butler as its president when the latter was imprisoned. Butler accompanied Rowan to Edinburgh, where he challenged the Lord Advocate to a duel for insulting remarks about his political writings, which had featured in a recent trial of Scottish radicals (the judge declined the challenge on account of his official position). Back in Dublin, Rowan joined Napper Tandy, both of them in Volunteer uniform and armed, in protesting against the proclamation which, in effect, proscribed the Volunteers. At that meeting, Rowan distributed an address headed 'Citizen soldiers, to arms!' This was too much for the authorities, who indicted him for seditious libel and brought him to trial in January 1794. Despite the efforts of his defence counsel, John Philpot Curran, Rowan was found guilty, fined £500 and sentenced to two years' imprisonment. His imprisonment in Dublin's Newgate was comfortable enough (all his meals were sent from home and his family and friends visited freely) but he was dangerously compromised by a visit from the Rev. William Jackson (subsequently arrested and found guilty by treason; he escaped hanging by taking poison in court) and decided to flee. Bribing a gaoler, he escaped in disguise and got away by boat to France. After a year or so in France, during which he was lucky to escape execution as a foreign spy, Rowan moved to the United States and stayed there for five years, living on money from his Irish estates sent to him by his wife. In America he met Wolfe Tone and supported his plans to persuade the French to intervene in Ireland.

ARCHIBALD HAMILTON ROWAN ESQ.
Late President of the Society of United Irishmen of Dublin.

Rowan welcomed the end of the Irish parliament, which he regarded as hopelessly corrupt, and the Union of 1800. In that year he sailed from America to Hamburg, where he was joined at last by his wife and children and where they lived for the next three years. In 1802 he petitioned the British government for permission to return home. Since he had some influential friends and no longer appeared dangerous his petition was granted, on condition that he forswore political activity. The rest of his life was passed in Killyleagh and Dublin. He supported liberal causes, in particular Catholic emancipation, and never lost his pugnacious spirit; in 1825 he went to London to challenge Sir Robert Peel to a duel for referring to him as an attainted traitor. He used to walk the streets of Dublin followed by a couple of huge Danish deerhounds, a striking figure still. He died in 1834, shortly after his wife, and was buried in Dublin.

Sources: *DNB.*
Webb, *Compendium of Irish Biography.*
Autobiography, ed. W.H. Drummond (Dublin, 1840).

79 *Scroll bestowing the Freedom of the Dublin Corporation of Glovers and Skinners on Archibald Hamilton Rowan, 1791*

PARCHMENT, IN CONTEMPORARY GILT FRAME; 77 x 50 CM (FRAME); ILLUMINATED ARMS AT TOP AND BOTTOM
ULSTER MUSEUM

As a prominent radical, Rowan had become popular with the citizens of Dublin. The guilds, which originated in medieval times, became in the eighteenth century supporters of patriotism and reform. In the early 1700s, the municipal government of Dublin had been dominated by a powerful oligarchy of aldermen, elected for life, who chose the lord mayor and sheriffs. They filled vacancies in their own ranks not by public election but by co-option, and selected the members of the city's Common Council from names proposed by the trade guilds. Agitation for reform, headed by the noted apothecary Charles Lucas, led to legislation in 1760 which allowed the guilds to elect directly their representatives on the Council. Lucas, 'the Wilkes of Ireland', went on to became a leading figure in the 'Patriot' party in the Irish Parliament.

80 *An Argument on behalf of the Catholics of Ireland*

By 'A Northern Whig' [Theobald Wolfe Tone]
Reprinted by order of The Society of United Irishmen of Belfast, 1791
Mr J.A. Gamble

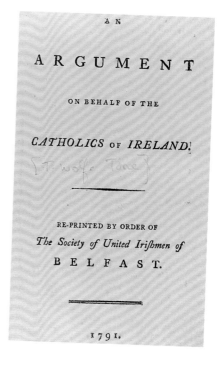

Tone's famous pamphlet, which was to mark the first step in his career as an Irish patriot, was published three weeks after it was written and sold for a shilling. Though addressed to Protestants in general, it was aimed specifically at radical Dissenters in the north who had qualms about Catholic emancipation. Tone dismissed the so-called revolution of 1782 as a 'bungling, imperfect business' which simply enabled Irishmen 'to sell, at a much higher price, their honor, their integrity, and the interests of their country'. Such was the nature of the Irish Parliament that no reform could be expected from it as currently constituted - 'no reform can ever be obtained which shall not comprehensively embrace Irishmen of all denominations'. Cleverly written, secular in tone, hard-hitting in its arguments, Tone's pamphlet presents his Protestant readers with a stark choice: accept the Catholics as allies and their emancipation as part of the reform programme, or abandon reform altogether. Like the enlightened middle-class Protestant that he was, Tone totally misunderstood the Catholic peasantry that made up the mass of the Irish population, underestimating both the strength of their Catholicism and their political ambition.

The pamphlet, first published in Dublin in 1791, was an immediate success, selling 6,000 copies within a few months; a further 10,000 were printed by the Belfast Society of United Irishmen, which its publication had helped to bring into being. It was credited with bringing about an important change in Presbyterian attitudes to the Catholics, a success that was probably somewhat exaggerated. It also made an impression on a new generation of Catholics agitating for reforms and was to lead to Tone's appointment as paid secretary to the Catholic Committee in 1792.

Sources: Marianne Elliott, *Wolfe Tone: Prophet of Irish Independence* (London, 1989).

81 *Billy Bluff and Squire Firebrand*

By [James Porter]
First edition, Belfast, 1796
P. and B. Rowan

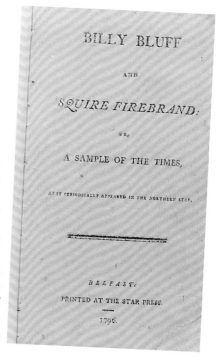

Billy Bluff and Squire Firebrand first appeared as a series of six letters to the editor of the *Northern Star*, the newspaper of the United Irishmen, between May and November 1796. They were immediately reprinted twice in pamphlet form. One of these printings - the only one up to 1840 to bear any printer's name - has the imprint 'Printed at the Star Press, 1796'; the other simply says 'Belfast, 1796' but is prefaced by 'To the Public in General and the Editor of the Northern Star in particular'. Further editions followed in 1797 and - 'printed privately' in Dublin - 1798. Another, incorporating some of the songs from *Paddy's Resource*, was published in Belfast in 1812.

The anonymous, but not unknown, author of *Billy Bluff* was the Rev. James Porter (1753-98), Presbyterian minister of Greyabbey, County Down, who also contributed to the *Northern Star* early in 1797 a series of articles under the name 'Sydney' which were addressed to the second Marquess of Downshire. Another nom-de-plume he used was 'A Man of Ulster'. Porter also contributed several of the patriotic songs that were later collected under the title *Paddy's Resource*, notably 'Green were the fields where my forefathers strayed o', and contributed to *The Press*, the *Star's* Dublin successor.

Porter, one of a number of Presbyterian clerical radicals, was a talented political satirist and his Billy Bluff letters were enormously enjoyed by the *Northern Star's* extensive readership in north Down. The letters recounted supposed conversations between a local landlord, Squire Firebrand, and his spy Billy Bluff, who informs him about the dastardly activities of the United Irishmen, such as reading newspapers and singing songs. The squire tells the horrified Billy, 'Tis songs that is most to be dreaded of all things. Singing, Billy is a d —d bad custom; it infects the whole country, and makes them half mad; because they rejoice and forget their cares, and forget their duty, and forget their betters'. In real life, the reactionary squire was the Rev. Hugh Montgomery, landlord of Greyabbey, and his ignorant informant one Billy Lowry, his bailiff. The other main character to be satirised, as Lord Mountmumble, was Lord Londonderry, father of Robert Stewart, Viscount Castlereagh, whose seat Mount Stewart was nearby. Londonderry was to prove a bad enemy. When Porter was arrested in 1798, accused of having intercepted a King's messenger, and was court-martialled in Newtownards, Londonderry sat among the officers of the court. Porter declared his innocence - and indeed seems to have had little or nothing to do with the activities of the local rebels when the rising came - but was found guilty and executed within sight of his own meeting house three days later. His wife did everything she could to save his life, by appealing in person to Lady Londonderry, who agreed to write to General Nugent on her behalf but - if the traditional story is true - was then obliged by her husband to add a postscript declining to interfere. Accompanied by her seven children, Mrs Porter then tried to speak directly to Nugent, but was turned away from his door.

Sources: F.J. Bigger, 'James Porter (1753-1798)', in *Irish Book Lover*, vol. 13, nos. 7 & 8 (1922).
A.T.Q. Stewart, *The Summer Soldiers*.

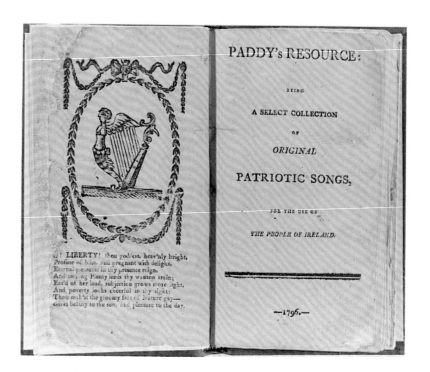

82 *Paddy's Resource*

ANONYMOUS, 1796
BEING A SELECT COLLECTION OF ORIGINAL PATRIOTIC SONGS FOR THE USE OF THE PEOPLE OF IRELAND, - 1796
MR J.A. GAMBLE

This is Part 2 of the famous United Irish songbook. Part 1, described as 'A Select Collection of Original and Modern Patriotic Songs, Toasts and Sentiments Compiled for the use of the people of Ireland' was published in 1795, price 1s. 1d. Porter's Billy Bluff describes *Paddy's Resource* to the Squire as songs 'all put into one book, your honour, and they called PADDY'S RACE-HORSE' - which was how the volume was referred to throughout the nineteenth century because of the popularity of Porter's satire. 'Such a parcel of lies and rebellion was never seen in a Christian country', says Billy. The Squire agrees, saying the Irishman's last resource is 'singing patriotic lies, national impudence, and united treason'. Like *Billy Bluff*, *Paddy's Resource* was immensely successful as popular radical propaganda.

Another prose satire, William Sampson's *Faithful Report of the Trial of Hurdy Gurdy*, had been published anonymously in the *Northern Star* in 1794. It was a parody of the trial of Thomas Muir, the Scottish radical, at which the music of that 'seditious organ' had been produced as evidence to support his transportation to Botany Bay.

Sources: F.J. Bigger, 'James Porter', in *Irish Book Lover*, vol. 13.
            Mary Helen Thuente, *The Harp Re-strung* (Syracuse, 1994).

83 *The Northern Star*

NEWSPAPER, PUBLISHED IN BELFAST
ULSTER MUSEUM

The *Northern Star*, the organ of the United Irishmen from 1792 to 1797, was established in Belfast early in 1792, after careful preparation by the committee of twelve proprietors that formed its board of directors. Pledges of support had been obtained from 136 leading citizens and the commercial viability of a radical newspaper had been explored in a businesslike fashion. The main existing paper, the *Belfast News-letter*, had earlier seen off two attempts to challenge its virtual monopoly - one by John Tisdall in 1783-86 with the *Belfast Mercury, or Freeman's Chronicle*, the other by William Magee with the *Belfast Mercury*, bought from Tisdall and transformed into the *Belfast Evening Post*; the *Post* survived only thirty weeks. Magee became one of the founding proprietors of the *Northern Star*. Tisdall printed the first seven issues and provided the printing equipment; thereafter one of his printers, John Rabb, succeeded him.

In its first year the *Star* had a cash-flow problem. Many potential buyers had current subscriptions with the *News-letter* and could not afford both. Single issues, sold at twopence to the *News-letter's* twopence-halfpenny, brought little profit. Advertising revenue was buoyant in 1792-93, however, and sales soon rose to a peak of 4,200, aided by a good distribution network. The *Star's* political message, of course, reached a wider audience, particularly in Counties Antrim and Down, less so in areas such as Tyrone, Armagh, and Londonderry which were farther from Belfast or had smaller proportions of Presbyterians; least of all in Cavan and Donegal. On the whole, the paper was sold by Protestants to Protestants. As well as the newspaper itself, increasingly a loss-making enterprise for both the *Star* and its rival (Henry Joy, the owner and editor of the *News-letter*, sold up in 1795), the *Northern Star* presses printed radical pamphlets such as *Billy Bluff* and *Paddy's Resource*, until prosecution and harassment put the whole enterprise out of business in 1797. By that time the editor, Samuel Neilson, who had also become sole proprietor, was a ruined man, his whole personal fortune sacrificed in the cause. It is true that the *Star* was uniquely disadvantaged as the forces of reaction gathered themselves to resist the United Irishmen in the period before the Rebellion, but it is also true that a severe economic depression in Belfast made it difficult for any newspaper to survive: the *News-letter* did so only by accepting a government subsidy.

Sources: John Gray, 'A Tale of Two Newspapers: the contest between the *Belfast News-Letter* and the *Northern Star* in the 1790s', in John Gray and Wesley McCann (eds), *An Uncommon Bookman: Essays in Memory of J.R.R. Adams* (Belfast, 1996).
Kevin Whelan, 'The United Irishmen, the Enlightenment and popular culture', in David Dickson, Dáire Keogh and Kevin Whelan (eds), *The United Irishmen* (Dublin, 1993).

84 *The Militia Act*

POCKET EDITION, DUBLIN, 1793, WITH SIGNATURE OF LORD GRANARD
P. AND B. ROWAN

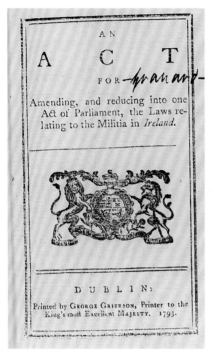

The Militia Act of 1793 was one of the most significant pieces of Irish legislation of the late eighteenth century, marking - as it did - a revolutionary change of policy on the part of the British government by ending the long prohibition against Irish Catholics bearing arms. In that respect it was one of a number of measures designed to placate the Catholics that the Irish administration felt obliged to adopt; others were the Catholic Relief Acts of 1792 and 1793 and the establishment of St Patrick's College, Maynooth in 1795. At the same time the Militia Act was a reactionary measure, designed to meet the menace of radical agitation from 'political' Volunteer units and the Society of United Irishmen; there was also a growing threat to public order from sectarian Protestant Volunteers and sectarian Defenders. Only the establishment of a Militia, it seemed, might enable the government to suppress the Volunteers and garrison the country as war with France drew off increasingly large numbers of recruits to the regular army. The new force would need to recruit Catholics as well as Protestants, however.

In the event, the Militia Bill was rushed through the Irish Parliament in record time and to general approval. The aristocracy and gentry welcomed the prospect of additional patronage, while the existence of such a force also gave prospects of employment in Ireland for the mass of the male population (most of whom were rural) when times were hard. Under this Act, each county and county borough was given a quota of recruits to provide the thirty-eight regiments, totalling nearly 15,000 men, that were established. Ballots of those eligible to serve were drawn up; substitutes were allowed, and volunteers; anyone refusing to serve could be fined £10. Unexpectedly, the embodiment of the new Militia caused serious disturbances, during May and June 1793, in nearly every county in Ireland. This violence met with a harsh response from the authorities: 230 people were killed. By the end of 1793, however, some 9,600 men had been enlisted. Target figures were raised later as need arose, till the total enlisted reached a peak of 32,500 in January 1799.

The Militia's military training was rudimentary at best, their officers were mostly incompetent, the rank and file were undisciplined when present and liable to desert at any time. Most of the men, in most of the regiments except those from the north, were Catholics, most of their officers Protestants. Yet the confident predictions of Tone and other exiles seeking French aid that the Militia would join the rebels proved to be well wide of the mark. In 1798 they obeyed their officers and could scarcely be restrained in their enthusiasm to extirpate their defeated opponents.

Sources: Thomas Bartlett, 'Defence, counter-insurgency and rebellion: Ireland, 1793-1803', in Thomas Bartlett and Keith Jeffrey (eds), *A Military History of Ireland* (Cambridge, 1996);
'An end to moral economy: the Irish Militia disturbances of 1793', in *Past and Present*, vol. 99 (May 1983).

85 *A Faithful Report of the Trial of the Proprietors of the Northern Star, 1794*

BY [WILLIAM SAMPSON]
BELFAST: [NORTHERN STAR], JUNE 1794
P. AND B. ROWAN

In the first of two trials in 1794 arising out of an accusation that the *Northern Star* had printed seditious advertisements in December 1792, the newspaper's proprietors were said by the attorney-general to be 'not engaging in such a business as this for fair gain and profit, for they appear to have circulated this paper at a price far below what was usual, which evinces that their only object was sedition'. In a subsequent trial the prosecution collapsed when it was proved that the item complained of - the address of the United Irishmen to the Volunteers in Dublin - had been published in the *Belfast News-letter* the previous day. Both trials were part of the government campaign to discourage the expression of radical opinions.

The anonymous author of this account (and of that of the second trial too) was the barrister William Sampson, a United Irishman who acted as defence counsel in several trials of radicals. He also contributed to the *Northern Star* (see *The Trial of Hurdy Gurdy*). Born in Londonderry in 1764, he had been an officer in the Volunteers before going to Trinity College and afterwards to Lincoln's Inn. His name was included on a list of those to be arrested in March 1798. He escaped to England but was arrested at Whitehaven and lodged in Carlisle gaol before being sent back to Ireland. He was eventually allowed to go to the Continent. From there he emigrated in 1806 to the United States, where he had a distinguished legal career and published several volumes, including his memoirs. His daughter Catherine married William, the son of his old friend Wolfe Tone. Sampson died in New York in December 1836 at the age of seventy-two.

Sources: Webb, *Compendium of Irish Biography.*

86 *Title page of the Report of the trial of William Drennan MD, 1794*

DUBLIN, 1794
REPRODUCTION

The trial of Drennan arose out of the Address to the Volunteers agreed by the Dublin Society of United Irishmen on 14 December 1792, which by the end of 1794 had become the basis for the prosecution of Archibald Hamilton Rowan and the proprietors of the *Northern Star* as well. As the author of the Address, Drennan must have expected to be proceeded against when Rowan was found guilty despite the brilliant oratory of his counsel, Curran. Drennan's legal team consisted of Curran, Simon Butler (first president of the Dublin Society of the United Irishmen) and Thomas Addis Emmet (another member), instructed by the attorney Matthew Dowling. The case for the crown was led by the attorney-general, Arthur Wolfe (who as Lord Kilwarden was to be murdered during the rebellion of Robert Emmet in 1803).

Drennan was acquitted mainly through Curran's destruction of the chief prosecution witness, William Paulet Carey. During the trial, Drennan excused the wobbly handwriting in a letter to his sister by saying 'I write this on my knee but my heart does not tremble, though my hand does', but it seems plausible that his subsequent disengagement from direct political action was the result of a decision not to face prosecution again.

Sources: John Francis Larkin (ed.), *The Trial of William Drennan* (Dublin, 1991).

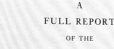

A
FULL REPORT
OF THE
TRIAL AT BAR,
IN THE
COURT OF KING'S BENCH,
OF
WILLIAM DRENNAN, MD
UPON AN INDICTMENT, CHARGING HIM WITH HAVING
WRITTEN AND PUBLISHED
A
SEDITIOUS LIBEL
WITH THE
SPEECHES OF COUNSEL, AND THE
OPINIONS OF THE COURT AT LARGE

DUBLIN:
PRINTED AND PUBLISHED BY
J. REA, 57, EXCHEQUER-STREET, AND
G. JOHNSON, 15, SUFFOLK-STREET.
1794.

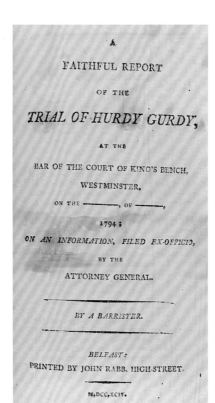

87 *The Trial of Hurdy Gurdy*

BY A BARRISTER [WILLIAM SAMPSON]
BELFAST, 1794
P AND B ROWAN

This burlesque of the trial of the Scottish radical Thomas Muir was originally published in the *Northern Star*, then issued as a pamphlet. Ridicule was a powerful and effective way of undermining respect for authority and spreading the spirit of radicalism. The popularity of *Hurdy Gurdy* also illustrates the links between Irish and Scottish radicals; there were United Scotsmen, and copies of the *Northern Star* circulated across the North Channel at one stage.

88 *William Wentworth, second Earl Fitzwilliam (1748-1833)*

MEZZOTINT BY JOSEPH GROZER AFTER JOSHUA REYNOLDS, 39.1 X 27.7 CM
NATIONAL GALLERY OF IRELAND, DUBLIN

Fitzwilliam was one of the Whigs, led by the Duke of Portland, who joined Pitt after the war with France broke out in 1793. Educated at Eton and Cambridge and connected with some of the most powerful Whig families in the country (he was the nephew and heir of Lord Rockingham), he was worth cultivating. Accordingly Pitt made him president of the council in June 1794 and when the Earl of Westmoreland was induced to resign later in the same year had him appointed lord lieutenant of Ireland. Fitzwilliam, who was the absentee owner of large estates in County Wicklow, was at first reluctant to accept the appointment. It was a tricky period in Anglo-Irish politics. Irish liberals and Catholics had been encouraged by recent reforms such as the Catholic Relief Act of 1793, put through by English pressure, against the wishes of the conservative clique that ran the Castle administration, but there was powerful opposition in Parliament and among the Ascendancy to further concessions on the Catholic question. In these circumstances the appointment of Fitzwilliam was ill-advised. As one historian puts it: 'Fitzwilliam's high principles were clouded by invincible self-righteousness and a complete lack of political finesse'. His short tenure as viceroy (he arrived in Dublin in January 1795 and departed in March) was a disaster. Egged on by Grattan and the Irish Whigs he exceeded his instructions and, moving with precipitate haste, dismissed the leading conservative John Beresford from office two days after arriving, sacked two under-secretaries (Hamilton and Cooke), sought the resignations of the attorney-general and the solicitor-general and ignored the lord chancellor. Then, without consulting his cabinet colleagues in England, he made known his support for the immediate admission of Catholics to Parliament. An outbreak of pro-emancipation petitions from Catholics and liberal Protestants throughout the country prompted Grattan to begin preparing an emancipation bill, raising Catholic hopes to fever pitch. On 21 February the British cabinet decided to recall Fitzwilliam and give him back his old post as lord president of the council. When Fitzwilliam finally departed from Dublin in March (he had been asked to stay on until his successor arrived) there were extraordinary scenes of grief and anger in the city. An enormous crowd turned out to cheer him, the horses of his carriage were unyoked and he was pulled through the streets to the dockside. Fitzwilliam chose to regard himself as having been recalled in disgrace. Two letters of his were published (without his orders, he said) implying that Pitt had allowed him to hold out hopes of emancipation and other reforms only to break faith as soon as the Irish parliament had voted generous taxation for the war against France. He blamed Pitt for taking the side of the corrupt Fitzgibbon-Beresford clique in Dublin Castle. Though none of his colleagues in the British

cabinet - not even his fellow Whigs - supported this view it was readily believed in Ireland. Many Irishmen lost confidence in the good faith of Pitt and in the capacity of the Dublin parliament to reform itself. The imprisoned leaders of the United Irishmen after the 1798 rebellion later asserted: 'Whatever progress the united system had made among the Presbyterians of the North, it had ... made but little way among the Catholics through the kingdom until after the recall of earl Fitzwilliam'.

The historian Lecky summed up the Fitzwilliam episode similarly: 'Great classes who were as yet very slightly disaffected now passed rapidly into republicanism, and Catholic opinion, which had been raised to the highest point of excited hope experienced a complete, a sudden and a most dangerous revulsion'.

It became widely accepted that only after all hope of constitutional reform had been extinguished by the recall of Fitzwilliam did the United Irishmen reorganise themselves and become a secret conspiracy dedicated to the overthrow of the British connection by armed force, with the aid of revolutionary France. This view of the Fitzwilliam episode as a 'tragic turning-point' in Irish history is open to question, however. Recent research suggests both that the radicalisation of Catholics was neither immediate nor universal and that separatist republicanism was already an established - if not always acknowledged - aim of some influential United Irishmen. To quote a recent essay, 'The Fitzwilliam débâcle, although an important political landmark for many Catholics, did not in itself transform the mass of the populace into revolutionary republicans'. What it did do was to damage Grattan and his Whig friends and strengthen the reactionary party in the Castle, with important results in the years that followed. Beresford, Cooke and company were restored by the next viceroy, Lord Camden, and the Catholic bill was not only easily defeated but was removed from the agenda for the time being. Apart from a brief period of office as president of the council in Grenville's government 1806-7, Fitzwilliam remained in opposition for the rest of his life. He was dismissed as lord lieutenant of the West Riding of Yorkshire in 1819 for condemning the Peterloo 'massacre'. He died in 1833.

Sources: *DNB.*
G.C. Bolton, *The Passing of the Irish Act of Union* (1966).
R.B. McDowell, 'The Fitzwilliam episode', in *Irish Historical Studies*, vol. XV, no. 58 (1966).
Deirdre Lindsay, 'The Fitzwilliam Episode Revisited', in Dickson, Keogh and Whelan (eds), *The United Irishmen* (1991).

89 *'McArt's Fort, from the Mountain'*

BY ANDREW NICHOLL, C.1828
WATERCOLOUR ON PAPER, 24 X 35.5 CM
ULSTER MUSEUM

McArt's Fort is the highest point of the Cave Hill which overlooks Belfast. When Wolfe Tone and his family were about to set out for America in June 1795 they travelled by way of Belfast, where they were entertained for three weeks by friends and supporters. A subscription - reportedly the substantial sum of £1,500 - was raised, and the Tone family was showered with presents and provisions for the journey. One incident which Tone particularly remembered and noted in his diary was a walk with his closest political allies - Thomas Russell, Samuel Neilson, Henry Joy McCracken, William Simms and others - to McArt's Fort, where they all swore

an oath 'never to desist in our efforts until we had subverted the authority of England over our country, and asserted our independence'.

Andrew Nicholl (1804-66) was born in Belfast and completed his apprenticeship as a printer in the offices of the *Northern Whig* before becoming a professional painter. He produced over one hundred watercolours of views around Belfast and along the Antrim coast c.1828, of which this is one. He painted in Belfast, Dublin and London, exhibiting in the Royal Academy and the Royal Hibernian Academy. In 1845 he accompanied Sir James Emerson Tennent to Ceylon, where he painted and taught; after 1850 he lived in London. Many of his paintings were engraved for use in Hall's *Ireland* and other publications. The Ulster Museum has a large collection of his watercolours and sketches.

Sources: R. B. O'Brien (ed.) *Autobiography of Wolfe Tone*, 2 vols, (London, 1893)
Marianne Elliott, *Wolfe Tone.*
Martyn Anglesea, 'Andrew Nicholl and his patrons in Ireland and Ceylon', in *Studies*, Summer 1982;
Introduction to *Andrew Nicholl's Paintings of the Antrim Coast in 1828* (Belfast, 1982).

6 'THE FRENCH ARE ON THE SEA'

The year 1796 might have been the great turning point in modern Irish history. The United Irishmen and their allies had attained a degree of support and organisation which - however exaggerated the estimates of their strength may have been - was certainly formidable and as yet comparatively unaffected by government counter-measures. In particular, Ireland was ill-prepared militarily to repel a large-scale foreign invasion assisted by internal support. The existence in France of a revolutionary government willing to consider such an expedition, the persuasive advocacy of Wolfe Tone and others, and the willingness of a successful young general to risk his reputation on the scheme were all propitious factors.

The crucial question, apart from that of political will, was the ability of the French to reach Ireland. The authorities in Ireland relied almost entirely on the British Navy to keep the French in Brest and Irish shores safe from invasion. Could the French transport a large force and land it? By sailing when they did, so late in the year, they achieved the vital element of surprise; by the same token, they were scattered by winter weather and had to abort their mission. As Tone remarked, it was England's greatest escape since the Spanish Armada. Later plans for invasion had much less real prospect of success, either because they were less formidable or because supporters of invasion in Ireland - what James Hope called the 'foreign aid men' - had become less influential, or both.

90 *The Port of Brest, 1794*

BY J.F. HÜE
MUSÉE DE LA MARINE, PARIS
REPRODUCTION

Jean-François Hüe, painter of landscapes, marine subjects and battle scenes, was born in 1751 and died in Paris in 1823. He was a pupil of Joseph Vernet, who painted a series of the ports of France; Hüe continued the series. This splendid picture of Brest is among those preserved in the Musée de la Marine. Received into the Academy in 1782, Hüe regularly exhibited marine works and landscapes in the Salon over a period of almost forty years, from 1781 to 1822.

Brest, shown here in all its bustle, was the chief naval port on France's western coast, the home of her Atlantic fleet and the point from which most of the expeditions to Ireland set out.

Sources: Bénézit, *Dictionnaire*

91 *Theobald Wolfe Tone (1763-1798)*

BY OR AFTER CATHERINE SAMPSON TONE
WATERCOLOUR, 11 X 9.2 CM (SIGHT) IN CASE 18 X 15.5 CM
ULSTER MUSEUM

This small portrait, showing Tone in profile wearing his French uniform, is mounted in a hinged case. When purchased at auction by the Ulster Museum in 1994 it was accompanied by a note, written on a separate piece of paper, which reads as follows:

> This Miniature Portrait of the famous patriot Theobold [sic] Wolfe
> Tone has been lithographed by Hullemandle [sic], who

110

attributed it to Catherine Samson [sic] Tone.
For many years it was in the possession of a Dublin
Merchant, a noted connoisseur & collector of antiques
& after his decease was treasured by his family
from whom it was purchased in January 1925.

Catherine Anne Sampson married Tone's son William in America. She was a daughter of William Sampson, a prominent United Irishman and friend of Tone, who was arrested and imprisoned in 1798. After his release he and his family settled in America, as did Mrs Tone and her children. Catherine painted a miniature of Tone which is now in the hands of a direct descendant and of which this portrait appears to be a copy.

Charles Joseph Hullmandel (1789-1850) was a leading English lithographer during the first half of the nineteenth century.

Theobald Wolfe Tone, the founder of Irish republican nationalism, was born in Dublin on 20 June 1763, the eldest son of a Protestant coachmaker, Peter Tone, and his wife Margaret. The Tones had sixteen children altogether, only five of whom were to live long enough to be adults. Wolfe Tone wanted to enter the army, but, since his father absolutely refused to support him if he did so, was obliged to abandon the idea and proceed to Trinity College, which he entered as a 'pensioner' undergraduate in February 1781. There he met Thomas Addis Emmet, 'the first of my friends', and others who were to figure - as friends or as foes - in his later career. If not quite a gentleman by background, Tone became one by taste and education, and certainly regarded himself as one. His intellectual liveliness, his wit and humour and his sociable manner made him good company wherever he found himself.

In 1785, while still an undergraduate, Tone eloped with a girl of sixteen, Elizabeth Witherington (he re-named her Matilda). He was to remain devoted to her for the rest of his life and she to him till the end of hers. 'If ever I succeed in life', he wrote, 'or attain at anything like station or eminence, I shall consider it as due to her counsels and example'. Early in 1786 he graduated from Trinity. For a time the young couple were obliged to live with Tone's father - now a bankrupt - at Bodenstown. Somehow the elder Tone scraped together the money to send his son to London, to study law at the Middle Temple. In London, he supported himself by journalism and forwarded to Pitt a proposal to establish a military colony in the Sandwich Islands, recently discovered by Captain Cook (Pitt did not reply). Returning to Dublin, Tone was called to the Bar in February 1789. He hated and despised the law, however, and never managed to make a living at it, turning instead to political journalism. For a time he was taken up by the moderate reformers of the Whig Club, which made him a member, but a chance meeting in the gallery of the House of Commons with a young ensign in the army, Thomas Russell, soon turned his mind in a more radical direction. Russell was to become Tone's most intimate friend and political ally, and the close friend of the whole Tone family. From this point onward, Tone was to devote himself to Ireland. For a man whose political career lasted less than nine years, over three of which he spent in exile, he was to leave an extraordinary mark on Irish history.

In September 1791 Tone published his influential pamphlet *An Argument on behalf of the Catholics of Ireland*. This brought him to the notice of the leaders of the Catholic Committee, who offered him the paid post of secretary. The pamphlet did much to break down Presbyterian prejudice against the Catholics (though it did not remove it entirely) but even more to encourage Catholics - or at any rate middle-class urban Catholics - to make common cause with radical Dissenters. This, the major aim of the Society of United Irishmen, was an alarming one for the government in Dublin. When the Belfast Society of United Irishmen was formed

in mid-October, when he himself was present, Tone's resolutions were unanimously adopted and the name of the association was his suggestion too, replacing Drennan's 'Irish Brotherhood'. Back in Dublin, Tone and Russell helped to establish the Dublin Society of United Irishmen on the Belfast model. Tone had been particularly impressed by the northern Dissenters' republicanism and lack of deference to aristocracy; there was more instinctive deference to rank in the south.

The Catholic Committee had been dominated by aristocratic leaders such as Lord Fingall, who was just as hostile to French Revolution ideas as upper-class Protestants were; so too were the Catholic bishops and clergy. In 1791, however, control of the Committee passed to a group of middle-class radicals led by John Keogh, a wealthy Dublin businessman. Keogh organised a Catholic Convention, which met in Dublin in December 1792 to press for further concessions in Ireland. Following the Convention a deputation of Catholics, led by Keogh and accompanied by Tone, went to London to present a petition to George III, travelling by way of Belfast and Donaghadee through Scotland. The outcome was the Catholic Relief Act of 1793, put through by British cabinet pressure. The Act's concessions, though important, did not make a great deal of practical difference for most Catholics, however, and were followed soon by repressive measures such as the Convention Act, an Arms Act, and the establishment of a militia. A bill to reform parliament was soundly defeated. Neither Catholics nor Protestant radicals were satisfied, and the ascendancy itself was divided and increasingly hostile to further concessions of any kind. The endowment of Maynooth College in 1795 did little to placate the Catholics while enraging diehard opponents. Henceforth Tone and many of his friends in the United Irishmen increasingly sought reform by revolutionary means, looking to France for help.

Tone's future - one of exile - was settled as a result of the visit to Dublin in April 1794 of an Anglican clergyman on a mission from France. The Rev. William Jackson was accompanied by an English friend, a lawyer named Cokayne, who was in fact a government spy. Jackson met some leading United Irishmen, including Tone. At the end of April, Jackson was arrested and a copy of a memorandum by Tone was found among his papers. Tone was saved from the consequences of his folly by Fitzgibbon and other powerful friends, who in return for an account of his part in the affair allowed him to leave the country and go to America.

Tone and his family sailed from Belfast in the American ship *Cincinnatus* in June. Five weeks out in an otherwise uneventful voyage, the *Cincinnatus* was stopped by three British frigates. A boarding party, sent across to press recruits for the Royal Navy, took all the deckhands except one and forty-eight of the male passengers. People such as Tone were usually left alone on such occasions, but he happened to be wearing trousers rather than breeches and therefore did not immediately look like a gentleman. But for the screams of his womenfolk he too would have been press-ganged.

In Philadelphia, Tone found that Hamilton Rowan had recently arrived from France. Through him, Tone was introduced to the French minister there. The statement he wrote for the Frenchman to forward to Paris emphasised the support a French invasion of Ireland would find among the people and the weakness of the government forces, and claimed that two-thirds of the British navy was composed of Irishmen, who could be subverted. Letters from friends in Ireland - Russell and Keogh in particular - urged him to make new efforts to negotiate with the French government on behalf of the United Irishmen. Besides, he found the Americans detestable - 'a selfish, churlish, unsocial race, totally absorbed in making money' - and America a cultural desert. Neither he nor Matilda wanted to settle there, and she supported his plans for going to France. The Americans supplied him with a passport, which happened to be in the name of 'James Smith', the pseudonym by which he was to be known until the last few weeks of his life. He set sail from New York on 1 January 1796, arriving at Le Havre a month later, after a crossing so stormy that he did not take his clothes off once. Matilda did not join him until May of the following year.

The Directory, as the government of France from September 1795 to October 1799 was called, was dominated by three of the five Directors - Barras, Reubell and Carnot. The last two, controlling foreign affairs and war respectively, were of particular importance to Tone's mission. Tone had an introduction to James Monroe, American ambassador in Paris (and later president of the USA), who provided him with an entrée to the Minister of Foreign Affairs, Delacroix (father of the painter). But it was a meeting with Carnot, at a public audience, that brought results. Though Tone's French was bad, the memorials that he was asked to produce, when translated, were much admired. What Tone argued for was the landing in Ireland of a large French force - 15,000 to 20,000 men under a well-known general - so that there would be a revolution rather than an insurrection and a civil war.

Carnot passed Tone on to General Henry Clarke, then aged thirty, whose Irish forebears had followed James II to France. Clarke was impressed by Tone's memorials and reported favourably to Carnot. Copies were sent to Truguet, Minister of Marine, and General Hoche. The Directory decided in favour of an Irish invasion and gave Hoche instructions to prepare for it. Its original plans for a wrecking diversion had turned, with the employment of Hoche, into a full-scale campaign for the liberation of Ireland. Tone's mission had succeeded. It received powerful support from Lord Edward FitzGerald and Arthur O'Connor, who visited the Continent in May 1796; O'Connor travelled into France to a secret meeting with Hoche which firmed up invasion plans. The result was the expedition to Bantry Bay in December - forty-three vessels, seventeen of them ships of the line, and 14,450 troops, with artillery, arms and ammunition to supply the Irish as well. Tone went with them, as Adjutant-General. Everything seemed set fair for the invasion of Ireland. Instead, to Tone's intense disappointment, the fleet was scattered and the landing never took place. As he rightly remarked, it was England's greatest escape since the Armada.

Tone's hopes were raised once more the following summer, when a Dutch expedition under Daendels and De Winter was gathered at the mouth of the Texel, only waiting for a favourable wind. But the wind never came, and Tone eventually had to disembark. Then Hoche died, aged only twenty-nine, and hopes of a major expedition to Ireland died with him. The year 1798 brought another attempt, but too little and too late in the case of Humbert's expedition. Without any hope of success, but feeling obliged to risk his life however hopeless the cause, Tone sailed for Donegal in the *Hoche* with Hardy's expedition. The fact that he was aboard was common knowledge, reported in the French papers, and he was under no illusion as to his likely fate if captured. 'In setting off for that last unfortunate expedition,' Matilda wrote, 'he told me he knew his life was gone...'. When the *Hoche* was engaged by Admiral Warren's squadron off the coast of Donegal, Tone fought with the bravery of one who would have welcomed death in action. Instead he survived. Rather than seek to hide himself among the French prisoners, he was the first to step ashore when they were eventually landed at Buncrana on 3 November 1798.

Tone asked to be treated as his rank in the French army demanded, but so far as his captors were concerned he was a traitor and would be treated as such, so he was separated from the other French officers and sent to Derry, where he was kept in chains. When he protested to Lord Cavan, the general of the district, he was told 'I look on you (and you have proved yourself) a traitor and rebel to your sovereign and native country, and as such you will be treated by me'; and he added, 'I lament as a man, the fate that awaits you'. The French general Hardy wrote to Cornwallis on his behalf but in vain.

Tone was sent to Dublin in irons and under heavy military escort. Approaching Dublin he insisted on changing into his full-dress French general's uniform for the last stage of his journey. He was taken to the Provost prison in the Royal Barracks - where he was tried by a military court on 10 November. Though reluctant to accept the word 'traitorously', he pleaded guilty to the charges and read out a personal statement explaining his motivation and regretting the way the rebellion had gone: '... if in consequence of the measures in which I have been engaged misfortunes have been brought upon this country, I heartily lament it ... for a fair and open war I was prepared; if that has degenerated with a system of assassination, massacre, and plunder I do again most sincerely lament it...' He asked only to die like a soldier, by firing squad. When he was sentenced instead to be hanged (though Cornwallis prevented the intention to display his head on a pike), he cut his throat with a penknife. Surgeons sewed up the wound and he survived another week, though seriously ill, dying on 19 November. Later Irish nationalists, unable to accept the fact of his suicide, suspected that the government had somehow murdered Tone in prison. At the time, however, there were no such rumours, and the authorities behaved openly and correctly so far as the inquest was concerned. Tone's family accepted his suicide as a fact. So too did Madden later, in his history of the United Irishmen. Besides, we know that Tone himself was determined not to die like a common criminal.

Matilda Tone was twenty-nine when her husband's death, at the age of thirty-four, left her destitute in France. The Directory gave her some immediate financial relief and said there would be a pension, but it took the intervention of the Bonapartes to secure payment at last in 1804. Successive French governments continued to pay it until her death in the United States in 1849.

Sources: *Autobiography of Wolfe Tone.*
            Frank MacDermot, *Theobald Wolfe Tone and His Times* (1939, revised and reissued 1968).
            Marianne Elliott, *Wolfe Tone: Prophet of Irish Independence.*

92 *Wolfe Tone memorabilia*

(a) **MS diary of Theobald Wolfe Tone covering the period of his first visit to Belfast and the establishment of the Society of United Irishmen.**
Trinity College, Dublin

Tone first visited Belfast on 11 October 1791, two months after the publication of his *Argument on Behalf of the Catholics of Ireland*. This had sought to reassure those, mainly Ulster Presbyterians, who had begun to express doubts about the political reforms being advocated, particularly in the direction of Catholic Emancipation. Tone was secretary to the Catholic Committee 'of which they [the people of Belfast] know wonderfully little', as he noted on the first day of his stay in the town.

The principal purpose of Tone's visit was the establishment in Belfast of the Society of United Irishmen. His diary entries suggest that, although the Society was undoubtedly first started there, a week after his arrival on 18 October, the idea had not been exclusively a Belfast initiative. Nevertheless he was glad to find 'the secret committee all steady sensible clear men and, as I judge, extremely well adapted for serious business'.

Among Tone's other entries in the first few pages of his Belfast diary, it is worth drawing attention to his satisfaction with 'a great deal of general politics being discussed'. In particular, the popularity of Thomas Paine's *Rights of Man* prompted him to refer to it as 'the Koran of Blefescu' (his nickname for Belfast).

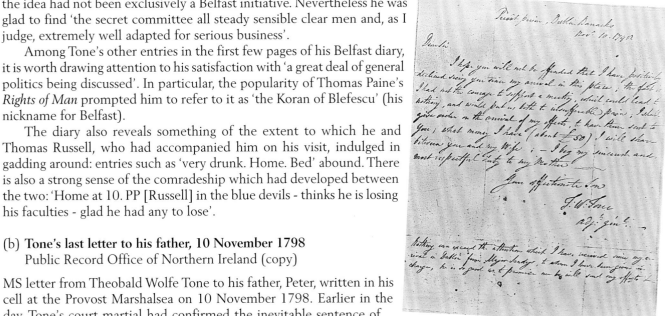

The diary also reveals something of the extent to which he and Thomas Russell, who had accompanied him on his visit, indulged in gadding around: entries such as 'very drunk. Home. Bed' abound. There is also a strong sense of the comradeship which had developed between the two: 'Home at 10. PP [Russell] in the blue devils - thinks he is losing his faculties - glad he had any to lose'.

(b) **Tone's last letter to his father, 10 November 1798**
Public Record Office of Northern Ireland (copy)

MS letter from Theobald Wolfe Tone to his father, Peter, written in his cell at the Provost Marshalsea on 10 November 1798. Earlier in the day, Tone's court martial had confirmed the inevitable sentence of death. The letter is signed 'T.W. Tone Adjutant general'.

He expresses the hope that his father would not be hurt by his refusal to see him before the sentence of death is carried out and ends: 'I had not the courage of supporting a meeting which would lead to nothing and would put us both to insufferable pain. I beg my sincerest and most respectable duty to my mother. Your affectionate son'.

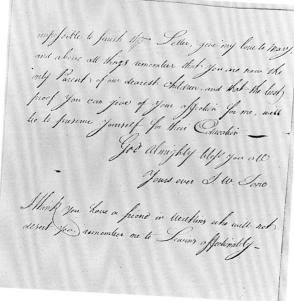

(c) **Tone's last letter to his wife Matilda, 10 November 1798, written from the Provost Marshalsea on learning that he had been sentenced to death.**
Public Record Office of Northern Ireland (copy)

Dearest Love
The hour is at last come, when we must part; as no words can express what I feel for you and our children, I shall not attempt it; complaint of any kind would be beneath your courage or mine; be assured I will die as I have lived and that you will have no reason to blush for me.

I have written on your behalf to the French government, to the Minister of the Marine, to General Kilmaine and to Mr Shee; with the latter I wish you especially to advise; in Ireland I have written to your brother Harry, and to those of my friends who are about to go into exile and who I am sure will not abandon you.

Adieu dearest love, I find it impossible to finish this letter; give my love to Mary (his sister) and above all things remember that you are now the only parent to our dearest children, and that the best proof you can give of your affection for me will be to preserve yourself for their education - God almighty bless you all. Yours ever
T.W. Tone

I think you have a friend in Wilkins* who will not desert you; remember me to Lewins affectionately.

* It is agreed by Tone's most eminent biographers that this is a reference to Thomas Wilson, a Scottish radical whom the Tones had met on their journey to the United States in 1795 and with whom they had struck up a warm relationship. Matilda Tone did in fact marry Wilson in 1816.

CARNOT.

93 *Lazare Carnot (1753-1823)*

COLOURED ENGRAVING
CHESTER BEATTIE LIBRARY, DUBLIN (REPRODUCTION)

Lazare-Nicolas-Marguerite Carnot was born at Nolay in Burgundy, the son of a lawyer and local judge. Although bourgeois in origin, he was admitted to the royal school for military engineers at Mézières in 1770 through the influence of a nobleman, and was commissioned as a lieutenant in the Corps of Engineers in 1773. For the next four years he served in garrisons in various parts of France, studying military engineering and literature and moving in intellectual circles wherever he went. He was elected to a number of local academies, including (1787) that of Arras, where he met Robespierre. He published several works on military engineering, including a well-received appreciation of Louis XIV's great engineer Vauban. Both his professional and his personal prospects were blighted by his common origins, however: he could not be promoted above the rank of captain, and his offer of marriage to the daughter of a minor nobleman was refused. Not unnaturally, Captain Carnot welcomed the Revolution.

In 1791 Carnot was elected to the Legislative Assembly as deputy from the Pas-de-Calais area, and served on the diplomatic and public education committees without distinguishing himself. He was nevertheless sent on a special mission to the Army of the Rhine in August 1792, the day after the Paris mob attacked the palace of the Tuileries and virtually overthrew the monarchy, and in September he was elected to the National Convention. He was absent from Paris on special mission during the debates on Louis XVI's trial, but returned in time to vote for the King's immediate execution. In the Convention, Carnot did not join the extreme radicals, but he supported many of the policies of the Jacobins. On a special mission to the Army of the North in March - August 1793, he uncovered the treason of General Dumouriez and forced him to flee to the Austrians. Carnot then became a member of the Committee of Public Safety, the body that ran the country during the Terror. His speciality was military affairs. The skill and success with which he raised, trained, equipped, transported and fed an army of nearly a million men, and thus enabled the Republic to triumph over its foreign and domestic enemies, earned him the title 'Organiser of Victory' and saved him from the guillotine when Robespierre and his supporters were overthrown on 9 Thermidor, Year II (27 July 1794).

In the new, more moderate regime set up in 1795, Carnot was one of the original five Directors. In this capacity, he continued to supervise military affairs. One of his appointments was that of the youthful Bonaparte to the Army of Italy. It was during this period that he met Wolfe Tone and was persuaded to lend his crucial support to French intervention in Ireland.

In 1797, however, when a royalist plot to overthrow the government was met by the military coup of 18 Fructidor (4 September), Carnot was compromised. He was forced to flee to Geneva to escape arrest. He was allowed to return under an amnesty of December 1799, granted by his protégé Napoleon as First Consul, and served as minister of war April-October 1800. As a member of the Tribunate, however, he alone voted against Napoleon's making himself first Consul for Life and (1804) Emperor. He retired into private life in 1807. He came out of retirement in 1814 to direct the defence of Antwerp against the advancing allies. Subsequently, during the Hundred Days, he served Napoleon as minister of the interior. On the final defeat of Napoleon he went into exile, first at Warsaw and later at Magdeburg, where he died on 2 August 1823.

Sources: *Encyclopaedia Britannica*, (15th edition).
               Samuel F. Scott and Barry Rothaus (eds), *Historical Dictionary of the French Revolution, 1789-1799* (2 vols., London, 1985), vol. 1.

94(a) & (b) *Two portraits of Paul Barras (1755-1829)*

LITHOGRAPH BY LEON MAUDUISON AFTER RAFFET (REPRODUCTION)
BIBLIOTHÈQUE NATIONALE, PARIS

Paul-François-Nicolas, Vicomte de Barras, Terrorist and Director, was born into a noble family in Provence and was educated by the Carmelites. At the age of sixteen he became a gentleman cadet in the Languedoc Regiment of the French royal army. In 1775 he got a commission in the Regiment of Pondicherry and from 1776 to 1783 served in India. There he fought against the British in the defence of Pondicherry in 1778. On his return to France he became disenchanted with the royal regime and in 1789 threw in his lot with the Revolution, joining the Jacobins. Elected in 1792 to the National Convention as one of the deputies for Var, he voted for the execution of Louis XVI. In 1793, when commissioner to the Army of Italy, he met Napoleon Bonaparte (then a captain of artillery) at the siege of Toulon and was favourably impressed by him. Toulon had been seized by royalists, who had opened the harbour to the British and Spanish fleets blockading the port. The siege lasted from September to December. When the British withdrew after setting fire to the arsenal, in the process destroying most of the ships in the harbour, the rebels were left to the mercy of the republicans. Barras, the commissioner, showed none at all, ordering the shooting of hundreds of prisoners.

In the Convention, Barras opposed the growing despotism of Robespierre and, appointed commandant of the Convention's armed forces (the Army of the Interior and the police), helped to overthrow the Robespierrists on 9 Thermidor. He subsequently became president of the Convention and brought in Bonaparte, now a general, to repress an uprising in Paris on 13 Vendémiaire (5 October 1795) - the occasion of the famous 'whiff of grapeshot'. Under the new constitution of 1795, Barras was elected to the legislative body, which made him one of the five Directors. All five were regicides. Barras was the only one of noble birth, and the only one to serve during the entire period of the Directory (one had to be replaced each year, after lots were drawn). Barras thus accumulated considerable power, which he enjoyed; he loved wearing the special costume, designed by the artist Jacques-Louis David, of a gold-embroidered coat of red velvet with white satin and a hat with huge tricolour plumes (b).

Barras was a leading figure in the coup of 18 Fructidor (4 September 1797) which removed two of the Directors - Carnot and Barthélemy - who were suspected of royalism. He cultivated the acquaintance of Bonaparte, claiming to have arranged the young general's marriage to Josephine de Beauharnais (a former mistress of his). Napoleon had his own ambitions, however, and when he overthrew the Directory in 1799 forced Barras to resign along with the other Directors. That was the end of Barras's influence in French history. Napoleon's police chief, Fouché, kept him under close surveillance, and he was twice exiled (to Brussels in 1801-05 and to Rome in 1813). The restored Bourbons would have nothing to do with him, but allowed him to live quietly on his estates. He died in Paris on 29 January 1829.

Barras was able, intelligent and ruthless, a cynical survivor and exploiter of the revolutionary upheavals through which he lived. He lived a life of great luxury, scandalous dissipation and extreme greed - in fact, he was a perfect example of all that was worst in the aristocratic stereotype of the pre-revolutionary period. Entirely bereft of republican virtues, he made a huge fortune from army contracts and diplomatic bribes.

Sources: Scott and Rothaus (eds), *Historical Dictionary of the French Revolution*, vol. 1.

95 *General Clarke (c.1766-1818)*

COLOURED ENGRAVING
CHESTER BEATTY LIBRARY, DUBLIN (REPRODUCTION)

Henri Jacques Guillaume Clarke was the descendant of an Irish Jacobite who had followed James II to France after the Boyne. Like his father before him, Clarke served in the Irish Brigade of the French royal army, in the regiments that chose to transfer to the British service when the Revolution came. Clarke threw in his lot with the Revolution, however, and as a fluent English speaker spent the years 1789-91 on the staff of the French embassy in London. During that period he visited Ireland. Fortunate to survive the Terror, he became a figure of some importance under the Directory, in the War Ministry of Carnot. When Wolfe Tone arrived in Paris in 1796 and approached Carnot about his plans for a French expedition to Ireland, Clarke was essential in helping to forward the project from his position as head of the Bureau Topographique et Historique Militaire. The Bureau, which had originally been established by Carnot under the Committee of Public Safety, was the most powerful of the nine bureaux under the Directory, and had a permanent staff. Its function was to co-ordinate plans for military operations directly with the generals. Tone therefore saw a lot of Clarke - this 'handsome, smooth-faced young man of thirty' - during the protracted preparations for the Bantry Bay expedition, and came to be very friendly with him.

The fall of Carnot in 1797 affected the careers of those, such as Clarke, who had been close to him. Clarke's took a great leap forward under Bonaparte, however, whom he served as Minister of War. As the caption to this portrait tells us, he ended up with the exalted title of Duc de Feltre, a marshal and peer of France.

Sources: *Autobiography of Wolfe Tone.*
            Marianne Elliott, *Partners in Revolution.*

96 *Laurent Jean-François Truguet (1752-1839)*

ENGRAVING
BIBLIOTHÈQUE NATIONALE, PARIS (REPRODUCTION)

Born in Toulon, the son of an admiral, Truguet followed his father into the navy.

He served as a naval officer during the American War of Independence, under d'Estaing, Grasse and Vaudreuil, and was made Chevalier of St Louis by the King in 1780. During the years 1785-86 he was engaged on hydrographical work in the Dardanelles. At the Revolution he threw in his lot with the reformers, unlike most of his fellow officers. Promotion followed and he became a 'contre-amiral' (rear-admiral) in 1792. During service in the Mediterranean in 1793 he bombarded Nice and other places belonging to the ruler of Savoy. The triumph of the Jacobins in the Convention led to his dismissal and imprisonment as a suspected counter-revolutionary, but he was released when Robespierre fell from power. Under the Directory he was appointed Minister of Marine, a post he held from November 1793 to July 1797, when his career was affected by the fall of his superior, Carnot. In 1799 he supported the coup of 18 Brumaire, by which Bonaparte overthrew the Directory and made himself First Consul. Truguet was re-employed in the navy and promoted to admiral in 1804. Later, in 1811, he was made maritime prefect of the coasts of Holland (that is, of the Napoleonic kingdom of Holland, which consisted of Holland and Belgium). After the restoration of the Bourbon monarchy he not only survived but prospered, becoming a peer of France in 1819, an honour he was to enjoy for the remaining twenty years of his life.

As Minister of Marine in 1796 and again in 1797, Truguet was deeply involved in plans for invading Ireland. He was a keen supporter of Hoche's great expedition, though as an experienced naval officer himself he had a far better appreciation than the impatient young general of the many genuine difficulties faced by the navy, and as minister he knew its impoverished and demoralised state better than anyone. That so formidable an enterprise was mounted at all was largely due to his hard work. Its complete failure was a great disappointment to him; he had looked forward to greeting the British peace envoy, Lord Malmesbury, with the words 'We have twenty thousand men in Ireland'.

Sources: J. Tulard, J. Fayard and A. Fierro, *Histoire et Dictionnaire de la Revolution Française* (Paris, 1987).
Marianne Elliott, *Partners in Revolution.*

97 *Three Portraits of General Lazare Hoche (1768-97)*

(a) Hoche, Général en Chef de l'Armée de Sambre et Meuse
By Ruotte after Dutaillis, c.1797
STIPPLE ENGRAVING, FULL LENGTH
MUSÉE CARNAVALET, PARIS (REPRODUCTION)

(b) Hoche, Général des Armées Françaises, dans le Nord et ensuite dans l'Ouest
By Duplessis-Bertaux, c.1797
MEZZOTINT IN CIRCLE, WITH LINE ENGRAVING AND TEXT BELOW
MUSÉE CARNAVALET, PARIS (REPRODUCTION)

(c) Hoche n'est Plus: Journée du 10 Vendémiaire an 6 ème
Anonymous, c.1797
LINE ENGRAVING IN OVAL, WITH VIGNETTES AND TEXT
MUSÉE CARNAVALET, PARIS (REPRODUCTION)

According to (a) and (b) above and most authorities, Louis-Lazare Hoche was born on 24 June 1768 at Versailles, where his father worked in the royal stables; a recent *Historical Dictionary of the French Revolution, 1789-1799*, however, gives his place of birth as Montreuil and his father's occupation as professional soldier. The town of Versailles certainly claims him; its Musée Lambinet has a large-scale portrait, a bust and other relics. With little formal education, his parents being 'pauvres et obscurs', he joined the army at the age of sixteen. When the Revolution

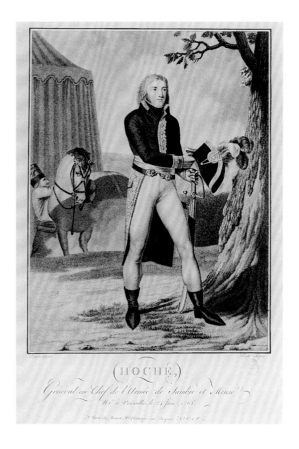

broke out five years later, he was a corporal in the French Guards. Like many able and ambitious young men of humble birth, Hoche welcomed the changes that swept away the privileges of the nobility and opened the way to promotion. When his regiment was disbanded, he joined the new National Guard with the rank of sergeant. In 1792, when France went to war, he was rapidly promoted, to lieutenant and then captain, serving at the siege of Thionville and the battle of Neerwinden.

In May 1793 he was named adjutant-general. Such were the (often justified) suspicions of disloyalty during that critical period that he was arrested the same summer and had to face a Revolutionary Tribunal. Since there was in fact no evidence against him, he was acquitted and given command of the garrison at Dunkirk. He conducted the defence of the town so competently that he was promoted first to the rank of brigadier and then (October 1794) to that of general of division. He had risen through the ranks in two and a half years and was still only twenty-six years old.

As commander of the Army of the Moselle, a poorly-disciplined and poorly-equipped force to start with, he drove the Austrians back across the Rhine, earning himself command of the Army of Italy. Scarcely had he reached Nice to take up his new post than he was arrested, taken to Paris and imprisoned. He stayed in prison until the coup of 9 Thermidor overthrew Robespierre and opened the doors for political prisoners. Restored to his rank, at the end of 1794 he was given command of the Army of the Coasts of Brest, with instructions to suppress the royalist insurrection in the Vendée area south of Brittany. His firm yet wise and moderate handling of the situation achieved good results; by mid-February 1795 he had pacified most of Brittany. In July of that year, however, the British landed a force of French royalists on the coast at Quiberon. The expedition went badly, however. Hoche was victorious, and afterwards executed many of the captured émigrés. His offer of religious toleration (a main cause of the revolt in this devoutly Catholic area had been the anti-clerical policies of the revolutionary governments in Paris) subsequently enabled him to make terms with the rebel chiefs; by mid-July 1796 he had proclaimed the insurrection at an end. The Directors gave him the title 'Pacificator of the Vendée'. The revolt had been a very bloody one, and was to leave a permanent legacy of bitterness and mistrust between conservatives and republicans.

As a good patriot, Hoche was outraged by the part Britain had played in the Vendée. This anti-English feeling was one of the reasons for his interest in Ireland, where French assistance to the United Irishmen might provide an effective way of taking revenge. When offered command of the Irish expedition in 1796 he threw himself into the preparations and staked his reputation on its success. Wolfe Tone has left a lively account of his first meeting with the general in Paris, which took place at the Luxembourg Palace on 12 July 1795 - the anniversary, as Tone noted, of the Battle of Aughrim.

Hoche proceeded to question Tone closely on the contents of the memorials with which he had been bombarding the French ministers, particularly on what support could be expected from the people, the likely attitude of the Catholic clergy, how the forces of the crown were likely to react; the militia, Tone thought, would 'come over to the cause of their country *en masse*'. Hoche made it clear that if he went to Ireland be would do so in force and bring 'great quantities of arms, ammunition, stores, and artillery, and, for his own reputation, see that all the arrangements were made on a proper scale'.

After many frustrating delays the expedition, with Tone as adjutant, sailed from Brest on 16 December 1796. Storms scattered the fleet, however, so that it arrived piecemeal at Bantry Bay. Worse, the frigate with Hoche on board did not appear. In the commander's absence his second-in-command, Grouchy, refused to take responsibility for landing and instead returned to Brest. When Hoche at last arrived, he could do nothing but follow. Because the failure had not been his fault, he was given command of another army, that of Sambre-et-Meuse, in February 1797. Reorganising his forces, he crossed the Rhine, defeated the Austrians in three battles and was on the way to further successes when news came in April that his rival Bonaparte had concluded an armistice with the Austrians at Leoben.

With the end of hostilities on the Continent, Hoche turned his thoughts to another invasion of Ireland, this time using the army and navy of France's Dutch allies in conjunction with another expedition from Brest. Before this could come to fruition, however, his health failed him. After a brief but miserable illness at his headquarters in Wetzlar - marked by convulsions, coughing fits and the spitting up of blood - he died on 19 September 1797; he was only twenty-nine. Had he lived, he would have had to deal with the ambitions of Bonaparte, his only rival in precocious military genius. As it was, the Directors made a posthumous national hero of him, with unprecedented displays of public grief.

Two of these three prints, (b) and (c), were clearly produced after his death, as tributes to Hoche's career and achievements. The idealised portrait by Duplessi-Bertaux (b) and its text constitute a high-class production, artistically much superior in every way to the other. The much cruder anonymous work (c), however, has the liveliness of caricature and - to judge from the evidence of the third, full-length portrait (a) - a better likeness of the man himself, lively and not too smooth.

The text in (c) is headed by the words 'il vécut assé pour sa gloire, trop peu pour Lapatrie' [he lived long enough for his glory, too short a time for the Fatherland]. Below, three vignettes shows the Pacification de la Vendée, his funeral, and a scene entitled 'il triomphà a quibron' [he triumphed at Quiberon]. At the bottom is an extract from the funeral oration given by the President of the Directory headed 'Hoche n'est Plus' [Hoche is no more] ...'

Of the artists responsible for these productions:

(a) Louis Charles Ruotte, engraver, was born in Paris in 1754 and died there in 1806. He engraved religious scenes, genre pictures and portraits, exhibiting in the Salons of 1793, 1795, 1796 and 1804.

(b) The Duplessi-Bertaux whose name appears here can probably be identified as Jean Bertaux, an etcher of the second half of the eighteenth century (dates unknown).

Sources: Scott and Rothaus (eds), *Historical Dictionary of the French Revolution, 1789-1799*, vol. 1.
Autobiography of Wolfe Tone.
Bénézit, *Dictionnaire.*

98 *Admiral Morard de Galles (1742-1809)*

ENGRAVING
BIBLIOTHÈQUE NATIONALE, PARIS (REPRODUCTION)

Justin Bonaventure Morard de Galles, born in 1741, entered the French navy in 1757, subsequently serving against the British, in the Indian Ocean under the great admiral Suffren, and later in the American War. In 1792 he was made contre-amiral (rear-admiral) and in 1793 vice-amiral. Shortage of experienced officers, insubordination among the lower ranks in the early years of the Revolution and the suspicion of revolutionary governments (the admiral, like so many others, was arrested and imprisoned under the Terror) did much to destroy the morale and fighting qualities of the navy. To make matters worse, French governments of the period all gave financial priority to land forces and the continental campaign. By the later 1790s, when Morard de Galles was again on the active service list, the navy was in a pitiable state.

At the best of times it was difficult to mount a successful combined operation on a large scale. The expedition to Ireland was beset by more troubles then most. Hoche was impatient to set out and, when delays arose, suspected Admiral Villaret and some of his officers of deliberately playing for time. In November 1796 he insisted on their dismissal, which made things worse. Villaret was replaced by

Morard de Galles, who accepted the appointment reluctantly. Things became so bad, and the time of year so late for sailing at all, that the Directors actually decided to cancel the expedition, only to find that it had sailed from Brest the day before, 16 December. Hoche insisted that he should travel with the admiral, on board the frigate *Fraternité*. When the fleet was scattered by storms and the *Fraternité* was blown far out to sea, the forces that arrived at Bantry found themselves bereft of decided leadership. When Hoche and Morard de Galles at length arrived, they were told that the ships had gone. Admiral Bouvet, the senior naval officer on the spot, had cut his cables and obliged the rest to follow him home, where he was disgraced and dismissed.

Morard de Galles's reputation also suffered, though he could scarcely be held responsible for what had happened; nevertheless it was effectively the end of his naval career. In his declining years, under Bonaparte, he was made a senator and a count of the Empire.

Sources: Tulard, Fayard and Fierro, *Histoire et Dictionnaire.*
            Marianne Elliott, *Partners in Revolution.*

99 *General Charles Kilmaine (1754-99)*

Engraving
Chester Beatty Library, Dublin (Reproduction)

Charles Jennings Kilmaine was born in Dublin in 1754. As a lad of fourteen, he went to Paris and enlisted in the Lauzun regiment of cavalry. He went to America with Lafayette and distinguished himself in several engagements, returning to France with strongly republican views. At the Revolution, he helped to keep his regiment's discipline intact and, when many of the aristocratic officers subsequently became émigrés or deserted, was rapidly promoted to command of a squadron and fought with notable bravery at the battle of Jemappes in November 1792. The National Convention starved the cavalry not only of equipment and arms but even of fodder for the horses; at one stage 6,000 of them were allowed to starve to death. Kilmaine and other officers used their private means to keep the men fed and prevent them from deserting. He took part in the campaign against the Allies in the north before being thrown into a Paris dungeon during the Terror. He escaped execution, however, and was released after the fall of Robespierre. Unemployed for a time, he was eventually given a division in the Army of Italy under Bonaparte and commanded the cavalry in all the famous victories of the campaign that drove the Austrians from Italy and forced them to make peace in 1797. He died in 1799.

Sources: Webb, *Compendium of Irish Biography.*

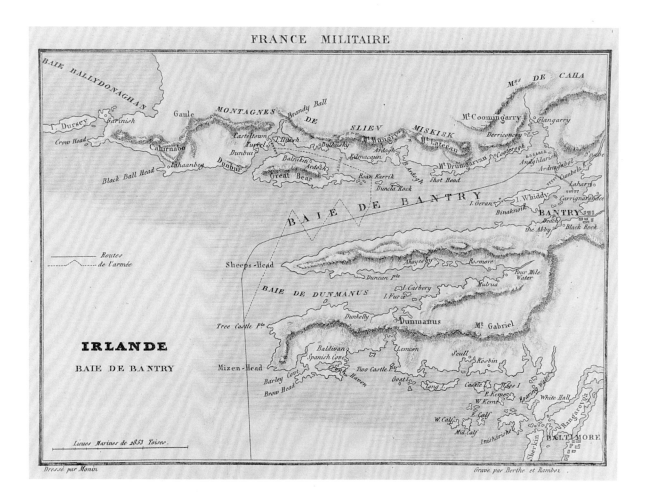

FRANCE MILITAIRE

IRLANDE

BAIE DE BANTRY

Dressé par Monin   *Gravé par Berthe et Ramboz*

100 *Baie De Bantry*

ENGRAVED MAP, 12 x 17 CM IN BORDER
FROM *FRANCE MILITAIRE* (1835)
ULSTER MUSEUM

This map of the coast of West Cork, showing the movements of the French expedition in Bantry Bay in December 1796, was engraved by Berthe and Ramboz for *France Militaire: Histoire des armées françaises de terre et de mer de 1792 à 1833* (5 vols. Paris, 1835); it comes from Vol. 2. The engraver L. Berthe, who was active in Paris from c.1777, was also responsible for a series entitled *Uniformes de l'infanterie française et etrangère.*

Sources: Bénézit, *Dictionnaire*

101 *End of Irish Invasion; -or- The Destruction of the French Armada*

BY J[AME]S G[ILLRA]Y
COLOURED AQUATINT, 25.4 x 36.8 CM, PUBLISHED IN LONDON 20 JAN. 1797 BY H. HUMPHREY
BRITISH MUSEUM, LONDON

This print shows French warships tossing helplessly among enormous waves, which are lashed to a fury by blasts from the mouths of (l. to r.) Pitt, Dundas, Grenville and Windham, whose heads emerge from the clouds. The French ship *Le Révolutionaire*, which has Charles James Fox as its figurehead, is about to founder.

124

_End of the Irish Invasion ;__ or __The Destruction of the French Armada._

Fox looks up despairingly. Playing cards (a reference to Fox's addiction to gambling) float in the water nearby. _L'Egalité_ is wrecked on the left, and another ship disappears in a whirlpool behind. _The Revolutionary Jolly Boat_ (left foreground) is being swamped by a blast from Windham: its occupants include the Irish playwright Sheridan and the Scottish advocate Erskine, both of whom were parliamentary friends and allies of Fox, as well as other liberals.

News of the arrival and dispersal of the French fleet at Bantry Bay had reached London on 31 December 1796. Its description, in the title, as the French Armada was more apt than Gillray could have known. Wolfe Tone, who was on board the flagship, wrote that the failure of the expedition was England's greatest escape since the Spanish Armada.

Sources: _BM Catalogue_, IV, no. 8979.

102 _Rigged model of a ship of 64 guns, c.1775_

BY AN UNKNOWN BUILDER
LENGTH 152, BREADTH 53.7, HEIGHT 127 CM; SCALE 1:48
DIMENSIONS OF SHIP (FROM THE MODEL): LENGTH ON GUNDECK 160 FT, BEAM 44FT; TONNAGE 1375 TONS
APPROXIMATELY
NATIONAL MARITIME MUSEUM, LONDON

This contemporary model of a British two-decker warship is probably a design for a class of 3rd Rates built about 1775. The rigging is modern (1930) but generally correct for the period. The long lateen yard on the mizzenmast was still a prominent

feature at that date, but only the after portion was used. The armament consisted of 26 24-pounders on the gun deck, 26 18-pounders on the upper deck, 10 9-pounders on the quarter deck and 2 9-pounders on the forecastle.

Warships were rated according to the number of guns they could carry, from more than 90 in a first-rate to fewer than 30 in a sixth-rate. The rate of a ship also determined the pay of its officers.

103 *Rigged model of a ship of 36 guns, c.1805*

BY AN UNKNOWN BUILDER
LENGTH 167, BREADTH 53.7, HEIGHT 120 CM; SCALE 1:48
DIMENSIONS OF SHIP (FROM THE MODEL): LENGTH ON LOWER DECK 144 FT, BEAM 37 FT; TONNAGE 900 TONS

APPROXIMATELY.
National Maritime Museum, London

This contemporary model accurately represents a 36-gun frigate built between 1796 and 1808, though it cannot be identified with any particular ship. The flag, if original, show that the rigging dates from 1801 or later, something that is confirmed by the solid bulwarks throughout. The sails appear to be original, a great rarity in models of this period. The vessel has its full complement of ship's boats - a launch and two cutters stowed amidships and a jolly boat hung on davits at the stern. The hull was coppered in 1960.

104 *Model ship, made by French prisoners of war in Ireland, c. 1804*

Dimensions of case: 23 cm high x 26.7cm long x 10.8 cm deep
Ulster Museum

The model, which is rigged, is made of bone; the case, covered with straw painted to resemble wood marquetry, is glazed at the front and sides and has a mirror at the back. The rigging, which is somewhat damaged, has not been restored.

Such models were usually made by prisoners of war for sale to the local population as a means of supplementing the few comforts of their incarceration. Little or nothing is known about this particular model, but it is thought to have been made by prisoners held at Newry, County Down.

7 IRISH CULTURAL REVIVAL

The United Irishmen were of course nationalists, but on the whole their nationalism was of an eighteenth-century kind, rather than that of later cultural nationalists who sought to strengthen the country's claim to independence by cherishing its distinctive music, literature and language. It was not that the materials for such a view were lacking - Irish was still spoken by a large part of the population, many country people (the large majority of the population at that time) had a keen appreciation of Irish poetry and legend, Celtic lore was in fashion, and antiquarians had been studying early Irish civilisation for years but that the nationalism of the Irish Patriots, like that of the American colonists, was in most cases based on geography and common interest rather than continuity of tradition. On the contrary, as the Dublin Society of United Irishmen declared, 'In associating, we have thought little about our ancestors and much of our posterity'. The Munster radical newspaper, the *Cork Gazette*, was positively hostile to Irish, denouncing its use as an obstacle to progress.

Some northern radicals, however, became enthusiastic students and admirers of Irish culture, or what they took to be Irish culture. Most were Presbyterians, such as the McCracken family and the Neilsons of Rademon. The *Northern Star* praised the Belfast Harpers' Festival of 1792, the work of Edward Bunting, and published the first Gaelic magazine. So far as it went, this was helpful, but radicals had no monopoly of such interest and seldom showed a sympathetic understanding of the Gaelic world.

105 *The Blind Harper*

By or after Thomas Robinson
Watercolour, 19.7 x 14.2 cm
Ulster Museum

This is believed to be a picture of Patrick Quin (c.1745-1812), one of the harpers who played at the Irish Harp Festival in Belfast in 1792. Quin had been a pupil of Patrick Linden of the Fews, County Armagh. His playing was so much admired that he was taken to Dublin in 1809 to become the first teacher at the newly-established harp school there, founded by John Bernard Trotter of Downpatrick. An engraving of Quin appeared in the Dublin *Monthly Pantheon* in the same year. Quin's harp, made in 1707 by Cormac O'Kelly of Ballynascreen, County Londonderry, later came into the possession of the Otways of Castle Otway, County Tipperary. It appears to be the one shown here, identifiable by a wolf dog carved on the front pillar.

Sources: Brian Audley, 'A new-discovered portrait of Patrick Quin, the Harper, c.1745-1812', in
             Treoir: The Journal of Irish Music, Song and Dance, issue 26, no. 4 (1994).

106 *Edward Bunting (1773-1843)*

By W. Brocas Jr, artist and engraver
Published by J. Sidebotham, Dublin, 1811: 29 x 9 x 21.8 cm; dedicated to the Harp Societies of
Dublin and Belfast
Ulster Museum

Edward Bunting, musician and composer, was born in Armagh in February 1773. At the death of his father nine years later, the boy was sent to live with an elder brother in Drogheda. There he showed such precocity as a musician that in 1784, aged only eleven, he was taken on by William Ware, organist of St Anne's parish

EDW^d. BUNTING ESQ^r.
Author of the *General Collection* of the Ancient Music of *IRELAND*.
To the
Harp SOCIETIES of DUBLIN AND Belfast
This Plate is Most Respectfully Dedicated by their Obet. Servt. James Sidebotham

church in Belfast, as his assistant. He lodged with the family of John McCracken, shipowner and father of Henry Joy McCracken and Mary Ann McCracken, and stayed with the McCrackens for the next three decades, becoming virtually a member of the family.

Bunting became interested in Irish music in 1792, when he was asked to transcribe the airs played by the ten harpers at the Belfast Harp Festival, organised by a committee of the Belfast Library and Society for Promoting Knowledge (the Linen Hall Library, as it came to be called). Bunting was so enthused by what he heard that he set out on a walking tour of Ulster, Connaught and Munster to collect other traditional airs, encouraged to do so by Dr James MacDonnell, the McCrackens, and their kinsman Henry Joy, all of whom were to remain his backers. It was resolved as early as March 1793 to publish Bunting's collection under the Society's patronage and in 1794 MacDonnell and Joy made the necessary arrangements with a London publisher, but it was November 1796 before the volume - the first of the three that constituted Bunting's life's work - at last appeared. It was an immediate success. Martha McTier wrote to her brother William Drennan:

'Have you heard Bunting's Irish music - well played - no - for you have not heard him - To me they are sounds might make Pitt melt for the poor Irish - not a copy is now to be got - but I hear they are very unjustly going to reprint them in Dub[lin]'.
A pirated edition did indeed appear, at a cheaper price, and badly affected sales of the original.

Bunting was sufficiently encouraged, however, to continue his work of collection. The 1798 rebellion and its aftermath interfered somewhat with the fieldwork, but interested individuals such as Thomas Russell, sometime Librarian of the Society (who had a copy of *Ancient Music* with him when a prisoner in Fort George), gave encouragement, and Bunting employed an Irish speaker from County

Down, Patrick Lynch, to collect with him in the West in 1802-03. Lynch was subsequently involved, on behalf of the prosecution, in Russell's trial for treason in October 1803 and was not employed by Bunting again. With continued support from MacDonnell, the McCrackens and the Belfast botanist John Templeton, Bunting compiled a second collection, which was published by Clementi & Co. of London in 1809, with lyrics by Mary Balfour (a friend of Mary Ann McCracken), the Scottish poet Thomas Campbell and William Drennan. This second edition, though it contained much that was new, suffered by comparison with Thomas Moore's recently-published *Irish Melodies*, in which Moore had used many of Bunting's earlier airs. The third edition, dedicated to Queen Victoria, appeared in 1840. In it, Bunting expressed the hope that 'as he was the first give to the world a regularly arranged selection of our national airs', he would 'terminate his labours by leaving behind him a complete, uniform, and, he trusts, very nearly perfect collection of Irish music'.

Recent expert opinion acknowledges Bunting's achievement, with an important reservation about the nature of it:

> Neither Bunting nor anyone else at that time understood that Irish traditional music was based on a quite different technical system from that of European art music, with the result that what seemed to them to be rustic crudities were tidied up for consumption by polite educated society. Yet the publication of the melodies he noted down marked the beginning of a serious interest in the music of Irish oral tradition. The pioneer work of Bunting inspired the many other collectors who worked throughout the nineteenth century. (Boydell)

His work could scarcely have come to fruition in his own day, however, without the energy and support of his friends in the Belfast Library, above all of James MacDonnell and the McCrackens. Left to himself, what someone called 'his spoiled, dilatory, wayward and more or less dissipated disposition' might have prevented the production of such a monument to his talents. Mind you, his dissipation sounds pretty innocent. In another letter to her brother, Mrs McTier reiterated what a treat it would be to hear Bunting play his Irish music, adding, 'sugar plumbs or sweetys is his greatest temptation, for he despises both money and praise ...'. Not surprisingly for one with such a sweet tooth, this engraving of him in his late thirties shows a portly figure. In 1819 he settled in Dublin, where he lived just long enough to have his photograph taken, before dying in 1843. The resulting daguerreotype forms the frontispiece of *Annals of the Irish Harper*, published in 1911.

Sources: D.A. Chart (ed.), *Drennan Letters*.
John Killen, *A History of the Linen Hall Library, 1788-1988* (Belfast, 1990).
Brian Boydell, 'Music, 1700-1850', in T.W. Moody and W.E. Vaughan (eds), *New History of Ireland*, vol. 4 (Oxford, 1986).
Charlotte Milligan Fox, *Annals of the Irish Harpers* (London, 1911).

107 *Contents page of a pirated edition of Bunting's first collection (1796) of Irish airs, published in Dublin*

ULSTER MUSEUM (ARMAGH MUSEUM COLLECTION)

108 *(a) Title page of Bunting's Ancient Music of Ireland, London, 1809*

ULSTER MUSEUM

This second collection of Bunting's Irish airs was hurried into print largely because

of the recent success of Thomas Moore's first two selections of *Irish Melodies*. The lyrics used were inferior to those of Moore, however, and since Moore had used many of Bunting's tunes sales of the latter's work were disappointing, despite the inclusion of many new airs and the use of high-quality paper and printing. Bunting and his backers in Belfast were disappointed.

108 (b) *Title page of Bunting's Ancient Music of Ireland, London, 1840*

ULSTER MUSEUM

The publication of Bunting's third and last collection came over thirty years after the second, and only after a good deal of patient work by his friends and admirers. After moving in 1819 to Dublin, where he married, he was appointed in 1827 to the post of organist of St George's Church, which occupied him for two days a week and paid a salary of £100 a year. The appointment was obtained, incidentally, through the influence of the attorney general of the time, the Belfastman Henry Joy. Another Belfastman, his old patron Dr James MacDonnell, in a series of letters from 1836 prodded and encouraged Bunting into completing his work. 'When you publish your music', he wrote, 'which I now never expect to see, as I am so old and you so indolent...'. Thus provoked, and with the enthusiastic help of Samuel Ferguson (also from Belfast) and George Petrie, his collaborators, Bunting got to work. MacDonnell not only gave sound advice and read the volume in proof but also arranged, through Lord Belfast, permission to dedicate the work to Queen Victoria.

His life's work done, Bunting died suddenly of heart failure on 21 December 1843, aged seventy.

109 *Interior of the Belfast Assembly Rooms in the 1790s*

COLOURED REPRODUCTION, AFTER AN ENGRAVING BY T. MALTON
ULSTER MUSEUM

The Assembly Rooms were the venue for the Belfast Harpers' Festival in 1792. The organising committee advertised the event widely, offering the inducement of a premium of some kind for every performer. Ten harpers took part in the meeting, which was held between 11 and 14 July (to coincide with Bastille Day celebrations). Newspaper reports of the event were not particularly enthusiastic; few of the tunes appeared to be new. While a Presbyterian radical later spoke of this Irish music as a 'beautiful fabric raised by our ancestors and preserved for us through so many ages ... which so often added splendour to the hospitable halls of our ancestors ... this monument of our ancient civilization', Wolfe Tone did not appear to enjoy it much. He noted in his diary for 11 July:

> All go to the Harpers at one; poor enough; ten performers, seven execrable, three good, one of them, Fanning, far the best. No new musical discovery; believe all the good Irish airs are already written.

On 13 July he wrote: 'The Harpers again. *Strum Strum* and be hanged ...' That Ascendancy attitude towards Irish culture was more typical of most Protestants than the enthusiasm of some Belfast Presbyterians.

Sources: John Killen, *History of the Linen Hall Library.*

110 *Dr James MacDonnell (1763-1845)*

BY CHRISTOPHER MOORE (1790-1863)
MARBLE BUST, 73.7 CM HIGH, SIGNED AND DATED 1844
ULSTER MUSEUM

James MacDonnell was one of the most talented and active citizens of Belfast in the late eighteenth and early nineteenth centuries. His background and interests were unusual for a leading member of the bourgeoisie. Born in 1763 at Cushendun, County Antrim, the second son of Michael Roe MacDonnell, he was a direct descendant of the famous Alastair MacDonnell, Montrose's ally in the 1640s. His mother brought James and his two brothers up as Protestants. A native Irish-speaker from the Glens of Antrim, who received instruction from a local hedge-schoolmaster in a cave at Red Bay, he also acquired an extensive education in English literature and the Classics in Belfast and was taught the harp by the blind Art O'Neill. He went on to study medicine at Edinburgh, where he graduated in 1784. On his return he set up as a doctor in Belfast, where his skills and sociable qualities soon gained him a successful practice and many friends. A reformer if not a radical in the 1790s, he strongly supported Catholic emancipation and was on very friendly terms with some of the most advanced radicals such as Henry Joy McCracken, Thomas Russell and Russell's friend Wolfe Tone. He was not himself a political activist, however, and disapproved of the revolutionary plans of the more militant United Irishmen. He remained on good terms with the McCrackens, nevertheless, and when Henry Joy was hanged in 1798 it was MacDonnell who was summoned by Mary Ann McCracken to try to revive the corpse (perhaps from prudence, he sent his brother instead). In 1803 he was induced to join other leading citizens in subscribing to a reward for the arrest of Thomas Russell, who as northern leader of Emmet's rebellion was subsequently hanged at Downpatrick. This action, which he was to regret greatly, caused a serious and prolonged rift with his radical friends, one of whom did not speak to him for over twenty years.

MacDonnell was involved, often as a prime mover, in most of the cultural and charitable developments of his day in Belfast - the Library, the Literary Society, the Academical Institution, the Natural History Society, the Ulster Gaelic Society and many others. As befitted his profession and his distinguished reputation as a doctor he was particularly active in medical matters, as chief founder of the Belfast Medical School, originator of the Fever Hospital (Ireland's first) and the Belfast Dispensary, and promoter of the town's General Hospital.

This bust of MacDonnell, appropriately enough, was done by the Irish sculptor responsible for the statue of Thomas Moore at Trinity College, Dublin. It was produced in 1844, the year before the sitter's death.

Sources: Charlotte Milligan Fox, *Annals of the Irish Harpers.*
Peter Froggatt, 'Dr James MacDonnell, MD (1763-1845)', in *The Glynns,* vol. 9 (1981).

111 *The O'Neill Harp*

ULSTER MUSEUM

This large high-headed harp, whose painted decorations include a vignette of a human face, has a one-piece sound box with a narrow brass strip along the middle with thirty-nine performations for strings; thirty-six brass pins survive. Though the harp is certainly of eighteenth-century date, there is no evidence to support the traditional story that it belonged to the well-known harper Arthur O'Neill (1737-1816).

Sources: Joan Rimmer, *The Irish Harp* (Cork, 1969).

111(b) *The Downhill Harp*

BY CORMAC O'KELLY OF BALLYNASCREEN, 1702
GUINNESS MUSEUM, DUBLIN

This famous instrument was played at the Belfast Harpers' Festival of 1792 by the blind harper Denis Hempson, then aged ninety-seven. It is a large low-headed harp consisting of a forepillar, neck and one-piece soundbox of alder; six hexafoil pierced soundholes; 32 string-holes in box, surrounded by perforated triangular brass plates; 30 pin-holes in neck; 27 surviving pins. A verse in English on the side of the soundbox gives the name of the maker and the date:

> In the time of Noah I was green
> Since his flood I had not been seen
> Until seventeen hundred and two I was found
> By Cormac O Kelly underground
> He raised me up to that degree
> The Queen of Musick you may call me

Sources: Joan Rimmer, *The Irish Harp.*

Further drawn by
John McCracken?

Hempson playing his harp (from Bunting's 1809 volume)

112 *Reliques of Irish Poetry*

BY CHARLOTTE BROOKE; SECOND EDITION (DUBLIN, 1816)
P. & B. ROWAN

Charlotte Brooke was born about 1740 at Rantavan, County Cavan, one of the twenty-two children of the notable Irish author (and friend of Alexander Pope) Henry Brooke and his wife Catherine, who was fourteen years old when they married. Charlotte was educated at home, where she studied Irish language and literature and collected and translated Irish poetry. *Reliques*, first published in 1789, consists of the Irish texts with her own translations into English verse. It was an important landmark in the development of an interest in Irish language and literature among Protestants in particular, doing what Bunting's work did for Irish music. Many of her translations were published in *Bolg an tSolair* in 1795. She was a close friend of the novelist Maria Edgeworth. She died in Dublin in 1793.

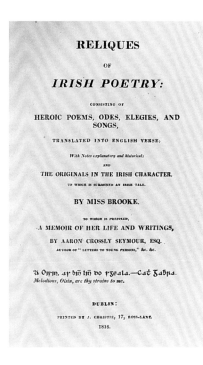

Sources: Webb, *Compendium of Irish Biography*.
            DNB.
            Brian Ó Cuív, 'Irish language and literature, 1691-1845', in *New History of Ireland*, IV.

113 *Bolg an tSolair: or, Gaelic Magazine*

PRINTED AT THE NORTHERN STAR OFFICE, BELFAST 1795 [NO.1]
ULSTER MUSEUM

The title page of this important and interesting publication describes the contents: *Containing Laoi na Sealge: or, The Famous Fenian Poem, called The Chase; with a* collection of *Choice Irish Songs, translated by Miss Brooke. To which is prefixed, an Abridgement of Irish Grammar; with a vocabulary and familiar dialogues.* The selling price, 1s. 1d., was a British shilling, equivalent to thirteeen pence Irish.

Bolg an tSolair was the first magazine in Irish, its publication by the *Northern Star* a sign of the serious interest in the language among the Presbyterian proprietors of the newspaper. They employed as editor Patrick Lynch, who ran an Irish School at Loughinisland, County Down, taught Irish at the Belfast Academy and also had private pupils. The first (and only) issue of the magazine ran to 120 pages. The destruction of the *Star's* presses by the Monaghan Militia prevented any continuation of what had evidently been intended to be a series.

Sources: Roger Blaney, *Presbyterians and the Irish Language* (Belfast, 1996).

113

114 *Introduction to the Irish Language*

BY WILLIAM NEILSON, DD (DUBLIN, 1808)
ULSTER MUSEUM

William Neilson was born on 12 September 1774 at Rademon, Kilmore, County Down, the fourth of the seven sons of the Rev. Dr Moses Nelson or Neilson, minister of the Presbyterian congregation there, many of whom were Irish-speaking. His mother, Catherine Welsh, was a direct descendant of the Scottish reformer John Knox. His father traced his descent from the O'Neills of Ulster and therefore changed his name from Nelson to Neilson; William was the only one of his children to do so. He was probably educated at the school of Classics and Irish run by Patrick Lynch of Loughinisland, as well as at his father's famous Classical Academy, where he assisted his father with the teaching after attending Glasgow University for four years (1789-93). He was then licensed as a Presbyterian minister and in December 1796 appointed to the congregation of Dundalk, where since 1700 every minister appointed had to be able to speak Irish. There he ran an inter-denominational academy similar to that of his father at Rademon. There too he published in 1804 his *Greek Exercises,* a popular text that ran to eight editions.

Neilson enjoyed preaching in Irish and in 1798 was arrested for doing so to his father's congregation. This proved to be a foolish blunder on the part of the authorities, for he had simply been preaching the Gospel and was vouched for as a loyal subject. In 1805 he went on a preaching tour of the North, delivering his sermons in Irish. His *Introduction to the Irish Language,* published in 1808, was said to have been begun by his father. It was dedicated to Lord Hardwicke, lord lieutenant of Ireland 1801-05, whom the author described as its patron. Patrick Lynch probably contributed something to it. Neilson's reputation as an Irish scholar was reinforced by the publication in 1810 of a book sponsored by the London Hibernian Society.

He was a founder member of the Gaelic Society of Dublin in 1806, was elected Moderator of the Presbyterian Church in the same year, and in 1808 was elected a Member of the Royal Irish Academy. In 1818 he resigned his post as minister in Dundalk to take up appointment as Headmaster of the Classical School and Professor of the Classical, Hebrew and Irish Languages at the Belfast Academical Institution, where he made special efforts to teach Irish. He died in Belfast, only three years later, just after he had been offered the chair of Greek at Glasgow. His funeral was attended by a huge number of mourners, reputedly 15,000.

Sources: Roger Blaney, *Presbyterians and the Irish Language.*

8 ORANGEMEN, DEFENDERS AND YEOMEN

Recent historical writing about the 1790s has tended to reconsider, if not substantially to question, the extent to which the events and personalities of the period were motivated by sectarianism. Whatever one's conclusions about the exact nature and extent of it, there is no doubt that it was particularly apparent in County Armagh. Several factors were involved: competition for land between Protestants and Catholics, evenly balanced in numbers, in what was then the most heavily populated county in Ireland; a particular perceived threat to Protestants engaged in the domestic linen industry; several disputed elections, which polarised political feeling; and the issue of whether or not Catholics should be allowed to bear arms.

The National Volunteers of the American War period had been Protestant formations, since only Protestants could bear arms. Some of them in County Armagh were closely identified with the Boyne Society, a forerunner of the Orange Order. When the Volunteers were suppressed in 1793, to be replaced by the new Militia, which was open to Catholics, Protestants lost their monopoly of arms and increasing tensions led to sectarian clashes between Protestant Peep O'Day Boys and Catholic Defenders, culminating in the so-called Battle of the Diamond, fought near Loughgall in 1795. The Diamond led directly to the formation of the Orange Order.

Faced with these developments, and the evident inability or unwillingness of local magistrates to do their duty, the government agreed to take up the idea of a yeomanry force, advocated by a Dungannon landowner, George Knox, and endorsed with enthusiasm by landowners elsewhere who were alarmed at the increasingly dangerous situation in their localities. To begin with, the yeomanry were not a sectarian force, but they were certainly joined with enthusiasm by Orangemen in Armagh and elsewhere and came to be seen as a Protestant counterweight to the largely Catholic (and therefore suspect) ranks of the Militia and became a vital element in the government's suppression of the United Irishmen.

115 *Framed folding wall chart, inscribed 1st Loyal Orange Boyne Society/ARMAGH 17th Octr 1798.*

PEN AND WATERCOLOUR ON PAPER,
ULSTER MUSEUM (ARMAGH MUSEUM COLLECTION)

This remarkable item, associated with the Loyal Orange Boyne Society, consists of two pictures displayed in a single folding wooden case. One depicts the organisation's symbols, derived mainly from Biblical scenes. The other also depicts Biblical stories, but uses representational landscapes. Both pictures were probably intended to explain to candidates for initiation the meaning of the stories used in the organisation's rituals.

The Boyne Society was set up at the turn of the seventeenth century, and was later superseded by the Orange, Arch Purple and Black institutions, all of which borrowed heavily from its symbolism. Indeed the similarity of this older symbolism with that of still-existing organisations makes the wall chart's emblems comparatively easy to interpret. The map-like landscapes of the second picture are more obscure. They are undoubtedly Biblical, but it is not always clear which picture refers to which story, so the interpretations given here are more speculative.

The secretive symbolism of the Boyne Society was inevitably, indeed intentionally, inaccessible to non-members. In the wall chart, some of the symbolic items are just thrown haphazardly together. In one cluster, the twelve stones of the Jordan stand next to Moses's grape-carrying spies from an earlier story while, nearby, Elijah looks at the 'cloud ... like a man's hand'. Other emblems are simply obscure, for example, the mysterious initials on the pillars, A and J, and G and H, two of which - G and H - reappear in the second pictures as geographical points on a river. There is also a plethora of additional imagery - all-seeing eye, sun, moon, beehive, cock, lamb and others - of the kind which crops up in the symbolism of many different eighteenth and nineteenth-century brotherhoods in Ireland and elsewhere.

Despite its similarity to that of other organisations, the symbolism of the Boyne Society had its own particular emphasis. The Boyne Society's *raison d'être*, of course, was to commemorate King William's victory at the Boyne. To clarify its message, however, it associates this victory with Biblical heroes who, like King William, can also deal successfully with water.

a) The Battle of Jericho. Here Joshua leaves twelve stones as a memorial to the fact that he was able to cross the Jordan by miraculously parting the waters.

b) The Two and a Half Tribes. After the battle of Jericho, the two and a half tribes of Reuben, Gad and Manasseh remain faithful to their fellow Israelites, even though they are on the eastern bank of Jordan's waters.

c) Gideon. Gideon defeats his enemies. First, however, he chooses his picked force of men stranded by a water test. Those who drink from the Jordan by lapping the water like dogs are deemed inadequate. His 'chosen few' are those who can handle water correctly.

d) Elijah. Elijah battles with Ahab, Jezebel and the prophets of Baal. He goes to heaven in a chariot of fire. He does this, however, having first crossed the Jordan like Joshua, by miraculously parting the waters.

e) Moses and the Exodus. Moses is here told to bring the Israelites out of Egypt into the promised land, a mission accomplished by parting the Red Sea's waters.

f) Noah's Ark. Faced by flood, Noah rescues pairs of animals and his own family, saving the sentient population from the encroaching waters.

g) David and Saul. The battle between the anointed King Saul, who has lost favour with God, and the anointed King David seems to mirror the history of William and King James. The three arrows and the cave of Adullam refer to the escape of David leading to the defeat of Saul.

h) The Ark of God ('TAOG'). Stories of the loss and rediscovery of the Ark of the Covenant have long been popular. Variants are found in the Orange Order's Royal Arch Purple degree, in the different Royal Arch degrees of Freemasonry, and even in Spielberg's film 'Raiders of the Lost Ark.'

It is likely that the last two stories, the conflict between Saul and David and the search for the lost Ark, neither of which is associated with water, and perhaps too the sojourn in the desert, provided the basis for Boyne Society ritual. But it is also

141

interesting that these ideas should have been interwoven with stories of water-competent heroes, men who, by one means or another, brought salvation by their dealings with water. Thus was the simple story of the Boyne and the 'Glorious Memory' of William III associated with illustrious figures from the Bible. And thus, through documents such as these, one can trace the origins of the rituals of the modern Orange associations.

Sources: C.S. Kilpatrick, 'The Period 1690-1911', in *History of the Royal Arch Purple Order* (Belfast, 1993).

116 *Killeavy Volunteers flag, 1778*

SILK WITH EMBROIDERED MOTIF AND LETTERING; 157.5 X 157.5 CM
ULSTER MUSEUM (ARMAGH MUSEUM COLLECTION)

The flag is of silk, originally green in colour. In the centre is an embroidered profile of King William III surrounded by a wreath of orange lilies and scrolls above and below. The scroll above contains the words OUR KING OUR COUNTRY, those below the words AND GREAT WILLIAM'S CAUSE and the letters B.O.S. 153. It was presented to Armagh County Museum in 1957 under the will of a Church of Ireland clergyman who was a descendant of the original owner and maker. Its existence was noted in 1898 in the *Ulster Journal of Archaeology*, second series, vol. 4, by an earlier member of the same family:

> I have in my possession a flag of the Corps of Killeavy Volunteers which belonged to my Great Grandfather, Mr Jonathan Seaver, J.P. of Heath Hall, who was a Captain in the Volunteers. It measures 62 x 62 inches. It is made of pure silk. The needlework is all by my Great Grandmother. The Volunteers had an Orange Lodge. I have no idea what B.O.S. stands for, could it be Black Orange Society?

In fact B.O.S. stands for Boyne Orange Society, a forerunner of the Orange Order. This rare, if not unique, survival illustrates the earlier history of the Orange movement, and demonstrates a direct link between some Volunteer companies of the 1770s and 1780s on the one hand and the Orange Order in Armagh and the local yeomanry on the other, for Jonathan Seaver was an officer in the Orior Yeomen and his son Thomas became treasurer of Armagh County Grand Order Lodge in 1797. Their home, Heath Hall, was near the village of Meigh in South Armagh, an area where sectarian tension was strong in the 1780s and 1790s.

Sources: C.S. Kilpatrick, 'The period 1690-1911', in *History of the Royal Arch Purple Order.*

117-120 *Orange Order demits, County Armagh, 1798-1804*

Demits were certificates of good standing, provided by local lodges or associations to members who were leaving the area, recommending them to lodges wherever they went - to all regular Orange Associations or Societies of the universe, as the formula puts it.

117 *Demit of Keeneary Loyal Orange Association No. 2 to David Kinkaid, 3 November 1798*

This certificate is a handwritten production from the Orange Society No. 2, Kinery, Loughgall, shortly before printed standard-format certificates came into use, following the establishment in Dublin of the Grand Lodge of Ireland. It reads:

> Keeneary Loyal Orang association No. 2

We the Master Warden and Secktary of the Royal orange asociation No. 2 held at Keeneary in the Kingdom of Ireland do hereby sertify that Brother David kinkaid has regularly received the first Degrees of a true orang Man and that of a Royal Mark's orang Man in this our Orang Association and that he was Beheaved himself During his Stay amongst us to the Entire Satisfaction of all. Regular Orang Associations of the unevors [universe] Do Recocknis and admit him as Such.

> Givin under our hand and Sail [seal] this 3rd of November 1798.
>
> | Master | James Blevens |
> |---|---|
> | Warden | ———————— |
> | Secktarey | henry hamill |

118 *Demit from the Royal Independent Orange Society No. 2, Kinery, Loughall to John Mences, 5 January 1799*

PRINTED, 31 X 20 CM, WITH SEAL
ULSTER MUSEUM (ARMAGH MUSEUM COLLECTION)

The earliest Orange certificates were handwritten. This one, from the Loughgall area, where Orangeism became formally established following the Battle of the Diamond nearby in 1795, is an early example of a printed version. Under the image of a crowned harp with the motto 'The King and Constitution' it reads:

ROYAL INDEPENDENT ORANGE SOCIETY, No. 2
We the Master and Secretary, of the Royal Independent Orange Society, Number Two, held at Kinery, in the Kingdom of IRELAND, do hereby CERTIFY, that Brother John Mences is qualified and has regularly

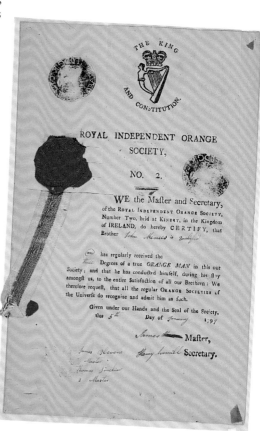

received the three Degrees of a true ORANGE MAN in this our Society; and that he has conducted himself, during his stay amongst us, to the entire Satisfaction of all our Brethren: We therefore request, that all the regular Orange Societies of the Universe do recognize and admit him as such.

Given under our Hands and the Seal of the Society,
this 5th Day of January 1799
James Blevens Master,
Henry Hamill Secretary.
James Blevens Master
Thomas Sinclair 2 Master

The Kinery Lodge was the second to be established following the fight at the Diamond. Of the officials listed here, one - Thomas Sinclair - had earlier been among the leaders of the Orange Boys, an organisation originating at Dyan in the early 1790s. He subsequently became a lieutenant in the Churchill Yeomanry, the unit raised by James Verner under the Act of 1796. Verner had five sons, all of whom became prominent Orangemen.

119 *Demit from Loyal Orange Association No. Six Hundred and Sixty One, to Serjeant Andrew Ross, 8 October 1798*

HANDWRITTEN, WITH WAX SEAL AND ORANGE AND PURPLE RIBBONS, 28 X 18.5 CM
ULSTER MUSEUM (ARMAGH MUSEUM COLLECTION)

Lodge No. 161, as this certificate tells us, was 'Held in His Majesty's 89th Regiment [of] Foot'. Regimental lodges were one of the main ways by which the Orange Order rapidly spread from Armagh to other parts of Ireland, since regiments moved around the country from one garrison town to another. The certificate reads:

To all whom it may Concern
We do hereby certify that the bearer hereof Brother Serjt And^w Ross of the above s^d. Regt is a regular made and he is true Brother Orangeman and has likewise obtained that sublime degree of a Brother March Orangemen And since his admission always behaved himself to the Intire satisfaction of all Our Brethen. We therefore request that all the regular Orange Lodges of the Universe do recognize and admit him as such.

Given Under Our hands and Seal of Our Lodge at Armagh this Eight day of October 1798.
W^m. Sturrock Master
And^w Burges Warden
Thos Burgess Sec^t

120 *Demit from Orange Lodge No. 25 to Aron Thompson, 7 July 1804*

HANDWRITTEN, 31 X 18.5 CM, WITH STAMP, WAX SEAL AND ORANGE AND PURPLE RIBBONS
ULSTER MUSEUM (ARMAGH MUSEUM COLLECTION)

This transfer certificate is for a man who was initiated into the Orange Order in 1798. It reads:

Lodge 25 Portadown
To All Whome It May Concern

We the Master, Deputy Master and Secetury of orange Lodge No. 25 Now Held In Portadown on the Irish Registry Do Hereby Certify That Our Well Beloved Brother Aron Thompson was Regularly Addmitted And Made An Orange Man In All Its various Degrees And Also Has Received that sublime order of A True Marks or purple Man...

    And Requesting All orange Lodges will Addmit Him And Recognize him As such.

    Gavin under our Hands And the Seal of our Body In our Lodge Room this 7th Day of July 1804-
Addmitted July 8th 1798 Declared off July 7th 1804

John Burleigh, G.M.
William Dawson, D.M.
Abr^m Dawson, Sec-

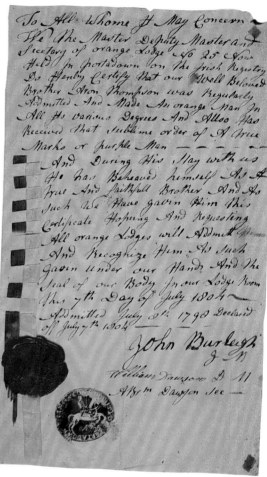

121 *Minute Book of the Grand Orange Lodge of Ireland, 1798-1818*

MS VOLUME, MODERN BINDING, PAGE SIZE 41 X 25 CM, 399 PAGES
GRAND ORANGE LODGE OF IRELAND

The Orange Order was founded in County Armagh following the affray between Peep O'Day Boys and Defenders in 1795 at the Diamond, near Loughgall. In its early years this new Protestant organisation was administered in a rather *ad hoc* way by the Armagh lodges which had founded it. This arrangement became increasingly unsatisfactory as membership spread to neighbouring counties and then, largely through military lodges, farther afield in Ireland and the British Isles.

    The Minute Book begins with the record of a preliminary meeting of deputies on 8 March 1798 in Dublin, in the house of Thomas Verner, 52 Dawson Street, and under his chairmanship, to consider the best mode of proceeding. The outcome of this was a letter, dated 10 March, from Verner to the Master of each of the 470 lodges in the country, to which 98 replied. At a subsequent meeting on 21 April, Verner was elected Grand Master of Ireland. Thereafter, all meetings and selected correspondence are covered until the emergency meeting of 18 November 1818, with an unexplained break of almost three years, from 24 September 1802 to 1 August 1805.

    Though the Minutes themselves are of a summary nature and therefore not very revealing about debates and divisions in the Order, they are a unique original source of information about its early development and concerns. Among other matters of interest are the following: the reluctance of some Armagh lodges and officials to submit to the discipline of the new body; the existence of lodges in many military regiments and close links with the Yeomanry in particular; the lack of any official line on the Union proposals in 1798-99 (no 'union debate' was to take place in lodges); an application for a new warrant for the North Cork Militia, the old one having been lost at Enniscorthy; the rejection or expulsion of members for having been papists or United Irishmen - the New Regulations of 1800 required members to declare that they were 'not nor ever was a Roman Catholic' and were 'not or ever will be a United Irishman'; strictures against establishing unauthorised degrees; a reprimand for reading the Book of Instruction in a common tap room; a rebuke to William Mackenzie for offending Catholics; the appointment of Sir Richard Musgrave as Grand Treasurer,

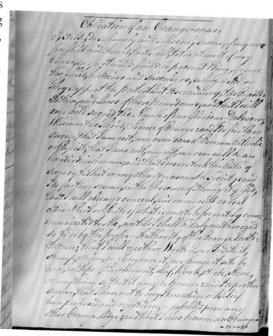

and the decision to purchase a copy of his book. The evidence of these Minutes clearly demolishes the standard academic theory, as expounded by Hereward Senior in his *Orangeism in Ireland and Britain, 1795-1836*, that the grass-roots movement of early days in Armagh was rapidly taken over by Irish Protestant grandees. This was far from being the case. The Verners and Blackers who emerged as leaders were at best minor gentry, and closely attuned to the views of their fellow-Orangemen.

122 *An Irishman's Letter to the People called Defenders*

BY [JOHN KELLS]
[DUBLIN, C.1793]; 8PP
AND
AN IRISHMAN'S SECOND LETTER TO THE PEOPLE CALLED DEFENDERS
[DUBLIN], 6 OCTOBER 1795; 12 PP

These slight pamphlets by an obscure barrister serve to illustrate two things: the general alarm created in conservative circles by the spread of the Defenders; and the difficulty of conveying in an exhibition such as this the nature and significance of a movement which was secret, largely oral in its internal communication, many-headed, and which left virtually nothing in the way of artefacts or relics. The Defenders are known rather by their actions and by the reactions of their opponents. Some rather scanty records of their aims, organisation and activities were collected by the lord lieutenant in 1795, at a time when alarm was created by the possibility - if not, at that time, seeming likelihood - that they might ally with the United Irishmen. This evidence has been collated and analysed by Professor Bartlett in 'Defenders and Defenderism'.

There were superficial similarities between the Defenders and their opponents in County Armagh, where both Defenderism and Orangeism originated in the increasingly sectarian rural feuding of the 1780s and early 1790s. Both Defenders and Peep O'Day Boys (Orangemen from 1795) were secret, oath-bound societies organised in lodges with masonic-style signs, passwords and rituals. Both were to spread farther afield, and in similar ways - the Defenders through recruitment of Catholic rural poor to the ranks of the new Militia after 1793, the Orangemen later, through military lodges after 1796. While Orangeism was, or became, a bastion of the established order, however, Defenderism was a revolutionary movement with strong millenarian tendencies, totally opposed to the state as it existed and if anything more ruthlessly cruel in its methods than its opponents, legal and otherwise. In 1791, a Protestant schoolmaster at Forkhill in County Armagh, his wife and his young brother-in-law had their tongues cut out. In 1795, near Drumsna in County Leitrim, eleven revenue officers were done to death with pikes, scythes and pitchforks as they fled from a building set on fire by local Defenders. Informers were disposed of, whatever their standing; one Michael Phillips, a Franciscan priest who volunteered information about Defenders in Roscommon, was murdered when he moved to Belfast in 1795 and was detected as a government agent. The expulsion of hundreds of Catholic families from Armagh and neighbouring counties to Connaught after the Battle of the Diamond was the other side of the same coin.

As the Defenders (under whatever name they used locally) spread in Ulster and north Leinster they became less purely agrarian in their aims and more politically radical. In Dublin, where they numbered several thousand at one point, they became an important, and potentially revolutionary, force in the sans-culotte world of artisans, small tradesmen and apprentices. Some of their oaths exhibited a curious mixture of militant Catholicism and radical ideas derived from France and America. A few Protestants even became members, though at rank and file level the movement retained its strongly sectarian character. The important development of the mid-1790s was the success, for a period of two years or so, of attempts to bring about an alliance between United Irishmen and Defenders, a formidable combination which struck terror into the hearts of government and its supporters, especially in Ulster, where it was most prevalent. After the failure of the Bantry Bay expedition in December 1796, which at first boosted expectations of French aid and encouraged recruitment, the continued failure of the French to appear, combined with determined action by the government to disarm and suppress suspected rebels and to encourage loyalists to organise themselves, turned the tide. The internal contradictions of the alliance began to manifest themselves. Many Defenders no doubt took part in the events of 1798, but of Defenderism as an organised element in the rebellion there was little sign.

Sources: Thomas Bartlett, 'Defenders and Defenderism', in *Irish Historical Studies*, vol. 24, no. 95 (1985).
Nancy J. Curtin, 'The transformation of the Society of United Irishmen into a mass-based organisation, 1794-6', in *IHS*, vol. 24, no. 96 (1985).

123-129 *The Irish Yeomanry, by Allan Blackstock*

The Irish Yeomanry was a locally-raised home defence force, started by the Irish government in October 1796 in response to the dual threat of invasion by the French and insurrection by the United Irishmen. The yeomanry was controlled and paid by the government but raised and officered by the landed gentry in rural areas, and by professional groupings and municipal bodies in towns and cities. There were two main types of yeomanry corps, cavalry and infantry, averaging 40-50 and 100 respectively. Rural corps were originally raised on the basis of baronial divisions but, as the force grew in strength from 1797, could include parish corps. Yeomanry corps were established in every Irish county and major town. The first levy was for 20,000, but the numbers grew to stand at around 50,000 at the time of the 1798 rising, peaking at over 80,000 in 1803, a level they remained at for most of the Napoleonic War.

The lord lieutenant, Lord Camden, initially hesitated over raising a yeomanry, fearing a resurrection of the Irish Volunteers who had adopted a political role and been instrumental in the achieving of 'legislative independence' for the Irish parliament in 1782. Once the government sanctioned the raising of yeomanry, 'offers of service' were solicited by those magistrates, gentlemen or professional groups who supported the measure. The offers would be submitted to the lord lieutenant. In practice, few proposals were rejected, as the yeomanry plan had been canvassed earlier and refusals were guaranteed to offend the prickly pride of the Irish gentry. Once a proposal was accepted, commissions were issued for the captain and his lieutenants to embody and discipline their men. The yeomen initially trained two 'exercise' days per week, for which purpose all corps had permanent sergeants attached. These men were ex-regulars, intended to give the yeomen the rudiments of discipline. The yeomen served voluntarily and could resign when they wished. They were not under the Mutiny Act, unless they voluntarily put themselves under its provisions by making a second offer to do emergency, full-time service in the event of invasion or insurrection. This was known as 'permanent duty'.

The yeomen themselves came from a reasonably wide social spectrum. At the upper end were the cavalrymen, who often owned their own horses and sometimes waived the right to pay, while the infantrymen were at the other end. In the north, infantry corps were frequently composed of weavers or smallholders. Urban infantry were different. As cavalry were felt to be unsuitable for service in towns and cities, some of the professional corps, such as the Dublin Lawyers' Infantry, had men of very considerable wealth serving in the ranks. Jonah Barrington tells the story, possibly apocryphal but doubtless illustrating a general truth, of wealthy and sedentary yeomen patrolling the streets in sedan chairs with their muskets sticking from the windows! Generally speaking, mounted yeomen thought themselves superior to infantry. The yeomanry institution as a whole was so status-conscious that when additional corps were added in 1798 precedence in each county had to be established by ballot to prevent disputes.

As a force, the yeomanry was very similar in appearance to the old Volunteers. The government had originally tried to make it as different as possible from the Volunteers, insisting, for example, that uniforms should be from a plain, standard pattern, blue for cavalry and red for infantry. More importantly, they tried to prevent the election of officers, one of the main democratic characteristics of the Volunteers. However, in the growing crisis of 1796, manpower was in short supply because of the war in Europe, and the United Irishmen were making a determined bid to attach the old Volunteers to their organisation by reminding them of their tradition of 'liberty' in 1782. In these circumstances, Camden's government made many compromises to volunteering traditions, without actually relinquishing the key controls of commissions and pay.

Apart from Antrim and Down, there were strong continuities in terms of membership and location between the Volunteers and the yeomanry, allowing for the lapse in time. In this respect the yeomanry, like the Volunteers, are best seen in the context of an ongoing tradition of Protestant self-defence which stretched back through the early eighteenth-century militia to the Williamite associations and, ultimately, back to the plantation requirements for those receiving land grants to arm their Protestant tenants. The government disavowed any intention of creating a denominationally exclusive force, but given the circumstances of its raising at a time when the United Irishmen were effecting an alliance with the Catholic Defender movement, it was inevitably going to be a predominantly Protestant organisation. Moreover, the delegation of local selection to the Irish gentry also militated against Catholic membership. Another ingredient was the fact that Camden's predecessor, Fitzwilliam, had promised emancipation and envisaged a largely Catholic yeomanry as one of its benefits. When Camden decided to raise yeomanry, there was a campaign by some within the Catholic Committee to prevent Catholic enlistment in a force organised by an administration dead set against emancipation. Despite these impediments, some Catholics did serve in many of the cavalry corps, where social position was felt to be a better indicator of loyalty than religion, and there were even corps raised by surviving Catholic aristocrats such as Lords Fingall and Gormanston. There were also poorer Catholic yeomen in areas of sparse Protestant settlement in the south and west. There were some Presbyterian yeomen in the force from 1796, particularly in the west of Ulster, but many more joined in Belfast, Down and Antrim at the time of the 1798 rising, and again after Robert Emmet's abortive rising in 1803.

In the popular mind, the yeomanry is associated with Orangeism. There certainly was a strong connection between the two organisations by the time of the rising, but it is a mistake to assume that this linkage went back to 1796. At that stage, the remnants of the Volunteer organisation provided a far bigger input than Orangeism, which was geographically limited to County Armagh and the fringes of the adjacent counties. The real liaison followed the Orange Grand Lodge's move to Dublin in early 1798. With rebellion a certainty, the Orange leaders offered tens of thousands of men for emergency military service. Fearing the political consequences of such a move, and wanting to retain a degree of control, the government compromised and allowed 5,000 Orangemen to enlist as supplementary yeomen in Dublin and Ulster.

The Irish Yeomanry was never considered as a permanent feature, and should not be seen as the forerunner of later developments in Irish police forces, which commenced under Sir Robert Peel's chief secretaryship in 1814. Rather, they were a wartime emergency force intended to take over the 'peacekeeping' duties of the regular army, which was badly depleted by the demands of war and had to retain its capability to move rapidly to the coast if an invasion occurred. Peacekeeping involved providing the local magistrates with additional force to deal with the increasingly difficult task of maintaining law and order. The yeomanry's first active role was in helping the magistrates carry out the provisions of the Insurrection Act early in 1797, then the disarming of disturbed districts under martial law later in 1797 and in early 1798. The first 'permanent' duty was undertaken in the spring of 1798, as part of the precautions for the expected rising. The yeomanry force was integrated more fully into the military system; county brigades were established, and a pre-arranged plan developed to overcome the inherent weakness of small scattered corps facing an enemy who had the natural advantage of surprise. Alarm posts were organised, where the various corps would meet before marching to the nearest defensible or strategic point. A system of fall-back positions to stronger garrisons was then arranged, all eventually leading back to major garrisons and fortified positions such as Enniskillen, Derry city, Coleraine, Belfast, Downpatrick, Newry and Blaris camp near Lisburn.

The rationale behind these contingency plans was that any sudden movement by the United Irishmen could either be prevented through the vigilance provided by such a network, or, if a rising occurred in force, to provide retreat options which would save the troops and yeomanry from being cut off in detail, then allow them to concentrate in one of the major garrisons and counter-attack from a position of strength. The yeomanry played a major role in these arrangements, forming a supplement to the attacking forces and garrisoning the strongpoints during the counter-attack.

The Down rising provides one of the best examples of this strategy in action. Nugent was able to draw his forces in to Belfast, Blaris and Downpatrick, then assess the rebel position and bring a combination of force against them from different directions. Various yeomanry corps from around Belfast, Hillsborough and Downpatrick fought at Ballynahinch alongside regulars, fencibles and militia. Nugent, a highly capable general who rose to become commander-in-chief in India, considered the yeomen as 'equal to the best troops' for this sort of conflict. Generally speaking, infantry corps were found to adapt better to the conditions of conflict in 1798, as cavalry proved useless against pikemen who were prepared to stand their ground.

The Irish Yeomanry's reputation has suffered from their involvement in the terrible carnage in the aftermath of battles, as well as their participation in the undoubtedly brutal disarmings of the previous two years. However, these lurid actions tend to obscure a less obvious and much less sanguinary aspect of the yeomanry's role. By their depth of numbers and advance organisation, they were able to *prevent* risings occurring, for example, in Tyrone and Armagh. Moreover, the system of yeomanry brigades formed initially as a counter-insurrectionary measure, continued to provide a vital addition to the stationary anti-invasion force, which could be called out on permanent duty whenever rumours of a French invasion caused tension to rise. By their very presence, the yeomen signified that the government was ready, and that any attempts at coordinated action by the 'disaffected' were doomed to failure.

The yeomanry can also be seen as the nucleus of a deliberately-created and popularly-based alternative to the United Irishmen, particularly in the north, where loyalism as a strategically organised movement lagged far behind the United Irish system. The fact was that the yeomanry accommodated both polarities within the old Volunteers. It therefore included the true whig libertarian traditions of the

Glorious Revolution and the Williamite tradition, those who could not forget 1688 and those who remembered 1690. The linkage with Orangeism can in many ways be seen as a mirror image of the United Irishmen's alliance with the Defenders, providing both depth of numbers and readiness for action. After 1798 Orangeism became the dominant tendency, particularly in the northern yeomanry, but by offering elements of both conservative and liberal ideologies, joining yeomanry corps proved an attractive option for many ex-radical Presbyterians and was officially encouraged from 1798. The yeomanry was reduced at the end of the Napoleonic War in 1815, but remained in existence until 1834, with the heaviest concentrations being in Ulster. The last surviving yeoman, James Fitzpatrick of Warrenpoint, County Down, almost lived to see his own centenary coincide with that of the 1798 rising, dying on 13 March 1898 at the age of 99.

123 *Two Yeomanry documents of 1796*

NATIONAL ARCHIVES, DUBLIN
REPRODUCTIONS

(a) Handbill, addressed 'To the Yeomanry' and signed 'Liberty', raising doubts about the nature of the oath required of Yeomen because it supports 'Laws, many of which, at present, form no Part of the Constitution ... viz a Convention Bill, a Gun-Powder Bill, an Insurrection Bill and last of all, the Suspension of Habeas Corpus Act ...'.

(b) Handbill, also addressed 'To the Yeomanry', countering (a) as 'intended to deceive and mislead you, by a false statement of facts, and a false interpretation of the Oath proposed to such persons as intend to associate in Yeomanry corps for defence of the Country, the preservation of the peace, and the protection of our lives and properties'.

124

124 *Belt plates of five Yeomanry units:*

Belfast Merchants Corps

Glenauley Infantry, with motto 'Croppies Lie Down'

C[rom] C[astle] I[nfantry], with motto 'Rebels lie Down'

Carlow Infantry

Royal Castlewellan Yeoman Infantry

<small>ULSTER MUSEUM</small>

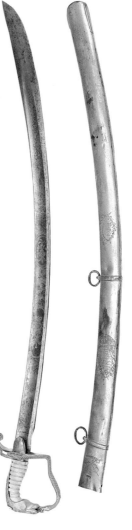

125 *Uniform of a private in the Aughnahoe Infantry*

<small>ULSTER MUSEUM</small>

Aughnahoe, near Aughnacloy, County Tyrone, was the estate of one of the Verner family.

126 *Sabre presented to Captain Thomas King in 1798 by his fellow officers of the Rathdrum Yeoman Cavalry, County Wicklow*

<small>INSCRIBED ON SCABBARD
ULSTER MUSEUM</small>

Thomas King was an attorney and magistrate who lived at Kingston, near Rathdrum, and commanded the Rathdrum Yeoman Cavalry. He was particularly active after the Rebellion, during the years 1800-03, in hunting down rebels in his area of Wicklow, employing a network of local spies to get information that might enable him to take Michael Dwyer in particular. King apparently served on almost all the courts martial held at Rathdrum and was regarded as merciless by his opponents. For that very reason of course, he was highly regarded by his fellow yeomen. In later life he wrote a successful treatise on the improvement of the potato industry.

Sources: Charles Dickson, *Life of Michael Dwyer* (Dublin, 1944)

127 *Drum of the Belfast Volunteers (Yeomanry)*

<small>ULSTER MUSEUM</small>

128 *Guidon of 'Colerain' Cavalry*

The original background colour is preserved on the reverse.

129 *Flag of Ballymena Volunteers*

The original Ballymena Volunteers were a unit of the National Volunteers, formed in 1778 as part of the Glorious Memory Battalion. As that name indicates, these

Volunteers were conservative and loyalist in outlook. Far from turning radical with the outbreak of the French Revolution, they paraded in 1791 and again in 1792 on the anniversary of King William III's birthday, rather than on Bastille Day.

It appears likely, however, that this interesting flag is not that of the 1778 Volunteers, who would have ceased to function after 1793, but rather that of a unit of the same name established under the Yeomanry Act of 1796. This view is supported by the imagery used in the central device, which features a Maid of Erin harp surmounted by a British royal crown of late eighteenth-century type, with clasped hands below (symbolising the Union?), enclosed in a wreath of palms. The harp on the reverse is a mirror image of the one on the front; as a result, the Maid appears facing right, which is heraldically unusual.

Whether Volunteer or Yeomanry, the flag was later adapted for use by an Orange association. The 'W III' on either side of the device is of a different date and material from the rest.

130 *Croppies Lie Down*

SHEET MUSIC
P. AND B. ROWAN

This edition of the famous loyalist ballad was published by the London music sellers, Corri Dussek & Co., on paper watermarked 1795. It is apparently the earliest printing and is extremely rare.

Seventeen different texts for 'Croppies Lie Down' were included in *A Collection of Loyal Songs As Sung At All The Orange Lodges in Ireland* (Dublin, 1798). Among those who later claimed authorship was Watson Taylor, secretary to the viceroy, Lord Camden. This claim was made to Thomas Moore some thirty years after the rebellion when the two men shared a coach journey. The most familiar text is that attributed to Captain Ryan, the yeomanry officer who was killed during the arrest of Lord Edward FitzGerald.

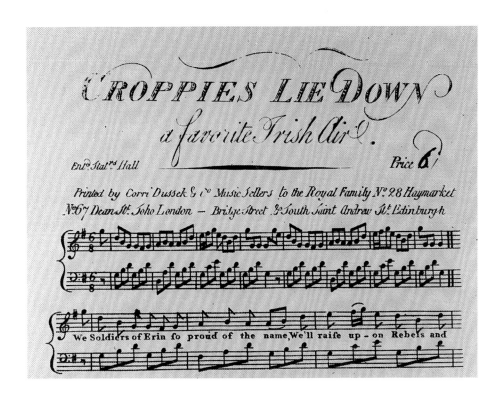

153

The term 'croppies' was originally applied to political radicals, of whatever religion, who wore their hair short in the style of French Jacobins. In 1798 the Grand Orange Lodge actually reprimanded one author who had altered the chorus to 'papists lie down'. Despite its original meaning, the term almost immediately acquired sectarian connotations for Protestants and Catholics alike, and the playing of the tune frequently sparked party clashes long after the Rebellion.

Sources: R.R. Madden, *Lives of the United Irishmen* (2nd series, 1848).
                G.-D. Zimmerman, *Political Ballads and Rebel Songs* (Dublin, 1967).

9 EVE OF REBELLION 1797-98

The appearance of the French at Bantry in December 1796 was a great encouragement to the United Irishmen and their Defender allies, and a great shock to the authorities and their supporters. Conciliating the Catholics was thought to have failed; in future coercion was to be used. As Lord Carhampton (commander-in-chief) put it later: '... if it shall please [Lord Camden] to permit them to go to war with us, and to permit us only to go to law with them, it will not require the second sight of a Scotchman to foretell the issue of the contest'.

In March 1797 General Lake began the disarmament of Ulster, to be followed by that of other areas. Enormous quantities of weapons were collected - in all, during 1797 and 1798, 48,000 guns and 70,000 pikes. The harsh methods used, predictable if the policy was to succeed in its aim, inevitably outraged the people who had to endure them and also more liberal politicians such as Grattan and his followers, who left Parliament in disgust. The execution of William Orr, under the Insurrection Act, was seen by many as judicial murder. Carhampton's successor Abercromby soon quarrelled with Camden and resigned, to be replaced by Lake. Informers among the United Irishmen enabled the authorities to arrest the Leinster Directory and, finally, Lord Edward FitzGerald, whose military talents made the conspiracy still formidable. Meanwhile, 1797 had passed without the expected French expedition, and the death of Hoche and the defeat of the Dutch at Camperdown seriously weakened the prospects for another major effort.

131 *John Jeffreys Pratt, second Earl and first Marquess Camden (1759-1840)*

BY SIR THOMAS LAWRENCE
OIL ON CANVAS, 74 X 61 CM
NATIONAL GALLERY OF IRELAND, DUBLIN

Only son of the first Earl Camden, lord chancellor of England 1766-70, Camden succeeded his father in the earldom in 1794. After taking his degree at Cambridge he became Recorder of Bath and MP for that city and held a number of political posts before being appointed lord lieutenant of Ireland on 11 March 1795 in place of Lord Fitzwilliam. His arrival in Dublin on 31 March was greeted by a riot.

Personally opposed to Catholic emancipation and parliamentary reform, Camden immediately restored to office the conservative officials whom Fitzwilliam had sacked. Thereafter he was largely the mouthpiece of Beresford, Foster, Cooke and Fitzgibbon. Grattan's Catholic relief bill of 1795 was rejected by a large majority in the Dublin parliament, which pleased the administration, but the establishment of St Patrick's College, Maynooth - a conciliatory if self-interested gesture - in the same year was approved by Camden, who laid the foundation stone himself.

Shortly after the new viceroy's arrival, Wolfe Tone left for America, but the Society of United Irishmen reorganised itself on a more radical basis and began to recruit increasing support, while the growth of Defenderism among Catholics and Orangeism among Protestants added to the growing unrest in the country. In these circumstances Camden alternated between panic and complacency. Panic led to repression, notably the suspension of Habeas Corpus in October 1796, the Insurrection Act and the establishment of the Yeomanry. Complacency left the defence of the country poorly organised, as became apparent when Hoche's invasion force arrived in December 1796 - which in turn created panic among the government's supporters. In March 1798 Camden, on his own responsibility, placed the whole of Ulster under martial law, and threatened to resign if a policy of concessions was adopted instead. If he did indeed, as nationalist historians used to believe, deliberately goad the country into a rebellion in order to bring the matter to a head, he made little or no effort to prepare for that outcome in military terms, with the result that, when the rebellion came in May 1798, instead of well-organised and instant repression there was panic again and frantic pleas for reinforcements from England. It was not the energy of the government that caused the rebellion to collapse. Camden begged to be superseded by a military man, gladly making way for Cornwallis, who arrived in Ireland on 20 June, when the rebellion was practically over. In the circumstances of the period 1795-98 - Great Britain's war with France at a desperate stage, militant political and social discontent in Ireland and the threat of a French invasion - it was inevitable that the administration in Dublin should have opted for maintaining the existing order, whatever its defects, rather than embark on a sweeping reform of the constitution - to risk re-thatching the house in the middle of a hurricane, as one conservative MP put it. Camden was bound to do what he did, more or less. He was, however, too indecisive to do it well.

Camden had a continuing, if undistinguished, political career after leaving Ireland; the sharp-tongued Canning described him as 'useless lumber in the ministry'. He was made a Knight of the Garter (1799), a marquess (1812), and chancellor of Cambridge University (1834). His last years were spent at his country house in Kent, aptly enough called The Wilderness, where he died in 1840 at the age of eighty-one.

Sources: *DNB.*
            McDowell, *Ireland in the Age of Imperialism and Revolution.*

132 *General Sir Ralph Abercromby (1734-1801)*

BY H. BONE, AFTER J. HOPPNER
ENAMELS
SCOTTISH NATIONAL PORTRAIT GALLERY, EDINBURGH

Abercromby was born in Clackmannanshire in Scotland to a Whig landowner who had married one of the influential Dundas family, a connection which was to be important for his son in an age when promotion in the Army or Navy, as in most official careers, depended largely on patronage and connections. He was educated in England, at Rugby School, then at the universities of Edinburgh and Leipzig, where he studied law. He wanted to be a soldier, however, and in 1756 his father eventually gave way and got him a commission as a cornet in the 3rd Dragoon Guards. In 1767 he married. By 1773 he had reached the rank of a lieutenant-colonel. Elected to Parliament for Clackmannanshire, he forfeited all chance of professional advancement by speaking out against the American War. He might have ended his life as a half-pay colonel if the French war had not broken out.

When it did, he immediately applied for a command. Such was his reputation and his parliamentary influence that he was at once promoted major-general and sent to Flanders. Defeat in the American War had destroyed the morale and discipline of the British army, political influence had undermined the professionalism of the officer corps and corruption and false economy had made the ranks miserable and dispirited. Abercromby was sent to the West Indies to capture the French sugar islands in 1795. The climate was a killer for European troops but he improved matters greatly by altering the uniform, forbidding parades in the heat of the sun, and establishing mountain stations and sanatoria. The aims of the expedition were largely achieved before he gave up his command because of ill-health.

In December 1797 he took over from Lord Carhampton as commander-in-chief in Ireland. It was to be a brief and controversial appointment, the military equivalent of the Fitzwilliam episode, for Abercromby did not get on with the administration in Dublin Castle and as a good professional soldier was appalled by the indiscipline and bad behaviour of the troops under his command. In his famous general order of 28 February 1798 he deplored the frequency of courts martial and the many irregularities and in a memorable phrase described the army as being 'in a state of licentiousness which must render it formidable to anyone but the enemy'. Abercromby's criticisms may have been largely justified, but his trenchant expression of them was tactless to say the very least and caused a political storm. On the ground that he had lost the confidence of the lord lieutenant and his advisers, the commander-in-chief insisted on resigning. He was succeeded, for lack of anyone better who was prepared to take on the job, by General Lake, who had thought him out of touch with Irish reality and 'quite in his dotage'.

Abercromby went on to become commander-in-chief in Scotland, before seeing active service again in Holland and then taking command in the Mediterranean. In October 1800 he was ordered to proceed to Egypt, to drive out or capture the French army left behind there by Napoleon. Landing at Aboukir he advanced on Alexandria, near which a decisive battle was fought on 21 March 1801. The French were completely defeated, three of their generals being killed. Abercromby as usual rode recklessly in front of his men, despite the fact that he was so shortsighted as to be almost blind. Wounded in the thigh by a musket ball, he died a week later. He was buried in Malta.

Sources: *DNB.*

133 *General Gerard Lake, first Viscount Lake (1744-1808)*

BY AN UNKNOWN ARTIST
ORIENTAL CLUB, LONDON (REPRODUCTION)

Lake was born 27 July 1744, the younger son of a landowner of Aston Clinton, Buckinghamshire. He entered the foot guards in 1758 as a career officer, serving in Germany during the Seven Years War and later in America, including the campaign

that ended in the defeat of Cornwallis at Yorktown in 1781. In 1790 he became a major-general and in 1793 - at the outbreak of war with France - was appointed to command the Guards Brigade in Flanders, serving on the continent until April 1794, when he became colonel of the 53rd foot and governor of Limerick. In 1797 he was promoted to lieutenant-general and given the task of disarming the United Irishmen in Ulster, a task which he carried out with considerable success. The brutality he employed, or allowed, in the process was certainly deliberate; he excused it on the grounds that it would be kinder in the long run. When Sir Ralph Abercromby resigned in April 1798, Lake was made commander-in-chief in Ireland. As such he was responsible for dealing with the rebellion in Wexford and in Ulster. On 21 June he routed the rebels at Vinegar Hill near Enniscorthy, following up his victory by severe repression under martial law.

The new viceroy, Cornwallis, himself then replaced Lake as commander-in-chief. When the French under Humbert landed at Killala in August, Lake was sent to the west, arriving at Castlebar just in time to see his troops routed by a smaller force. Regrouping at Tuam, he tracked Humbert and forced him and his Irish allies to surrender at Ballinamuck, County Longford on 8 September. Afterwards, while the French were treated with all the courtesies of war, the wretched Irish were ruthlessly hunted down by Lake's men.

In 1799 Lake returned to England and soon afterwards was appointed commander-in-chief in India, where he arrived in July 1801. He was MP for Aylesbury 1790-1802, and in 1799 was also put into the Irish parliament for Armagh city (invariably put at the disposal of government by the Protestant primate who controlled the borough) in order to vote for the Union. In India, Lake had a brilliantly successful career: at Laswari in 1803 his Sind opponents lost 31 battalions, trained and officered by Frenchmen, along with over 400 pieces of artillery. When his old superior and critic Cornwallis took up the governor-generalship again in 1805, however, Lake was superseded as commander-in-chief. Cornwallis died within a few months, whereupon Lake resumed his pursuit of the war with 'matchless energy, ability and valour'. Lake was thanked by Parliament and (in September 1804) rewarded with a peerage as Baron Lake. After returning to England he was promoted to a viscountcy. He died in London on 20 February 1808, after catching a chill when attending the court martial of a fellow officer.

This portrait of Lake, by an unknown artist, may be a later copy of an early-nineteenth century work. To judge by contemporary engravings, it is a good likeness.

Sources: DNB.

134 *Arthur Hill, second Marquess of Downshire (1753-1801)*

BY P. CONDÉ AFTER A MINIATURE BY R. COSWAY (1786); OVAL IMAGE 10 x 8.5 CM
NATIONAL PORTRAIT GALLERY, LONDON

Arthur Hill was the only surviving son of Wills Hill, Earl of Hillsborough and (1789) first Marquess of Downshire. Before 1789 he was known by the courtesy titles of Lord Kilwarlin (in Ireland) or Lord Fairford (in England); between 1789 and 1793, when his father died, as Earl of Hillsborough. On his mother's side, he was a cousin of Lord Edward FitzGerald, the United Irishman. During the 1790s the Downshires controlled eight or nine seats in the Irish Parliament.

As a leading supporter of the Ascendancy in a period when all it stood for was under attack, Arthur Hill had no great liking for either Presbyterians or Catholics, especially the latter. In September 1792, when Wolfe Tone and a delegation from the Catholic Committee in Dublin came north on a mission to settle sectarian

ARTHUR MARQUIS of DOWNSHIRE.
1786.

tension between Catholic Defenders and Protestant Peep O' Day Boys in south Down, as part of their policy of uniting Catholics and Dissenters, they called on Lord Downshire and his son. 'Very long conversation on the subject of our mission', Tone recorded in his diary. 'Lord Downshire's faculties quite gone, Lord Hillsborough's sharp enough; a high aristocrat. Angry at the committee's interference. No notion of any mode of settling the disturbances but by a strong hand. Talks of more regiments of light horse, and calls the committee and the Defenders "Dublin Papists, and country Papists"... On the whole, his lordship was just civil, and no more'.

As a leading reactionary, colonel of the Downshire Militia and great northern magnate, Downshire played an active part in opposing the United Irishmen and rallying loyalists. In a dramatic episode designed to overawe the Belfast radicals, he and Castlereagh - accompanied by Lord Westmeath, colonel of a militia regiment, and John Pollock, crown solicitor - entered the town on 16 September 1796 with cavalry and informers and arrested Neilson, Russell and others, who were then despatched to Dublin under armed escort. Perhaps more important in the long run, Downshire became the spymaster of the informer Samuel Turner, whose reports enabled the government to arrest the Leinster Directory of the United Irishmen shortly before the outbreak of the Rebellion in 1798. The story is told in detail in *Secret Service under Pitt*. It began on the night of 8 October 1797, when a mysterious figure - muffled in a cloak, his face covered with a slouch hat - turned up at Downshire's house in London and asked to see him immediately. In a private interview he revealed himself as a northern Protestant, high in the counsels of the movement, who had become convinced that the object of the Catholics in it was not just radical reform but the ruin and destruction of the country and the establishment of a tyranny with murders, assassinations and the seizure of Protestant property. He offered to report all he discovered but would not appear in court to prosecute anyone arrested as a result. In a second interview the following day in an empty house nearby, Downshire took down the names of the United Irishmen's executive committee and other information. On the basis of what he had heard, he then approached Pitt and the informer was taken on. No one, not even the Cabinet, was told the man's identity; he was known only as 'Lord Downshire's friend'. As intelligence, his reports were of enormous value to the government; because his evidence could not be used in open court, however, much of what was revealed could not be used to prosecute the people concerned.

During the rebellion, Dowshire's house at Blessington, County Wicklow was burned, and the Downshire Militia saw service in the south. Having earned the gratitude of government by his resolute behaviour up to and including 1798, he then drew down its anger by becoming equally resolute in opposing the Union. The government's revenge was to dismiss Downshire from the governorship of the county from which he took his title, from the colonelcy of the Downshire Militia, from the Privy Council and from a sinecure in the court of Chancery. His formidable widow believed that his death in 1801 was hastened - if not actually caused - by this treatment and swore revenge on Castlereagh whom, as the architect of the Union, she felt to have been responsible for it. This feeling was not in the least mitigated by the fact that, under the terms of the Act of 1800, Downshire was the chief beneficiary of the compensation money paid to owners of extinguished boroughs, receiving altogether £52,750 for the seven seats of Hillsborough, Blessington, Fore (two each) and half of Carlingford (one seat) - money which went some way towards paying his debts of more than £300,000.

Richard Cosway, whose original miniature must have been done in 1786 on the occasion of Lord Hillsborough's wedding (the title 'Marquis of Downshire' is clearly post-1793), was born in 1740 and died in 1821. He was a fashionable painter and miniaturist, who was elected to the Royal Academy in 1771 and was a favourite of the Prince Regent.

The engraver Condé, who was of French origin, flourished between 1785 and 1800.

Sources: W.J. Fitzpatrick, *Secret Service under Pitt* (London, 1892).
Tone's *Autobiography.*
A.P.W. Malcomson, 'The Gentle Leviathan: Arthur Hill, second marquess of
Downshire, 1753-1801', in P. Roebuck (ed), *Plantation to Partition* (Belfast, 1981).

135 *Caricature portrait, believed to be that of the Rev. John Cleland (1805)*

BY AN UNKNOWN HAND, REDRAWN BY DEIRDRE CRONE
ULSTER MUSEUM

John Cleland (c.1754-1834) was the second son of a minor County Down landowner, Moses Cleland of Rathgael, near Bangor. Unusually for a clergyman of the established church, he was educated at Glasgow University, the seminary of several of the northern Presbyterian ministers who were to be his opponents in the 1790s. In 1789 he was appointed incumbent of the parish of Newtownards, a post which he held until 1810. In addition, he later acquired two other church appointments as an absentee pluralist - Chancellor of Lismore, County Waterford (1796-1834) and Precentor of Armagh (1802-34).

In Newtownards he also acted as land agent for Lord Londonderry, whose Mount Stewart estate included the town itself and much of the surrounding countryside. Londonderry himself lived and died a Presbyterian, but his son Robert, Viscount Castlereagh, joined the Church of Ireland and became a leading figure in the Protestant ascendancy. As a conservative landowner, however, Londonderry was utterly unsympathetic to radical, let alone revolutionary, ideas and as agent, magistrate and sub-sheriff Cleland proved his enthusiastic tool. Most of the tenants were Presbyterians, many of them enthusiastic for reform. In common with Catholics, Presbyterian farmers had a particular dislike of tithes, and when in 1792 Cleland began to demand tithes in townlands of the parish which had never before paid them he became a hated figure. The extraordinary zeal he showed as a magistrate in rallying opposition to the radicals in north Down also made him a marked man, the subject of at least one assassination attempt by the United Irishmen. During the year or so before the outbreak of the rebellion Cleland gave crucial service to the authorities as spymaster of the informer Nicholas Magin (or Mageean) of Saintfield, whose reports enabled General Nugent to concentrate his forces and deal piecemeal with the rebel threat in Antrim and Down. What with government reward money and the profits of the land agency, Cleland became a rich man.

In 1805 he married the heiress to a property in the neighbouring parish of Dundonald and went to live there at Stormont (or Stormount as it was called before the name was frenchified). He died in 1834, at the age of eighty. Stormont Castle was sold to the government in 1920 by a descendant of this noted loyalist and the Parliament Building of Northern Ireland was erected in the grounds.

This caricature, believed by the Cleland family to be of Cleland, was published in 1805 during the contested election for County Down in that year.

Sources: Peter Carr, *'The Most Unpretending of Places': A History of Dundonald, County Down*
(Dundonald, 1987).
Trevor McCavery, *Newtown: A History of Newtownards* (Dundonald, 1994).
J.B. Leslie and H.B. Swanzy, *Biographical Succession Lists of the Clergy of the Diocese of
Down* (Enniskillen, 1936).

136 *The Rev. William Bruce, DD (1757-1841)*

BY JOSEPH WILSON (C.1784)
OIL ON CANVAS, 73.6 X 60.6 CM, NOT INSCRIBED
ULSTER MUSEUM

William Bruce, born in Dublin on 30 July 1757, was the second son of the Rev. Samuel Bruce, minister of the Strand Street Presbyterian congregation. He was educated at Trinity College, where he graduated in 1776, and studied theology in Glasgow and Warrington; he was granted his DD by Glasgow later, in 1786. In 1779 he was ordained into the Presbyterian Church in Lisburn, County Antrim. Then he became an enthusiastic Volunteer, even appearing in the pulpit in his regimentals. In 1782 he returned to Dublin, to take charge of his father's old congregation. The following year he took part in the great Volunteer Convention in Dublin, as a delegate for Carrickfergus. In 1790 he went north again, to Belfast, as minister of the First Presbyterian Church in Rosemary Street, an appointment he held until 1831. At the same time he became principal of the Belfast Academy, at that time the town's only institute of higher education, remaining in charge till 1822. A leading figure in the intellectual life of Belfast, he was one of the founders of the Literary Society (1801) and served as its president for several terms, and was president of the Linen Hall Library (which has another portrait of him) 1798-1817. He retired to Dublin in 1836 and died there on 27 February 1841.

Bruce is a good example of a moderate reformer of the 1780s who instead of becoming radical in the 1790s became increasingly conservative. Wolfe Tone records dining at McTier's in October 1792 when Bruce was also a guest and engaging in 'a furious battle, which lasted two hours, on the Catholic question'. Later, Bruce was to enlist as an infantryman in the Belfast Yeomanry. His imposing figure, guarding the Long Bridge, was the last sentry to be passed by General Nugent and his troops as they marched out on 12 June 1798 to do battle with Munro and his United Irishmen at Ballynahinch.

When all was over, Bruce preached a powerful headmasterly sermon linking the evils of the day to the decline in parental authority. 'Do not let any father hope', he declaimed, 'to receive respect or obedience from a rebel or an atheist'.

Martha McTier, who was present, told her brother, William Drennan, that some of the congregation approved, while others could scarcely keep their seats. 'I expressed disappointment that "Croppies lie down" was not sung after it', she wrote tartly.

This picture, which is now attributed to Joseph Wilson on stylistic grounds - was probably painted in the early 1780s, when Bruce was much involved in the Volunteers. The sitter's coat, green with gold braid and epaulettes, appears to be a civilian one trimmed with military accessories.

Sources: Eileen Black, *Irish Oil Paintings, 1572-c.1830*
             Tone, *Autobiography.*
             R.B. McDowell, *Ireland in the Age of Imperialism and Revolution.*

137 *Rev. Samuel Barber (1738-1811)*

ARTIST UNKNOWN
MINIATURE
ULSTER MUSEUM

Samuel Barber was one of the handful of Presbyterian clergy who were active United Irishmen. Born at Killead, County Antrim and licensed by the Presbytery of Templepatrick, he preached in various parts of south Antrim for a number of years before finally being ordained minister of the Rathfriland congregation in County Down in 1783. He played a prominent part in the Volunteers, as captain of the Rathfriland corps, and was an ardent and outspoken patriot. In 1786, in reaction to a provocative pamphlet by the Protestant bishop of Cloyne on the tithe question in Munster, Barber published a broadside of his own making it clear that the Presbyterians were 'not in love with their chains' and that the sooner the established church was abolished the better. He was a strong supporter of Catholic emancipation and opposed the powerful influence of the conservative and rather anti-Catholic Hill family, which had substantial property close to Rathfriland. In 1790, along with other radicals, Barber helped to organise support for the candidacy of Robert Stewart against Arthur Hill, Lord Hillsborough, in the electoral contest for the county. In 1798 he was arrested for treason on 3 June, a few days before the rebellion in Ulster began, and was imprisoned in Downpatrick gaol for the next two years, despite all efforts to have him released on the grounds of age, infirmity and (he said) innocence of the charge.

Sources: A.T.Q. Stewart, *The Summer Soldiers.*
             W.D. Bailie, 'The Rev. Samuel Barber, 1738-1811', *in Challenge and Conflict:
             Essays in Presbyterian History and Doctrine* (Belfast, 1981).

138 *Memorabilia of the Rev. Samuel Barber, including his petition to Lord Castlereagh, November 1798*

MS PAPER, 25 X 20 CM
ULSTER MUSEUM

Written from 'Downpatrick jail', Barber's petition relates the circumstances of his arrest, his trial by court martial on a charge of having uttered seditious words and his sentence to two years' imprisonment (which he chose in preference to banishment for seven years). The prosecution, he says, 'was entirely conducted by Mr. Savage Hall, who as is well known to the whole neighbouring Country, has long cherished an Enmity towards me'. The petition concludes:

'Conscious of being a good subject, & a diligent Christian Minister, I implore your Lordship to obtain a remission of the remaining part of the Sentence, in favour of a man now Sixty years of Age. I have already suffered Enough. Severe justice for a hasty but not a malevolent expression has been sufficiently expiated. Restore me to my afflicted family. Restore me to my beloved Congregation, who will receive me with joy, & will join me in grateful acknowledgement to yr. Lordship.' This copy of the petition is in the handwriting of Barber's legal adviser, Thomas Mercer. The appeal failed, Castlereagh refusing to intervene.

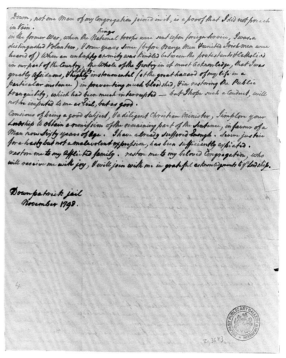

139 *William Tennent (1760-1832)*

BY AN UNKNOWN ARTIST
ULSTER MUSEUM
REPRODUCTION (DETAIL)

William Tennent was the eldest son of the Rev. John Tennent, minister of the Presbyterian congregation at Roseyards, near Ballymoney, County Antrim. Born on 26 June 1760, he served his apprenticeship in Belfast with John Campbell, a merchant and banker. By 1783, when he joined the newly-founded Chamber of Commerce, he had become a junior manager in the New Sugar House, where he was later a partner. He also held partnerships in a distilling firm and an insurance company and became one of the town's most successful younger merchants. In the 1790s he held radical political views and was deeply involved in the activities of the United Irishmen, being an original shareholder of the *Northern Star* and - it is thought - chairman of a later, more extreme 'Jacobin' committee of the United Irishmen. An informer reported on 'Mr Tennent's' presence at a meeting of conspirators, but since no Christian name was given he escaped with his neck. He was arrested in 1798 on suspicion and sent to Fort George in Scotland, where he spent the next three years. This confinement damaged both his health and his commercial prospects, though his brother Robert - a naval surgeon who returned to Belfast in 1799 - probably nursed his business interests. At any rate, when released he soon recouped his fortune, becoming a founding partner in the Commercial Bank, in 1810 (it became the Belfast Banking Company in 1827 and is now part of

the Northern Bank). In 1813 he purchased the manor house and most of the estate of the Maguires of Tempo, County Fermanagh, which later became the property of his son-in-law Sir James Emerson Tennent; he also invested heavily in the property disposed of by the debt-ridden second Marquess of Donegall in the 1820s.

After 1798, Tennent abandoned active politics. He remained a man of liberal views, however, playing a very active part in Belfast public life as a police commissioner, water commissioner, manager of the Academical Institution, vice-president of the Chamber of Commerce, treasurer of the First Presbyterian Church and so on. He died of cholera during the epidemic of 1832. Most of his seven or eight children were illegitimate but, characteristically, all were acknowledged, educated and provided for.

This portrait, by an unknown (and undistinguished) artist was painted about 1810.

Sources: Eileen Black, *Irish Oil Paintings, 1572-c.1830*.
W.A. Maguire, 'Banker and Absentee Landowner: William Tennent in County Fermanagh, 1813-32', in *Clogher Record*, vol. 14, no. 3, (1993).

140 *Portrait of a young man, possibly a United Irishman*

BY THOMAS ROBINSON (D.1810)
OIL ON CANVAS, 76.8 x 63.1 CM; SIGNED AND DATED 1798
ULSTER MUSEUM

A number of things lend support to the suggestion that this portrait may show a United Irishman: the date; the very anonymity of the sitter; the subject's appearance - short hair, brown coat; the map he is shown holding, which appears to illustrate areas (south of England, northern France) and towns (London, Paris, Brest and Calais) which would have been of significance to someone involved in or sympathetic to the movement. The artist's presence in Lisburn during the late 1790s would certainly have put him in the way of meeting such people. There is no documentary evidence for this identification, however.

Sources: Eileen Black, *Irish Oil Paintings, 1572-c.1830*.

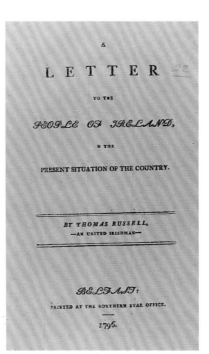

141 *Thomas Russell, A Letter to the People of Ireland, in the Present Situation of the Country. Belfast: Printed at the Northern Star Office. 1796.*

<small>MR J.A. GAMBLE</small>

Russell's open description of himself on the title page of his pamphlet as 'an United Irishman' is an indication of the self-confidence of the Belfast radicals in 1796.

142 *General Lake's Proclamation, 13 March 1797*

<small>AS PRINTED IN *REPORT FROM THE SECRET COMMITTEE OF THE HOUSE OF COMMONS*, 1798 (APPENDIX IX)
ULSTER MUSEUM</small>

The first part of the Proclamation reads as follows:

> Whereas the daring and horrid outrages in many parts of this province ... have increased to such an alarming degree, as from their atrocity and extent to bid defiance to the civil power, and to endanger the lives and properties of his Majesty's faithful subjects.
>
> And whereas ... several persons .... have been forcibly and traitorously deprived of their arms, it is therefore become indispensably necessary for the safety and protection of the well disposed, to interpose the King's troops under my command; and I do hereby give notice that I have received authority and directions to act in such manner as the public safety my require.
>
> I do therefore hereby enjoin and require all persons in this district (peace officers and those serving in a military capacity excepted) forthwith to bring in and surrender up all arms and ammunition which they may have in their possession to the officer commanding the King's troops in their neighbourhood.
>
> I trust that an immediate compliance with this order may render any act of mine to enforce it unnecessary.

The near-miss of the Bantry Bay expedition of December 1796 had filled the northern radicals with renewed hope. In the spring of 1797 the chief secretary in Dublin, Thomas Pelham, wrote to Lake to tell him of the lord lieutenant's decision to proclaim the disarmament of Ulster. Issued at Belfast on 13 March, above Lake's name, the proclamation put the North virtually under martial law. Given the circumstances, and the earlier arrests of leading United Irishmen, the new regulations should scarcely have come as a surprise, but they apparently did. The immediate reaction was to hide arms formerly held by Volunteers, including the six cannon of the Belfast Blue Battalion.

Despite Lake's impatience with legal restraints, and some nasty work by units such as the Ancient Britons around Newry, which created the impression that the utmost brutality was everywhere employed, the disarmament was in general carried out within the law. It was in fact successful, and greatly weakened the plans of the more advanced radicals for an uprising. The more moderate, even in Belfast, were by that time having second thoughts.

Sources: A.T.Q. Stewart, *The Summer Soldiers.*

143 *Memorabilia associated with the execution of William Orr (1766-97)*

(a) Memorial exhortation to vengeance, printed on cloth. (b) Watch-paper with 'Let ORR be the watch-word to LIBERTY!' (c) and (d) Printed memorials, on paper, linking Orr with four United Irishmen, soldiers of the Monaghan Militia, executed on 16 May 1797.

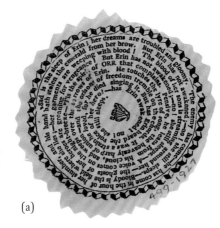

(a)

William Orr was a well-to-do young farmer from Farranshane near Antrim. A 'New Light' (i.e. theologically liberal) Presbyterian, he had been active in the Volunteers. In the 1790s he supported radical reform, joining the United Irishmen sometime after 1794 and contributing occasionally to the *Northern Star*. In September 1796 he was arrested on a warrant issued by the Rev. George Macartney, vicar of Antrim and a magistrate, and charged under the Insurrection Act with swearing in as United Irishmen two soldiers of the Fifeshire Fencibles. He was lodged in Carrickfergus gaol, where he remained for a whole year before being tried in September 1797.

(b)

The evidence of the two soldiers was not very reliable - one of them was thought to be deranged - but the government, especially Castlereagh, was anxious to frighten the New Light Dissenters and decided to make an example of Orr. Orr's defence was arranged by a Belfast Catholic solicitor and United Irishman, James McGuckin, who was later arrested and turned informer. John Philpot Curran, the noted liberal barrister, was the leading defence counsel. The prosecution was led by Arthur Wolfe, later a judge, who as Lord Kilwarden was piked to death in the Emmet rebellion in 1803. Despite the fact that it was carefully handpicked by the prosecution, the jury found Orr guilty only after being locked in all night, and then with a recommendation to mercy. The judge sentenced Orr to hang nevertheless. In view of the evidence of false testimony and of tampering with the

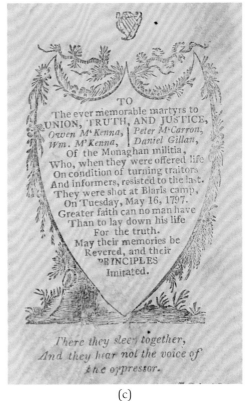

(c)

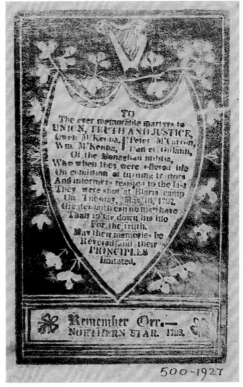

(d)

jury it was for a time doubtful if the sentence would be carried out. Orr's brother tried to save him by forging his signature on a document confessing his guilt, but Orr himself at once repudiated the ploy in a letter to the viceroy. Even Lady Londonderry was moved to intercede with the viceroy, but in vain. Orr was hanged at Carrickfergus on 14 October, behaving with impressive fortitude and exclaiming, 'I am no traitor. I die for a persecuted country ... I die in the true faith of a Presbyterian'. His dying declaration, already printed, was widely distributed and read; it denounced the conduct of the trial and asserted his innocence, while making it plain that he was indeed a United Irishman.

Orr became a martyr at once, not only among northern Presbyterians but in many parts of Ireland, where 'Remember Orr' became a watchword. Mourning cards sacred to his memory were circulated, relics preserved, gold rings engraved with his name (Henry Joy McCracken wore one at the battle of Antrim). William Drennan dashed off one of his best poems, 'The Wake of William Orr', which when published in the *Press* became immediately famous. Far from dampening the ardour of the United Irish conspirators, the judicial murder of Orr (as it was widely regarded) increased their determination to rise. In 1798 Orr was indeed remembered.

Sources: A.T.Q. Stewart, *The Summer Soldiers.*

THE DYING DECLARATION
OF
WILLIAM ORR, of Ferranſhane, in the County of Antrim, Farmer.

TO THE PUBLICK.

MY FRIENDS AND COUNTRYMEN,

In the Thirty-first Year of my Life, I have been sentenced to die upon the Gallows, and this Sentence has been in Pursuance of a Verdict of Twelve Men, who should have been indifferently and impartially chosen; how far they have been so, I leave to that County from which they have been chosen, to determine; and how far they have discharged their Duty, I leave to their God and to themselves.———They have in pronouncing their Verdict, thought proper to recommend me as an Object of humane Mercy; in Return, I pray to God, if they have erred, to have Mercy upon them. The Judge, who condemned me, humanely shed Tears in uttering my Sentence, but whether he did wisely in so highly commending the wretched Informer, who swore away my Life, I leave to his own cool reflection, solemnly assuring him and all the World, with my dying Breath, That that Informer was foresworn. The Law under which I suffer, is surely a severe one; may the Makers and Promoters of it be justified in the Integrity of their Motives and the Purity of their own Lives—by that Law, I am stamped a Felon, but my heart disdains the Imputation. My comfortable Lot and industrious Course of Life, best refute the Charge of being an Adventurer for Plunder: but if to have loved my Country, to have known its Wrongs, to have felt the Injuries of the persecuted Catholic, and to have united with them and all other Religious Persuasions in the most orderly and least sanguinary Means of procuring Redress:—If those be Felonies, I am a Felon, but not otherwise. Had my Councils, (for whose honorable Exertions I am indebted) prevailed in their Motion to have me tried for High Treason, rather than under the *Insurrection Law,* I should have been intitled then to a full Defence and my Actions and Intentions have been better vindicated, but that was refused, and I must now submit to what has passed.

TO the generous Protection of my Country, I leave a beloved Wife, who has been constant and true to me, and whose Grief for my Fate has already nearly occasioned her Death. I leave five living Children, who have been my Delight—may they love their Country as I have done, and die for it, if needful.

LASTLY, a false and ungenerous Publication having appeared in a Newspaper, stating, certain alledged Confessions of Guilt on my Part, and thus striking at my Reputation, which is dearer to me than Life, I take this solemn Method of contradicting that Calumny.———I was applied to by the High Sheriff and the Rev. William Bristow, Sovereign of Belfast, to make a Confession of Guilt, who used entreaties to that Effect; this I peremptorily refused; did I think myself guilty, I should be free to confess it, but on the contrary, I glory in my Innocence.

I trust that all my virtuous countrymen will bear me in their kind Remembrance, and continue true and faithful to each other, as I have been to all of them, with this last Wish of my Heart, nothing doubting of the Success of that Cause for which I suffer, and hoping for God's merciful Forgiveness of such Offences as my frail Nature may have at any Time betrayed me into. I die in Peace and Charity with all Mankind.

WILLIAM ORR.

CARRICKFERGUS GAOL,
OCTOBER 5, 1797.

N. B. *The above Declaration was made and read by* WILLIAM ORR, *in the Presence of the Rev. Mr. Savage.*

144 *The Dying Declaration of William Orr*

FROM *THE PRESS,* 17 OCTOBER 1797
P. AND B. ROWAN

Written by Orr in Carrickfergus Gaol and dated 5 October, the declaration was printed in time to be distributed to the crowd at his   execution nine days later. It begins:

My Friends and Countrymen

In the thirty-first year of my life, I have been sentenced to die upon the gallows, and this sentence has been in pursuance of a verdict of twelve men, who should have been indifferently chosen ... . The judge, who condemned me, humanely shed tears in uttering my sentence; but whether he did wisely, in so highly commending the wretched informer who swore away my life, I leave to his own cool reflection, solemnly assuring him and all the world, with my dying breath, that the informer was forsworn.

145 *The Press, Dublin radical newspaper, 1797-98*

BOUND VOLUME
P. AND B. ROWAN

The *Press,* published in Dublin between 28 September 1797 and 6 March 1798, ran to sixty-eight issues, the last of which was seized by the authorities before it could be distributed. Arthur O'Connor was its virtual proprietor, though the nominal one up to the end of December 1797 was Peter Finnerty. When Finnerty was found guilty of libel, O'Connor's name was then entered at the Stamp Office as the printer. The early issues of the *Press,* which appeared three times week, had a print run of

3,000 or so. When O'Connor's connection with it became known, however, this figure doubled to 6,000, the maximum capacity of the presses. Apart from O'Connor himself, notable contributors included William Drennan, whose poem on the execution of William Orr first appeared in the *Press*, and the barrister Sampson.

Like the *Northern Star*, whose place as the chief organ of the United Irishmen it took, the *Press* was literally destroyed by militia - in this case by troops of the Cavan Militia, who smashed the type and presses after occupying the office on 6 March 1798.

Three selections from the newspaper were subsequently published in London, Dublin and Philadelphia, under the title *Beauties of the Press*.

Sources: Madden, *Lives of the United Irishmen*.
Kevin Whelan, 'The United Irishmen, the Enlightenment and Popular Culture', in Dickson, Keogh and Whelan (eds), *The United Irishmen (1993)*.

146 *Edward John Newell*

ENGRAVING FROM MADDEN'S *Lives of the United Irishmen*, AFTER A SELF-PORTRAIT BY THE AUTHOR OF *The Apostacy of Newell, containing the Life and Confessions of that Celebrated Informer* ... [BELFAST] 1798. P. AND B. ROWAN

Edward John Newell was born in Downpatrick, County Down, in 1771. After an unhappy childhood and schooling he had a restless and unsatisfactory career, first as a runaway sailor, then as a painter and glazier and student of engraving in Dublin. In 1796 he moved to Belfast, where he practised as a painter of miniatures and taught drawing. Already a Defender, he moved in radical circles in that capital of radicalism and joined the United Irishmen. Through friendship with a local tax official named Murdoch (whose wife he later seduced) he was recruited as an informer and began to supply the authorities with valuable information about the Belfast radicals. Claiming to have been given unlimited powers by General Lake and Colonel Barber, he was responsible for the arrest of a number of leading figures, including William McCracken, Henry Joy's brother. His own brother put a notice in the *Northern Star* to say that his family disowned him because he was 'in the practice of going through the town of Belfast disguised in the dress of a light horseman, with his face blackened and accompanied by a guard of soldiers, pointing out certain individuals who have in consequence been immediately apprehended and put in prison ...'

Later, in hiding, he wrote his autobiography, which has been described as 'a clever, moralizing amalgam of spicy detail about his own private life and revelations relating to his employment as a government agent'. Published in Belfast, it was a considerable success. When about to leave for America, Newell was murdered at Roughfort, County Antrim.

Sources: R.B. McDowell, *Ireland in the Age of Imperialism and Revolution*.
A.T.Q. Stewart, *The Summer Soldiers*.

147 *Leonard MacNally (1752-1820)*

ENGRAVING, 16 x 11 CM
NATIONAL GALLERY OF IRELAND, DUBLIN

Leonard MacNally was born in Dublin in 1752 and brought up to the grocery trade. Having greater ambitions, however, and greater abilities, he soon abandoned commerce for the law, studied at the Middle Temple in London and was called to both the English and the Irish Bar, practising in England before returning home.

LEONARD MAC. NALLY ESQ.
Barrister at Law

John Philpot Curran, the great liberal lawyer, thought highly of him and befriended him. MacNally's appearance was singular. Barrington describes him as follows: 'His figure was ludicrous; he was very short, and nearly as broad as long; his legs were of unequal length, and he had a face which no washing could clean; he wanted one thumb, the absence of which gave rise to numerous expedients on his part; and he took great care to have no nails, as he regularly eat every morning the growth of the preceding day ... He possessed, however, a fine eye, and by no means an ugly countenance ... in a word, McNally was a good-natured, hospitable, talented, dirty fellow, and had, by the latter qualification, so disgusted the circuit bar, that they refused to receive him at their mess ...'

His disrepute at the bar was increased in the 1790s by the unpopularity of his political opinions, which led him to join the United Irishmen and to act as defence counsel in the trials of some leading radicals. These included Napper Tandy, in his case against the lord lieutenant in 1792, and later T.A. Emmet, Jackson and Tone. Not until after his death, when his son applied for its continuation, did it become known that ever since 1798 MacNally had been receiving a government pension of £300 a year for betraying his clients' defence secrets to the crown.

MacNally was the successful author of a dozen plays and a number of legal works, one of which netted him the large sum of £2,500. He also wrote the words of the popular song 'Sweet Lass of Richmond Hill', the lass in question (of Richmond, Yorkshire, not Richmond, Surrey) being the girl he married in 1787. The poem was set to music by James Hook and first performed at a concert in Vauxhall Gardens in 1789. Barrington relates an amusing story about his duel with MacNally in 1794, fought in the middle of the review ground in the Phoenix Park after an exchange of words in court, when Barrington was seconded by 'a huge, wicked, fighting King's County attorney' and his opponent by the United Irishman John Sheares, with Henry Sheares and Bagenal Harvey standing by as 'amateurs' (all three, as Barrington remarks, were soon afterwards hanged and beheaded for high treason). When Barrington fired, MacNally was hit in the side, which could have been fatal for him. Much to Barrington's relief it was not, for the following reason: 'The ball appeared to have hit the buckle of his gallows [galluses, meaning suspenders or braces], by which it had been partially impeded, and had turned round, instead of entering his body. Whilst I was still in dread as to the result, my second, after seeing that he had been so far protected by the suspenders, inhumanly exclaimed, "By J——s, Mac! you are the only rogue I ever knew that was *saved* by the *gallows*".

Execrated by the loyalists whilst alive as the friends of rebels, MacNally has been execrated by nationalists ever since for his betrayal of them. The motivation of this complex character, who was both intelligent and successful, is hard to fathom. Unlike some other informers, he left no justification or explanation of his conduct.

Sources: W.J. Fitzpatrick, *Secret Service under Pitt* (1892).
Hugh B. Staples (ed.), *The Ireland of Sir Jonah Barrington: Selections from his Personal Sketches* (Washington, 1967).
Webb, *Compendium of Irish Biography*.
Percy A. Scholes, *The Oxford Companion to Music* (10th edition).

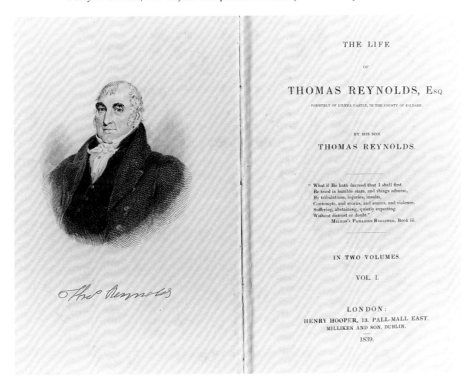

148 *The Life of Thomas Reynolds, Esq., ... by his son Thomas Reynolds (London: Henry Hooper ... and Milliken and Son, Dublin: 1839)*

2 VOLS, DMY 8 VO., PORTRAIT
P. AND B. ROWAN

Reynolds was born in Dublin in 1771, son of a wealthy Catholic family. He was a member of the more conservative wing of the Catholic Convention of 1792 but a year or so later converted to Protestantism and became the brother-in-law of Wolfe Tone. In 1798, when he was living in some style as tenant of the Duke of Leinster in Kilkea Castle, County Kildare, he was recruited into the United Irishmen by the Duke's brother, Lord Edward FitzGerald, and was appointed treasurer of his district and colonel of a regiment. He became convinced that he had taken the wrong turning when FitzGerald showed him detailed plans for the intended rising. In March 1798 he gave the information that enabled the government to arrest the members of the Leinster Directory at Oliver Bond's house in Dublin. This did not prevent the military sacking his castle and lands. Although given a pension and several official positions, he always felt ill-treated. He died in Paris in 1836.

JEMMY O'BRIEN,
with his Working Tools

149 *James O'Brien, United Irishman and informer, 'with his working tools'*

IRISH SCHOOL, C.1800
ETCHING, 21.7 x 12.4 CM
NATIONAL GALLERY OF IRELAND, DUBLIN

This caricature of the notorious informer shows him with one hand holding a dagger, with which to stab his supposed friends in the back, while the other rests on a copy of the Bible (with which to swear their lives away). The picture on the wall looks like Pitt. A victim of the informer's work hangs from a gibbet outside the window.

150 *John Philpot Curran (1750-1817)*

BY T.H. SWEETMAN (FL. 1812-31)
OIL ON CANVAS, 25.4 x 21.6 CM, SIGNED AND DATED
ULSTER MUSEUM

Curran, famous as one of the finest orators of his day and particularly eloquent as counsel for the defence in court trials, was born in County Cork in 1750. His father, to whom it is said he owed little more than his ugly looks, was seneschal of the manor of Newmarket; his mother, a woman of strong character and ready wit, was a much greater influence in his life. The eldest of five children, he was brought up in a rough and ready way, speaking Irish with the peasantry as well as English. Educated by the local Church of Ireland clergyman and then - partly at his teacher's expense - at Middleton School, he was intended for the church. In 1769 he entered Trinity College as a sizar (scholarship winner) where, though a keen classical scholar, he was often in trouble for drunkenness and brawling. There he abandoned the idea of becoming a clergyman, going on instead in 1773 to study law at the Middle Temple in London. The following year he was called to the Irish bar. As a student he had taught himself to speak by practising in front of a glass and arguing cases in his room. He married a cousin in 1774.

He was assisted in his early legal career by Arthur Wolfe (Lord Kilwarden) and Barry Yelverton (Lord Avonmore) and became a K.C. through the influence of the latter. The case that first made his name was in Cork in 1780, when he took on the role of counsel for the plaintiff - a priest who had been horsewhipped by Lord Doneraile - when no one else would touch it, and won. A Captain St Leger, a relative and accomplice of Doneraile, afterwards challenged Curran, in the first of the five duels he fought; the others included the lord chancellor, Fitzgibbon, and the chief secretary, Hobart. In Parliament, to which he was elected first in 1783, he was a member of Grattan's party and a passionate advocate of Catholic emancipation.

During the 1790s Curran took part as defence counsel in almost all the trials of leading United Irishmen, from Rowan in 1792 to Tone and others in 1798, despite threats and menaces from his reactionary opponents (but for the protection of Kilwarden he would probably have been arrested himself); his last appearance in connection with 1798 was in 1800, when he acted for Napper Tandy. He entirely disapproved of Robert Emmet, who was secretly engaged to his youngest daughter; she was subsequently obliged to leave his house.

In 1806, Curran was made master of the rolls, a judicial post from which he retired in 1814. The last part of his life was embittered by domestic trouble - his wife eloped with a clergyman, and only one of his children was mentioned in his will. He died in London in 1817 and was buried there, but in 1834 his remains were transferred to Glasnevin cemetery in Dublin, to a tomb paid for by public subscription and designed by his friend, the poet Thomas Moore.

This unprepossessing portrait by the obscure Irish artist Thomas Sweetman was painted in 1809. To judge by the descriptions of Curran it may nevertheless be a good likeness, for 'In figure he was under the middle height, with intensely bright black eyes, perfectly straight jet-black hair, a thick complexion, and a protruding under-lip on a retreating face' *(DNB)*.

Sources: *DNB.*
             Eileen Black, *Irish Oil Paintings, 1572-c.1830.*

151 *Bank of Ireland banknote, 1797*

BANK OF IRELAND

The wars with France put a great strain on the economy of the British Isles. By 1797 British public expenditure had risen to £57.75 million and revenue only to £20 million. This, and other factors, reduced the gold reserves of the Bank of England from £7 million in 1794 to £400,000 in August 1796. By February, rumours of the French landing in Wales had created further panic and virtually no gold was left. A Sunday emergency meeting chaired by Pitt produced an Order in Council removing the obligation of the Bank to redeem its notes in gold. Up to this date, and again from 1821 to 1914, the basis of the currency was gold - banknotes were not legal tender and silver was only valid up to £25.

Ironically, the economic situation in Ireland was not as bad, but it would not have been possible to permit Bank of Ireland notes to be exchangeable with gold as all that remained would have streamed out of the country. The lord lieutenant sent a note to the Irish House of Commons on 2 March 1797 asking it to adopt the English position.

In the north things were rather different. The only bank there closed in Belfast in 1797. Another did not open until 1808. As a result gold remained in wider circulation, partly at the insistence of landlords and the linen trade.

173

152 a & b *French Revolutionary paper money*

ULSTER MUSEUM
(A) *ASSIGNAT* FOR 500 LIVRES, DATED 20 PLUVIÔSE, AN 2 (8 FEBRUARY 1794)
(B) *MANDAT TERRITORIAL* FOR 100 FRANCS, DATED 28 VENTÔSE, AN 4 (18 MARCH 1796)

In November 1789 the French National Assembly ordered the nationalisation of church land, which amounted to almost ten per cent of the country. Interest-bearing bonds called *assignats* were issued backed by this land. Early assignats were for high values, but as uncertainty led to the hoarding of coin denominations became smaller. Interest payment lasted only a year. Inevitably discounting ensued, with resultant inflation. By 1795, the year French currency was decimalised, the notes were worth less than one per cent of their face value.

Conventional printing from hand-engraved copper plates was not up to supplying the huge numbers required, so a process of stereotyping from cast metal plates was used instead. In spite of the legend threatening death to forgers this was a problem, but, more seriously, the British government tried to hasten the destabilisation of the revolutionary state by running a sophisticated system of large-scale forgery, disseminating the notes through Flanders and Jersey.

The discreditation of the assignats brought their withdrawal by early 1796 and replacement by *mandats territorial* at the rate of 30 : 1. The new notes were also supposed to be backed by land but equally failed to command public confidence. In February 1797 they too were demonetised.

153 *Naval Cat O'Nine Tails (sealed pattern)*

OVERALL LENGTH 45 IN., HANDLE 19 IN.
NATIONAL MARITIME MUSEUM, LONDON

The 'cat' consists of a wooden handle covered with green baize and red baize, cut in a zig-zag pattern, coarsely sewn with twine. A label is attached, sealed with the Admiralty seal of a foul anchor. Nine rope tails are attached, each with a single knot at the end. The sealed pattern served to instruct the contractor who made the cat, which was the instrument used to inflict corporal punishment awarded by court martial on Royal Navy ships for offences against the Naval Discipline Act. In addition to such formal punishments, sailors were subjected to informal floggings with a knotted rope's end (this was called 'starting') or the rattan cane of the bosun's mate, not to mention casual blows.

One of the chief complaints of the sailors who mutinied at Spithead and the Nore in 1797 was not flogging itself but the savage misuse of it by sadistic captains and their officers. The Regulations laid down a maximum number of strokes, but such limits were usually disregarded and savage floggings were very common. The effects were terrible. Six blows, laid on by a brawny bosun's mate, as hard as he could at the full length of his arm, tore the flesh; after a dozen the back looked like 'so much putrefied liver'; after a time the bones showed through. To maintain the severity, the man wielding the cat would be changed after every two or three dozen lashes.

The severity of flogging was gradually reduced during the nineteenth century, as a result of public pressure, but the cat was not finally put back in its bag until 1879.

Sources: G.E. Manwaring and Bonamy Dobrée, *The Floating Republic: An Account of the Mutinies at Spithead and the Nore in 1797* (Penguin Books, 1937).

154 *General H.W. Daendels (1762-1818)*

MEZZOTINT BY CHARLES W. HODGES, AFTER A PAINTING BY MAASKAMP, 1795
RIJKSMUSEUM, AMSTERDAM
REPRODUCTION

Herman Willem Daendels was born at Hattem in Gelderland in 1762 and practised as a lawyer there. In the 1780s he became leader of the Patriot party in his native town. The Patriots were liberal reformers who opposed the conservative rule of William V of Orange, hereditary stadtholder of the Dutch republic. When the King of Prussia intervened on behalf of the Orange party and besieged Amsterdam in 1787, Daendels was one of the city's defenders. Following the defeat of the Patriots he was exiled to France, where he spent the next eight years. When the Revolution broke out in 1789, Daendels welcomed it with enthusiasm and joined the Revolutionary army which invaded and 'liberated' Holland, setting up in 1795 a client state known as the Batavian Republic. Daendels became a general in the Batavian Army.

The Dutch in the 1790s still had a considerable navy, and following the failure of the attempted French invasion of Ireland in December 1796 another major expedition was planned for the summer of 1797. This was to consist of the Dutch fleet, carrying 15,000 Dutch troops, which would set out from the River Texel

175

under Daendels and Admiral De Winter, and 6-8,000 French troops under Hoche from Brest. Wolfe Tone, who was to become very friendly with Daendels, and admired him, was appointed adjutant-general in the service of the Batavian republic for the occasion. Hopes of success were so high that he ordered a green uniform to wear in Ireland, before setting off for the Texel early in July. The mutinies in the English fleet blockading the Texel made the moment even more propitious, but contrary winds frustrated all efforts to set out until the mutinies were over, by which time political changes in France had weakened Hoche's position. The sudden death of Hoche in September, at the age of twenty-nine, seriously undermined plans for any expedition to Ireland, though Daendels was still enthusiastic for a bold stroke of some sort against Great Britain. The disastrous defeat of the Dutch fleet off Camperdown in October 1797 finally brought such hopes to an end. Under later Dutch regimes Daendels served as a colonial governor in Java and West Africa. He died in 1818.

The English artist Charles Howard Hodges (1764-1837) was a mezzotint engraver and portrait painter who settled at Amsterdam in 1794. During the period of the Batavian Republic he produced high-quality prints of a number of prominent people, including the two commanders of the proposed invasion of Ireland in 1797, General Daendels and Admiral De Winter.

Source: *Encyclopaedia Britannica* (15th edition).
            Herman Willem Daendels 1762-1818, catalogue of an exhibition at the Rijksmuseum (Utrecht, 1991).

155 *Admiral J.W. De Winter (1761-1812)*

BY DANIEL ORME (1766-1832)
MINIATURE ON IVORY
NATIONAL MUSEUM OF SCOTLAND (SCOTTISH UNITED SERVICES MUSEUM), EDINBURGH

Jan Willem De Winter became vice-admiral of the Dutch navy when Holland was liberated by the French and became the Batavian Republic and an alley of France. When the French Directory in 1797 decided to get up another expedition to invade Ireland, the Dutch navy under de Winter was to transport 15,000 Dutch troops to Ireland as part of a joint venture with the French from Brest. By July, 80 ships were waiting at the month of the River Texel for a favourable wind and a break in the British blockade, which was being conducted by Admiral Duncan from his headquarters at Yarmouth. Wolfe Tone's diary records his good opinion of De Winter and his high hopes of reaching Ireland soon. But week after week the wind prevented the Dutch from getting out. On board the Dutch flagship Tone and De Winter practised flute duets as they waited in vain for a fair wind, while the troops, 'packed like sardines', consumed their provisions in idleness and boredom. By the end of August the plan had collapsed; early in September most of the troops were disembarked and Tone left to consult with General Hoche.

When all realistic hope of a major Dutch expedition had passed, the Batavian government, for political reasons and contrary to the strong advice of De Winter, ordered the fleet to set to sea. As soon as Duncan heard that the Dutch had emerged he hurried to look for them and came up with them off Kamperduin (Camperdown). The two fleets were fairly equal in numbers, though the Dutch were inferior in manoeurability and gunpower. The 68-pounders of the British broke the Dutch line in two places and thereafter, in ship-to-ship close fighting, got the better of the Dutch despite a prolonged and bloody contest. Casualties were heavy on both sides - De Winter lost 1,000 of his total force of 7,000 - but nine of his sixteen ships of the line were taken and at last, with the *De Vrijheid* mastless and surrounded by five British ships, he hauled down his colours and surrendered his sword to Duncan on the bloody quarter-deck of the *Venerable*.

The Dutch prizes were so badly damaged that none of them could be used again; one could not even make it to port in England but sank in the North Sea. The defeat marked Holland's final exit from the ranks of European sea powers.

De Winter was a prisoner in England for a few months. During that time this portrait of him was painted and given to Duncan.

Sources: Tone, *Autobiography*, vol. 2.

156 *Admiral De Winter's sword, surrendered to Admiral Duncan following   the Dutch defeat at the Battle of Camperdown.*

NATIONAL MUSEUMS OF SCOTLAND (SCOTTISH UNITED SERVICES MUSEUM), EDINBURGH

This sword is of a style known as a 'shashqa' and is actually from the Caucasus region of central Asia. It was a fashion amongst Dutch naval officers of the period to carry non-European swords, an idea inspired by the Netherlands' strong trading interests in the East.

When De Winter was about to hand over his sword to Duncan on board the *Venerable* in a formal gesture of surrender, Duncan is said to have stopped him with the words, 'I would much rather take a brave man's hand than his sword'.

157 *Admiral Duncan, Viscount Duncan (1731-1804)*

BY SIR WILLIAM BEECHEY RA
OIL ON CANVAS
SCOTTISH NATIONAL PORTRAIT GALLERY, EDINBURGH

Adam Duncan was the second son of Alexander Duncan of Lundie in Perthshire. He entered the Royal Navy in 1746, in a ship commanded by his maternal uncle, and saw service in various ships till the end of the Seven Years War in 1763, by which time he was a post captain. The Admiralty found no further employment for him for the next fifteen years, which he spent mostly in Scotland. In 1777 he married a daughter of Robert Dundas of Arniston, the influential lord president of the court of session. A new command followed in 1778 and thereafter he was fairly constantly employed in ships of the line, becoming a rear-admiral in 1787, a vice-admiral in 1793 and a full admiral in 1795.

In February 1795 Duncan was appointed commander-in-chief in the North Sea. With his fleet based at Yarmouth, he was engaged in blockading the coast of the Low Countries for the next two years. Then in spring of 1797 it became known that the Dutch fleet, moored at the mouth of the River Texel, was getting ready for sea. Duncan's role became crucial, but just at that point the naval mutiny which had broken out in the ships at Spithead and the Nore spread to Yarmouth and practically paralysed the fleet there too. His own flagship, the *Venerable*, and one other obeyed the order to sail. Even this was possible only because of Duncan's popularity with the sailors and his intimidating size and strength (he once lifted an agitator in one hand and held him over the side of the ship). The two ships kept up the pretence of a blockade by continually sailing into sight of the Dutch and making signals to the non-existent fleet before disappearing below the horizon. Fortunately, the Dutch were not ready to sail and, when they were, were prevented from getting out by a persistent westerly wind till the sailing season was too far advanced. Wolfe Tone, who had been on board the Dutch flagship, was bitterly disappointed to be thwarted once more and left for France.

For political reasons, however, the Dutch government was anxious to make a demonstration and, much against the advice of De Winter, 'insisted on his going to

sea to show they had done so', as the Dutch admiral later told Duncan. Accordingly the Dutch fleet of nineteen vessels set sail early in October, while Duncan was revictualling most of his ships at Yarmouth. Summoned by a despatch, he weighed anchor at once and sighted the Dutch on the morning of 11 October about seven miles from shore off the village of Kamperduin (Camperdown). The wind was blowing straight on shore and it was clear that if not attacked at once the Dutch would soon be in shallow coastal waters where they would be safe. The Admiralty's 'Fighting Instructions', however, expressly forbade Duncan from placing his fleet between the enemy and the shore in such circumstances. Boldly, the sixty-six year old admiral ignored the regulations, broke the Dutch line and engaged the enemy from leeward, preventing their retreat. It was an enormous risk. The Dutch fought very hard, and inflicted heavy losses, but in the end lost most of their fleet.

Camperdown was a famous victory and made Duncan a national hero. Coming after the naval mutinies and depressing military and financial developments, the news was received with wide enthusiasm. Duncan was at once raised to the peerage as Baron Duncan of Lundie and Viscount Duncan of Camperdown. (Years later, in 1831, his son was given the earldom of Camperdown that many people felt the father should have had). He died suddenly in 1804. A huge figure (by contemporary standards, especially among sailors, almost a giant) of 6 feet 4 inches in height and correspondingly broad, Duncan was frequently painted. His fame as the victor of Camperdown is evident from the number and variety of the representations of Duncan himself and of the battle.

Sources: *DNB.*
             Manwaring and Dobrée, *The Floating Republic.*

158 *Admiral Duncan*

BY JAMES TASSIE
PASTE MEDALLION,
SCOTTISH NATIONAL PORTRAIT GALLERY, EDINBURGH

James Tassie (1735-99) was a famous Scottish modeller who began his working life as a stonemason. In 1763 he went to Dublin, where he worked as laboratory assistant to Dr Henry Quin, King's Professor of Physics in the College of Physicians. Together they perfected the secret 'white enamel composition' which Tassie was to use in the making of his remarkable reproductions of gemstones and his medallion portraits. This portrait of Duncan is an excellent example of his skill.

Sources: *DNB.*
            Eoin O'Brien and Anne Crookshank, with Gordon Wolstenholme, *Portraits of Irish Medicine* (Dublin 1984).

159 *'The Battle of Camperdown'*

BY OR AFTER P.J. DE LOUTHERBOURG
OIL ON CANVAS, 52 X 76 CM
NATIONAL MUSEUMS OF SCOTLAND (SCOTTISH UNITED SERVICES MUSEUM), EDINBURGH

The battle of Camperdown was one of the greatest sea battles of the Revolutionary Wars. Following the mutinies in the British fleet in the summer of 1797, order had been restored by concessions on pay and some improvement in conditions for the seamen, and by punishing the ringleaders of the rising at the Nore: 412 men were court-martialled, 59 sentenced to death (of whom 29 were hanged), 9 flogged

(one seaman on the *Monmouth* got 380 lashes) and 29 imprisoned for periods ranging from one to eight years; a particular example was made of Richard Parker, 'President of the Delegates', who was hanged on board HMS *Sandwich* on 30 June. The whole episode had been a severe shock to the government and to national opinion, which had regarded the Navy as the bulwark of the country but had done nothing about the miserly and inhumane way it was run.

Admiral Duncan, whose North Sea fleet was engaged on the vital business of blockading the revolutionary Dutch fleet at the mouth of the Texel throughout 1797, found himself reduced at one point to only two ships - *Venerable* and *Adamant*. Fortunately, at that point no hostile force was ready to sail. By the time the Dutch were ready in July he was being reinforced; Wolfe Tone's diary records the anxious counting of the British fleet that went on almost daily as the Dutch waited for a fair wind and tide. At last, in late September when all danger seemed over, Duncan took most of his ships to Yarmouth for refitting and revictualling. De Winter put to sea with his entire fleet on 3 October, a pointless gesture and dangerously late in the season. News of this reached Duncan on 9 October. Two days later his ships found the enemy nine miles off the Dutch coast. Without waiting to form the usual line of battle, Duncan ordered his captains to engage as they came up and to get between the Dutch and the shore - a very hazardous manoeuvre in the circumstances. The Dutch line was broken in two places. Thereafter it was a question of gunnery. The Dutch, outgunned, fought with obstinate courage. On the British side, the ships which had been in a state of mutiny were especially anxious to demonstrate their skill and loyalty. One of them, the *Ardent*, had more casualties than any other ship, losing one-third of her whole company. The stain of the mutinies was thus wiped out.

The Dutch fleet consisted of four 74-gun battleships, seven 64s, four 50s, two 44-gun frigates, two of 32 guns and some smaller vessels. Duncan had seven 74s, seven 64s, two 50s, two frigates, a sloop and some cutters. Eleven of the Dutch ships were taken. When the action ended, the ships still engaged were in only nine fathoms of water, within five miles of a dangerous lee shore and threatened by an approaching gale. The importance of Duncan's victory at the time is reflected in the instant status of national hero that it bestowed on him, the title of viscount that he received, and the number of representations it evoked. The earldom his son was given in 1831 showed that his place in the national pantheon was no less secure a generation later.

This picture, which gives some idea of the ferocity with which the battle was fought, is a copy of the larger work by de Loutherbourg now in the Tate Gallery. It is not signed, and may not be by de Loutherbourg himself. Philippe Jacques (or Philip James) de Loutherbourg was born in Germany in 1740 and studied painting in Paris, where he exhibited at the Salon in 1763 and became a member of the Académie Royale in 1767. In 1771 he came to London, where he began by designing scenery and costume for David Garrick's play productions. He first exhibited at the Royal Academy in 1772 and became an R.A. in 1781, painting landscapes, marine subjects and battle scenes. He died in London in 1812.

Sources: *DNB.*
              Encyclopaedia Britannica (11th edition).
              Manwaring and Dobrée, *The Floating Republic.*

The Apotheosis of HOCHE.

160 *The Apotheosis of Hoche*

BY J[AMES] G[ILLRAY]
COLOURED ENGRAVING, 48.9 X 38.1 CM, PUBLISHED IN LONDON 11[JAN.?] 1798 BY H. HUMPHREY
BRITISH MUSEUM, LONDON

This complicated engraving, a parody of the religious art with which people were
familiar, shows the French revolutionary general Lazare Hoche on his journey
heavenward to join the gods. Hoche is seen as a handsome young man, seated on
a rainbow, playing a guillotine as if it were a lyre. He wears only a cloak and a sash
which contains a pair of pistols, and has just kicked off his jackboots. A noose is
about to encircle his neck. His head is surrounded by rays of glory, framed by the
winged heads of Jacobin cherubs shouting hymns of praise (open books show the
Marsellois Hymn and Ça Ira). The cherubs wear caps of liberty and blood gushes
from their necks.

Above Hoche are three cloud levels. The largest supports the Jacobin table of
the law (as in French prints of the 'Declaration des Droits de l'Homme') which
contains a reversal of the Ten Commandments: *Thou Shalt Murder* etc. All of this

181

is set round with winged heads of monsters and animals. The central design is surrounded by armies of Jacobins, naked except for caps of liberty and sabots. Those on the left are led by victims of the Revolution, identified by placards as Roland, Condorcet etc.

On the ground below the rainbow the republican army charges unarmed fugitives. A heap of headless corpses and severed heads lies in the foreground; soldiers fire at a prisoner; corpses hang from a tree; a sign points to La Vendée [the royalist area 'pacified' by Hoche], which is full of burning houses and churches, fugitives etc. Above this blazing scene flies a Fury, flaming sword in one hand, bottle of poison or vitriol in the other. Liquid gushes from her horrible breasts, her hair is made up of serpents, fire comes from her mouth. She is followed by a swarm of little monsters. Another swarm, of Jacobins, scatters *Assignats* (revolutionary banknotes). All the crimes of the French Revolution are displayed in this ghastly panorama.

The sudden death of Hoche, aged only twenty-nine, in September 1797 was followed by magnificent funeral celebrations in Paris which are parodied in this print.

Sources: *BM Catalogue*, VII, no. 9156.

161 *Evidence to Character! - being a Portrait of a Traitor, by his Friends & by Himself*

BY J[AME]S GILLRAY
COLOURED ENGRAVING, 18 X 25.8 CM, PUBLISHED IN LONDON 1 OCTOBER 1798 BY J. WRIGHT
BRITISH MUSEUM, LONDON

This important and effective propaganda print is a burlesque of the trial of Arthur O'Connor at Maidstone in May 1798. O'Connor (as he looked, not caricatured), wearing leg-irons, stands at the bar making a confession, viz. *I confess, that I became an United Irishman in 1796 & a Member of the National Executive, from 1796, to 1798. I knew the offer of French assistance was accepted at a meeting of the Executive in Summer 1796: I accompanied the Agent of the Executive (the late Lord Edward Fitzgerald) through Hamburgh to Switzerland, had an interview with General Hoche (who afterwards had the command of the expedition against Ireland) on which occasion every thing was settled between the parties with a view to the descent. I knew that in 1797 a Fleet lay in ye Texel with 15000 Troops destined for Ireland I knew of the loan negociating with France for Half a Million for the new Irish Government.*

This was the gist of the information given to the authorities in Dublin by O'Connor and his fellow-prisoners in August 1798 in return for their lives, after the failure of the rebellion. A copy of *The Press by O'Connor* hangs from his pocket. Round his neck is a noose held by the hand of Justice emerging from the clouds; her other hand holds balanced scales.

At the trial, many leading members of the liberal opposition to Pitt's government, whom he knew and who thought they knew him, gave evidence on O'Connor's behalf, with the result that he was acquitted of treason (whereas his travelling companion, Father O'Coigley, was hanged). The subsequent revelation that he was in fact a leading figure in the United Irishmen made these witnesses look complete fools and was a gift to government propagandists. The words attributed to them by Gillray correspond closely with their actual words as reported in the published account of the trial.

Lady Holland, a leading Whig, noted in her journal for 29 August 1798: 'Opposition knocked up by the confession [of O'Connor and the other Dublin prisoners] ...In fact too much power thrown into the hands of Government owing to the vile and foolish conduct of Opposition'. And Lord Carlisle wrote the following day, 'If there is a lower political hell than any we before have witnessed, I think the opposition have found it out for themselves, by their connection with O'Connor and such worthies'. When Fox came across O'Connor again, in Paris in 1802, he showed his contempt for him.

Sources: *BM Catalogue*, VII, no. 9244.

162 *Arthur O'Connor, Esqr*

LATE MEMBER IN THE IRISH PARLIAMENT FOR THE BOROUGH OF PHILIPSTOWN
BY W. WARD AFTER J. DOWLING [HERBERT]
MEZZOTINT, 38 x 28CM PLATE; 'LONDON. PUBLISHED APRIL 18, 1798, BY J. DOWLING'.
P. AND B. ROWAN

Arthur O'Connor was born near Bandon, County Cork in 1763, one of the nine children and the fifth and youngest son of a wealthy and well-connected Protestant named Roger Conner and his wife Anne, sister of Lord Longueville. When they grew up, the two youngest boys, Roger junior and Arthur, abandoned the name Conner and pretended to be descended from the ancient O'Connor kings of Ireland. Both became United Irishmen.

O'Connor was educated at boarding schools in Munster and later, aged sixteen, went on to Trinity College, Dublin, where he read the works of Adam Smith, studied economics and discarded revealed religion. He was a frequent visitor to the gallery of the Irish House of Commons and particularly enjoyed the polished invective of some of the leading speakers. In 1782 he joined the Volunteers - his first claim, subsequently much exaggerated, to military experience. Spurning a family living in the church, he opted for the Irish bar, to which he was called in

1788 though he never practised as a lawyer; he did not need to earn a living, since his father had settled £1,500 a year on him. Instead, he built a house near Kinsale and settled down as a country gentleman, serving in 1791 as high sheriff of County Cork. In the same year he entered Parliament, through the influence of his uncle, for the borough of Philipstown in King's County. Though he later claimed to have been a lifelong republican, in fact he supported the administration and was silent even on the Catholic relief acts of 1792 and 1793. In London in 1792 he made the acquaintance of the wealthy young English radical Francis Burdett, who fell under his spell and apparently wanted him to marry his sister-in-law. From London, O'Connor and his friend John Hely-Hutchinson, son of the provost of Trinity College and later a British general, travelled to France in uniform (O'Connor's that of a Volunteer) and were received by Lafayette at his headquarters at Sedan shortly before he fled from France upon the collapse of the monarchy. O'Connor was later to exaggerate this brief visit into a claim to have served on Lafayette's staff.

Despite the September massacres in France, O'Connor returned to England strongly pro-French and republican. He welcomed the execution of Louis XVI and was disgusted when some MPs went into mourning. When France declared war on Great Britain and Holland in February 1793 he blamed Pitt and published (under a pseudonym) an anti-war pamphlet.

Back in Ireland, O'Connor became the close friend of Lord Edward FitzGerald and his wife Pamela; FitzGerald called him 'twin of my soul'. Following the sudden recall to England of the viceroy Fitzwilliam in 1795, Grattan's doomed bill to admit Catholics to Parliament was debated. O'Connor's speech for the bill, an outstanding one, brought him fame and popularity overnight among Irish Catholics and reformers and English Whigs. Though it cost O'Connor his seat and his uncle's favour, it brought him the admiration and friendship of all the leading opposition politicians in London - Fox and his circle - whose testimony was later to save him from the gallows. In 1796 he and Fitzgerald went to Hamburg and on to Switzerland, from where O'Connor travelled into France for a secret meeting with General Hoche at which the invasion of Ireland and a simultaneous rising of United Irishmen and Defenders was discussed and agreed.

Returning to Ireland, O'Connor took a house near Belfast and announced himself as a candidate for a parliamentary seat for County Antrim. Since he had no local connections and no election was due till the following year, this move had more to do with providing him with a platform for subversive propaganda than with any desire to get back into Parliament. His address to the electors of Antrim was published three times in the *Northern Star*. O'Connor was at his Belfast address when the French appeared off Bantry in December 1796; his own steward in County Cork wrote to say that 'God blew a storm and sent them to rout'. When the government launched a recruiting campaign O'Connor's reaction was to publish a still more seditious address, in which he said that it was nonsense to summon Irishmen to resist invasion when they were already under the heel of an invader. This led to his arrest and confinement in Dublin Castle for six months. In August 1797 FitzGerald and Thomas Emmet put up bail to have him released, untried.

While O'Connor was in prison, the *Northern Star* in Belfast had been suppressed and its presses broken by the Monaghan Militia. Joining the FitzGeralds in Kildare, he helped Lord Edward to organise and train the United Irishmen for the expected rising. He also set up and ran a successful, and highly inflammatory, newspaper called *The Press*, whose nominal publisher was convicted for seditious libel in December 1797. O'Connor suddenly left for London at the end of the same month en route for France, presumably to press once more for French aid. Curiously enough, he then hung about London for nearly two months, staying at Burdett's house and cultivating the Whig politicians. During this period he made a fictitious sale of his Irish property to Burdett, to save it from being confiscated if things went wrong. John Binns, a member of the radical London Corresponding Society, chartered a small ship for the journey and a merchant named Bell supplied foreign currency. In London, O'Connor was introduced to an Irish priest, James O'Coigly or Quigley, who was also going to France. They arranged to travel together, O'Connor under the name Colonel Morris, Quigley as Captain Jones. The whole party was arrested at Margate on 28 February 1798 by Bow Street runners and taken back to London for questioning. They were subsequently tried for treason at Maidstone in May, when O'Connor was acquitted largely because Fox, Sheridan, Erskine and other Whig leaders appeared in court to give evidence of his loyalty and good character. Quigley, from whom O'Connor was careful to distance himself, to such an extent as to weaken the priest's defence, was found guilty and was executed. O'Connor was rearrested in court, after trying to escape with help from his friends, to answer a charge of treason brought by the Irish government, and was taken to Dublin. He was in prison there with other leaders of the United Irishmen when the rebellion broke out.

In order to save further bloodshed, O'Connor, Thomas Emmet and William MacNeven made a bargain with the government by which, in return for the lives of themselves and a large number of fellow-prisoners, they undertook to tell the story of the United Irish conspiracy and its relations with the French. The English Whigs now learned that O'Connor had used and hoodwinked them. The prisoners were all to be exiled to a neutral country, but the USA would not take them in 1798 and the government refused to let them loose on the Continent while the war with France continued. O'Connor remained in prison till the Peace of Amiens in 1802, confined with twenty of the most prominent prisoners in Fort George in Scotland, before going to France by way of Hamburg. In prison he had challenged Emmet to a duel, which fellow-exiles prevented from taking place afterwards only with difficulty. Emmet thought O'Connor a bad and dangerous man, who if he got the chance might make himself dictator of Ireland under French auspices. Through the influence of a French officer of Irish descent, General Dalton, whom he had impressed, O'Connor was given the rank of *général de division* by Napoleon. He never served in the field, but was confined to intelligence work relating to Ireland and Irishmen during the period 1804-5, when his military service ended. He continued to draw the full pay and allowance of a general until the fall of Napoleon, however. Under Louis XVIII he was retired on a pension, which he continued to enjoy under succeeding regimes till the end of his life, a period of forty-seven years.

In 1807, then aged forty-four, O'Connor married Eliza de Condorcet, the seventeen-year-old daughter of the great French mathematician and philosopher. He became a French citizen in 1818. He died in 1852 at the age of eighty-eight.

Was O'Connor 'a cunning and ambitious demagogue' or a disinterested patriot? The author Benjamin Constant, who met him in Paris, summed him up as 'more ambitious than a friend of liberty'. His uncle Lord Longueville wrote of him in 1798: 'Of all the bad men I ever met he is the worst'. Martha McTier, William Drennan's sharp-tongued sister, wrote to her brother in 1802: 'I never liked him but on paper; powerful indeed he was there. He has a bad, a very bad countenance and will never rest till he is somehow exalted. I like him not and hope he may never come to Ireland'. Wolfe Tone, on the other hand, called him 'a noble fellow'. Whatever the final verdict, he was one of the most interesting and influential of the United Irishmen and - had there been a successful French invasion - might well indeed have been exalted.

William Ward the Elder (1766-1826) was an English engraver who worked mainly in mezzotint. The painter of the portrait, whose name is curiously given here as 'J. Dowling', was John Dowling Herbert (1762/3-1837), a minor Irish artist who had been an assistant to both Robert Home and Gilbert Stuart when they were in Dublin. He was the author of *Irish Varieties*.

Sources: *DNB.*
Webb, *Compendium of Irish Biography.*
Frank MacDermot, 'Arthur O'Connor', in *Irish Historical Studies*, vol. XV, no. 57 (1966).

163 *Memorial to the Rev. James O'Coigly, Maidstone*

PHOTOGRAPH (M.P. VIDEO, MAIDSTONE)

In 1898, the centenary of the Rebellion, this brass monument and three commemorative windows, in memory of Father James O'Coigly [Quigly], were erected in the Catholic church of St Francis in Maidstone, Kent, where he had been tried and hanged. The inscription on the monument reads: *Pray for the soul of Revd. James O'Coigly, a native of Ireland, who was put to death on Pennenden Heath, June 7th 1798; underneath, in Irish and English; This memorial & three windows over the altar have been erected by a number of his fellow countrymen as a record of their admiration for his love of creed & country for which he died.*

According to his own words, written as he awaited execution and afterwards edited by his kinsman Valentine Derry and published in London, James Coigly or O'Coigly claimed descent on his mother's side from a landed Jacobite family, the O'Donnellys of Tyrone, eight of whom - Coigly's great-grandfather and seven of his brothers - were slain at the battle of the Boyne; his great-grandfather Coigly, he claimed, had invented and constructed the famous boom at Derry in the siege of 1689 and was afterwards killed with three of his brothers at Aughrim. Coigly's father, 'a plain honest farmer' in County Armagh, gave his son a superior education. He was sent to Paris in 1785 to study for the priesthood. There he headed a successful agitation, against the superior of the college backed by the archbishop of Paris, to improve the rights of the students and reform abuses in the administration. At the outbreak of the Revolution he was nearly 'lanternized' by the mob, escaping from France with difficulty. Returning home, he found the inhabitants of County Armagh 'engaged in a civil war, and *religion made the pretext!*' A good case has been made for identifying Coigly as the author of a well-informed pamphlet, published in Dublin in 1792, entitled *An Impartial Account of the Late Disturbances in the County of Armagh; Containing, All the principal Meetings, Battles, Executions, Whippings, &c. of the Break-o-day Men and Defenders, since the Year 1784, down to the Year 1791... By an Inhabitant of the Town of Armagh.*

Coigly did minister for a time as a priest in Dundalk, County Louth, but he appears to have spent most of his time trying to establish peace in Armagh and working for the union of Catholics and Dissenters (Defenders and United Irishmen) there and in neighbouring areas - 'Witness my efforts in 1791, 1792 and 1793, at Randalstown, Maghera, Dungiven, Newtown [Limavady] and Magilligan ...'. In these efforts, which were clearly the programme of the United Irishmen, he acknowledged 'the spirited exertions of that truly respectable, virtuous and enlightened body the Dissenters of the county of Antrim, but chiefly and in particular those of Belfast'.

Coigly's family were to suffer for his political activities. 'The church and king mob, calling themselves Orangemen', he wrote, 'commenced their bloody system by attacking my father's house about two years ago [1796]'. The raiders proceeded to smash or carry off everything in the house, and then went on to commit similar outrages at the house of Coigly's elder brother. Unable to get anyone prosecuted, Coigly was only confirmed in his radicalism. Subsequently he travelled to England and thence to Paris by way of Hamburg. In Paris, he drew unfavourable comment from Wolfe Tone early in 1798. He had joined the circle of Napper Tandy, which intrigued to undermine Tone and Lewins as United Irish representatives. Tandy, wrote Tone, 'began some months ago by caballing against me with a priest of the name of Quigley, who is since gone off, no one knows whither; the circumstances of this petty intrigue are not worth recording. It is sufficient to say that Tandy took on him to summon a meeting of the Irish refugees, at which Lewines and I were to be arraigned .. by himself and Quigley.'

Coigly had gone to Ireland. On the way back, in London, he was introduced to Arthur O'Connor and accompanied him when he set out for France. The party was arrested at Margate in Kent when waiting to board ship. After being examined in London, Coigly was taken to Maidstone with the others and tried there for treason at the end of May. He was hanged on the gallows at Pennenden Heath on 7 June. Reading of it in the French papers, Tone wrote in his diary: 'Quigley, the priest, is found guilty; it seems he has behaved admirably well, which I confess was more than I expected; his death redeems him'.

Sources: Howell's *State Trials*, vol. 27.
Rev. Brendan McEvoy, 'Father James Quigley, Priest of Armagh and United Irishman', in *Seanchas Ardmacha*, vol. V (1970).
David W. Miller, 'Politicisation in Revolutionary Ireland: The Case of the Armagh Troubles', in *Irish Economic and Society History*, vol. 23 (1996).

164 *The Life of the Rev. James Coigly, An Address to the People of Ireland, as written by Himself, during his Confinement in Maidstone Gaol (London, 1798)*

P. AND B. ROWAN

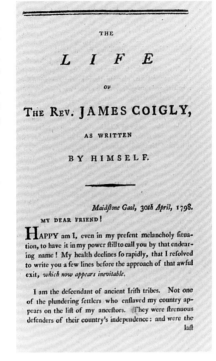

165 *Recollections of the Life of John Binns: Twenty-nine Years in Europe and Fifty-three in the United States. Written by Himself with Anecdotes, Political, Historical, and Miscellaneous (Philadelphia, 1854). First edition 12 mo., engraved portrait.*

P. AND B. ROWAN

Binns, born in Dublin in 1772, settled in London in the 1790s. There he became a notorious radical democrat, particularly associated with the more extreme elements of the London Corresponding Society. He was also a United Irishman. In 1798 he was arrested along with O'Connor and Coigly, en route for France, and was tried at Maidstone for high treason but was acquitted. In the United States he established the *Democratic Press* and lived to a ripe old age.

166 *Lord Edward FitzGerald (1763-98)*

BY HUGH DOUGLAS HAMILTON
OIL ON CANVAS, 71.1 x 55.9 CM
ULSTER MUSEUM

Lord Edward FitzGerald was born in London on 15 October 1763, the twelfth of the nineteen children of the first Duke of Leinster and his wife Emily Lennox, sister of the third Duke of Richmond. After her husband's death in 1773 the Duchess of Leinster scandalised her family by marrying her children's tutor, William

Ogilvie, with whom she had already begun a passionate liaison, and bore him two children, three if her last by Leinster was really Ogilvie's. The whole family decamped to France six weeks after the Duke's funeral. There the secret marriage contracted in Dublin was confirmed by an official ceremony. From 1776 to 1779, Edward lived with his mother (and the rest) in the Château of Aubigny, which belonged to his uncle, the Duke of Richmond. His upbringing made him a cosmopolitan figure, at ease with French as much as English and imbued with enlightened ideas. As a younger son with little property of his own, he needed to adopt some profession and settled on the army. After studying at a military academy in Paris, he got a lieutenant's commission in the 96th Regiment of Foot, but served first with the Sussex Militia, under the eye of his uncle.

Young Edward was eager for some real action, however, and having joined the 96th at Youghal he exchanged into the 19th and embarked for the American War early in 1781. He saw action against the colonists in South Carolina and enjoyed the experience, until badly wounded and left for dead on the battlefield of Eutaw Springs. His life was saved by a slave named Tony Small, scavenging among the bodies after the battle, who took him to his own quarters and dressed his wounds. When he recovered and went home, Edward took Tony with him as his personal servant. The black servant in his striking costume, who was to become a devoted companion, was a familiar if exotic sight on the streets of Dublin in the 1780s and 1790s.

In 1783 Edward FitzGerald was put into the Irish House of Commons for the borough of Athy, through the influence of his brother the Duke of Leinster. By that time, the reform movement mobilised outside Parliament by the Volunteers had lost most of its impulse. For a while, Edward turned to his English cousin Charles James Fox as his political mentor but was soon back in Ireland, where he lived pleasantly with his mother and stepfather at Frescati, the villa in Blackrock that was their home during these years. Afterwards, Ogilvie recalled that in 1784 and 1785 Edward 'was with us, indeed, wherever we went, and those were the happiest days of any of our lives'. Disappointed in love, when his prospective fiancée's parents turned him down, he entered the Royal Military College, Woolwich. In 1787 he visited Gibraltar, Portugal and Spain. In 1788 he joined his regiment, the 54th, in Nova Scotia and was stationed at New Brunswick, Halifax, Quebec and Montreal. He enjoyed military life, and was well liked by the soldiers. The writer William Cobbett, at that time sergeant-major of the 54th, who grew to hate the army and wanted to leave it, later wrote: 'Lord Edward was a most humane and excellent man, the only really honest officer I ever knew in the army'. In 1789 he travelled from Frederickstown to Quebec, with Tony and another officer, camping out in the wilderness. In June he lived with the Indians near Detroit and was made a Chief of the Bear tribe. He then travelled down the Ohio and Mississippi rivers to New Orleans. Indian life and the life of the settlers he came across, which he admired as more natural and egalitarian than that of the 'civilised' world he came from, made a great impression on him, confirming his rejection of conventional social values.

In 1790 he was returned to Parliament for County Kildare. A passionate affair with the lovely Elizabeth Sheridan, wife of the playwright turned politician, followed, ending only when she died of consumption after giving birth to their daughter (who was brought up as Sheridan's). The quickening pace of politics thereafter increasingly claimed FitzGerald's attention. The publication of the *Rights of Man* made a great impression on him, transforming him from a follower of Rousseau to a disciple of Paine, and from a radical to a republican. In October 1792 he visited Paris, where he not only met Paine but lodged with him and was completely captivated by him.

In November, at a meeting of British residents in the city, he joined in toasting the progress of liberty and the Revolution and drinking to 'The people of Ireland, and may Government profit by the example of France, and reform prevent revolution'; along with other young noblemen present, he renounced his (courtesy) title. As a result he was dismissed from the army. Lastly in this eventful year, just before Christmas he married, after a short acquaintance, the beautiful Pamela, the young ward of Madame de Genlis - probably her daughter by the Duke of Orleans (Philippe Egalité, who voted for the execution of his kinsman Louis XVI and was himself executed under the Terror). Pamela had previously, when on a visit to England, been briefly engaged to the widowed Sheridan. The marriage turned out to be a happy one; Pamela shared her husband's radical views and took an active part in the intrigues of his revolutionary friends.

Returning to Dublin with his bride, Edward denounced the government for prohibiting a meeting of radical Volunteers and spoke and voted against the Arms Bill and the Insurrection Bill. He became friendly with Arthur O'Connor, and joined the United Irishmen, recruiting for the cause in Kildare. In May 1796 he and Pamela went to the Continent, via Hamburg, in order to make contact with the French. There he was joined by O'Connor. They persuaded Reinhard, the French envoy in Hamburg, to take them seriously and travelled together into Switzerland. From there, O'Connor crossed into France and met secretly with Hoche to make plans for an invasion of Ireland. The FitzGeralds returned home by way of London, where they stayed with the Duchess at Ealing, leaving their son, 'little Eddy', with her to bring up.

Back in Ireland, FitzGerald and O'Connor prepared for the expected French expedition. When it finally arrived, in Bantry Bay at the end of December 1796, both the time and the place of its arrival caught the United Irishmen (and Dublin Castle) entirely by surprise. Though it failed to land, the more optimistic of the Irish revolutionary leaders - FitzGerald among them - were greatly heartened and believed the French would come again. All over the country there were reports from United Irish representatives of floods of recruits and a fever of expectation. The arrest and imprisonment of his friend O'Connor pushed FitzGerald to the forefront of the planning for an armed insurrection. With the Sheares brothers, he was the first to put forward a practical plan to achieve the aims of the United Irishmen by violent means; unlike them, he knew from his experience as a soldier just what such a plan would involve. As his most recent biographer puts it:

'Although the violence he advocated would be controlled and as short-lived as possible - a rising, a *coup d'état*, banishment without retribution of the tyrannical government and then a National Convention to determine the form of the new republic - it was violence none the less, and the military campaign at the centre of the plan would be surrounded by casual murder, reprisals, looting, burning, execution and torture on both sides. There was nothing noble about this, it was the plan of a practical political revolutionary, a man impelled by abstract principles of equality and fraternity, but a man of violence all the same'. [*Citizen Lord*, pp 221-2]

At the 1797 election he gave up his seat, convinced that no good could come from the unreformed Parliament; Grattan retired at the same time, and for the same reason. Meanwhile, Lake had disarmed Ulster, and the United Irish leaders had became disunited. In August, FitzGerald put up bail to have O'Connor released from Dublin Castle. They joined with others, including Leonard MacNally the informer, in establishing a new newspaper, *The Press*, to replace the *Northern Star*, which had been put out of business. Through informers such as MacNally and Samuel Turner, and by observation of his movements, the Castle soon had plenty of evidence, if not the kind of evidence to satisfy a court, of FitzGerald's militant republicanism. In fact, Lord Edward himself recruited to the cause Thomas Reynolds, who became a colonel of the United Irish forces in Kildare and was to be responsible for the arrest of the Leinster Directory. In December, in mysterious circumstances, O'Connor suddenly left Ireland for London, en route for France, leaving FitzGerald to become the military leader of a rising with or without French help. He drew up detailed plans to secure the capital and to mobilise the movement's forces throughout the country, based on the figures provided from the various areas to the National Executive meeting of 28 February 1798 - 110,000 in Ulster, 100,000 in Munster, 45,000 in the Dublin area. Foolishly, FitzGerald entrusted a copy of this paper to Reynolds, who was horrified by what it contained and made contact with the government. Reynolds also found out that the next meeting of the Leinster provincial committee was to be at Oliver Bond's house in Dublin on 12 March. This news too he passed on, but did not reveal where FitzGerald was to be found; instead, he dropped him hints of his impending arrest. When the members of the Leinster Committee were arrested next day, only FitzGerald of the five-strong National Committee remained at liberty. Warrants for his arrest were issued, and Frescati (the villa at Blackrock) was searched. So was Leinster House, where FitzGerald, alerted by the faithful Tony, escaped just in time. The search of the pregnant Pamela's bedroom, where she was convalescing from an illness, revealed letters from O'Connor and Coigly and a plan for the capture of Dublin. There was now enough evidence to convict her husband, if only he could be found. Rumours of his appearance in various parts of the country were rife, but in fact he remained in Dublin, heavily guarded and changing his lodgings frequently. Some of the officials at the Castle - Lord Chancellor Fitzgibbon, now Earl of Clare, among them - would have been glad to let him leave Ireland, but he felt himself obliged to stay and see the business through. Appeals from his family had no effect. His daring life on the run during this period made him a figure of legend, the charismatic chief who alone could unite the demoralised movement and yet lead it to victory. A proclamation offered a thousand pounds for his capture, but to no avail until, after several near shaves, he was surprised in a house in Thomas Street on 19 May by Major Swan, Captain Ryan and Major Sirr. FitzGerald fought ferociously against capture with his special zig-zag dagger, slashing Swan and disembowelling Ryan (who died later of his wounds) until shot twice in the shoulder by Sirr. He was then put into a sedan chair and taken under heavy escort to Dublin Castle, where his wound was dressed by the Surgeon General. The magistrates then removed him to Newgate gaol and locked him up. Thomas Russell, one of the inmates, was allowed to stay with him on the first night; thereafter no one was allowed to see him except guards and doctors, until near the end, when he was obviously dying. Then, Lord Clare arranged for his brother Henry and his sister Louisa to visit him; Clare himself, who accompanied them, broke down in tears. The wound to FitzGerald's shoulder, from which the two pistol balls had not been removed, had become infected in the unusually hot summer weather and septicaemia set in. The Surgeon General, who visited the patient each day along with a doctor engaged by the FitzGerald family, dithered about an operation until it was too late. Early on the morning of 4 June, after a violent struggle, Edward FitzGerald died.

Without his leadership or that of any other senior figure (Samuel Neilson had been arrested in the street outside when discovered making preparations to rescue him), the rising went ahead as planned on 23 May. Without central direction, however, the scheme for a co-ordinated national effort, beginning with the seizure of Dublin, fell apart. Like his own death, what ensued was a bloody mess. Alone of his class, this cosmopolitan aristocrat had made the journey from idealist reformer to violent republican revolutionary . That in itself made him stand out. When to this uniqueness is added unselfishness of motive, reckless courage and singular charm, it is little wonder that Lord Edward Fitzgerald emerged in nationalist mythology as the leading figure in the pantheon of heroes of 1798.

Sources: Stella Tillyard, *Citizen Lord: Edward Fitzgerald, 1763-1798* (London, 1997).

167 *Arrest of Lord Edward Fitzgerald*

BY GEORGE CRUIKSHANK, FROM MAXWELL'S *REBELLION*
ULSTER MUSEUM
REPRODUCTION

Fitzgerald was captured on 19 May 1798 when hiding in the house of a feather merchant in Thomas Street, Dublin. He had stayed at several safe houses in the city since the arrest of the Leinster Provincial Committee at Oliver Bond's house on 12 March. Cruikshank's bedroom setting of the arrest imitates many nationalist depictions of the same incident. The arrest was in fact effected after Lord Edward had grappled on the staircase with his pursuers, led by Major Sirr, Captain Swan and Captain Daniel Ryan. On 31 May, Ryan died of wounds inflicted during this struggle. Fitzgerald, whose injuries had not initially been considered life-threatening, died on the following day.

168 *Nightly Visitors, at St Ann's Hill; 'In glided Edward's pale-eyed Ghost, And stood at Carlo's feet.'*

BY J[AME]S G[ILLRA]Y
COLOURED AQUATINT, 34.2 X 24.8 CM, PUBLISHED IN LONDON 21 SEPTEMBER 1798 BY H. HUMPHREY
BRITISH MUSEUM, LONDON

Charles James Fox is shown in bed, at home in his house at St Ann's Hill, his nightcap a bonnet rouge with cockade. His sleep is disturbed by ghosts which stand in a row at the foot of the bed, emerging from clouds. Except for Lord Edward FitzGerald, who stands above the rest with bloodstained hair and shirt, they are headless, with nooses around their bleeding necks. Lord Edward reproaches Fox with the words:

> Who first seduced my youthful Mind from Virtue? -
> Who plann'd my Treason, & who caus'd my Death? -
> Remember poor Lord Edward, and despair!!!

192

Fox replies:

> Why do'st thou shake thy Goary Locks at me!
> Dear, bravest, worthiest, noblest, best of Men!
> Thou can'st not say, I did it! -

The bodies are those of Grogan and Harvey [here Hervay], both of whom were hanged in Wexford, Quigley (executed at Maidstone), and the Sheares brothers (executed in Dublin). On the floor to left is an open book, partly hidden by the bedclothes, entitled *Plan of the Irish Rebellion*. Above Fox's head two devilish naked cherubs carry a paper inscribed *Confessions of O'Connor, Ol Bond*.

Fox opposed the government's Irish policy, and had given evidence which helped to save O'Connor from the gallows at his trial in Maidstone. Subsequently O'Connor and others prisoners in Dublin gave evidence about the United Irish conspiracy in return for their lives. Oliver Bond, who had been arrested and sentenced to death, was also reprieved by this so-called Kilmainham Treaty, but he died in prison in September 1798.

Fox had indeed known FitzGerald - they were in fact cousins - and was admired by him. He had not turned the younger man to republicanism and revolution, however: that was the effect of reading Paine's *Rights of Man*.

Sources: *BM Catalogue*, VII, no. 9244

169 *Crests of the Lemon and Johnston families*

OIL ON CANVAS, 51 x 49 CM
ULSTER MUSEUM

Presented to James Lemon Donaghadee.
by the Duke of Leinster.
1798.

According to the tradition of the Lemon family of Belfast, this curious item was the gift of William, second Duke of Leinster, to James Lemon of Donaghadee, County Down and his wife Elizabeth née Johnston. The story is preserved in a typescript, attached to the back of the picture, which reads as follows:

> In 1798 Lord Edward Fitzgerald, who was married to a French woman, was endeavouring to arrange an invasion in Ireland by the French. His brother, the Duke of Leinster, did not want to associate himself with this venture and fled with his valet on horseback to Donaghadee and was hidden in the house of James Lemon who eventually smuggled him on board his sailing packet boat for Scotland.
>
> The Duke, while in his house, found out the crest of James Lemon and of his wife Elizabeth (nee Johnston), the Lion the Lemon's and the Flying Spur the Johnston's.
>
> As an appreciation the Duke got the two crests combined and sent it to James Lemon.

It is certainly true that Leinster was embarrassed by his younger brother's revolutionary opinions and actions, and by the unwelcome suspicions that these brought upon himself and other members of the family. Leinster House in Dublin was watched by government spies and searched in pursuit of Lord Edward or evidence against him. Leinster left Ireland in the autumn of 1797 in order to accompany his sick wife to England, where she died soon after. Donaghadee had a packet service to Portpatrick in Scotland and provided a swifter and less conspicuous passage than a Dublin departure would have done. The Lemon legend is therefore not implausible in a general way; the details, however, are hard to verify. On the other hand, the tale would have been a very odd one for respectable people to invent without foundation; and the provenance of the object and its accompanying documentation, donated to the Museum by a direct descendant of James Lemon, is excellent.

170 *Presentation Sword in the style of the Light Cavalry, 1796 pattern*

BY JOHN ASHE RAINEY, DUBLIN, 1798
BLADE 94 CM, WITH SPEAR POINT; SCABBARD
MR NEVILLE WHITTLEY

This fine Dublin-made sword has a stirrup guard and bars in gilt brass, and a ball quillion. Between the bars is a crowned Maid of Erin, a *GR* cypher on the semi-circular bar, and above this the inscription *On parade March 18 1798*. The grip is of bone, bound with silver wire, and there is a slit for a sword knot at the top of the guard.

The langet on the left side is inscribed *God/Save the/King*. The blade, which is blued half way, is decorated with gilt astrological signs, trophy of arms, Moor's Head and small stars. The lower part of the blade, which is of plain steel, has sun, moon, stars, astrological signs and stylised Moor's Head etched upon it.

The right side of the blade is similarly decorated. The right langet is inscribed:
On parade 1798/This sword was/Presented by the Non-Commissioned Officers/ & Privates of the 5th Comp/of 2nd Royal Dublin/Infantry to Alderm^n Ja^s Vance/their Cap^in in Testimony/of the Affectionate/regard they have for/him as a Loyal/Soldier and/much respected/Fellow Citizen.

The scabbard is of red leather with gilt locket, middle band, and chape, and loose rings on the locket and middle band. Inscribed on the locket is *John Ashe Rainey Fecit DUBLIN*. The leather is decorated on both sides at the top with a gilt crown over a three-piece scroll inscribed *Prosperity to Ireland*, in a gilt rectangle with rising and setting suns, in the centre the royal arms, and down at the chape a gilt crowned Maid of Erin.

The 2nd Royal Dublin Infantry was a regiment of Yeomanry. Judging by the splendid style of this sword, the non-commissioned officers and privates of the 5th Company must have been men of some substance.

The maker, Rainey, is known to have been practising as a Dublin cutler in the early 1800s. This sword shows that he was producing reputable work for the leading citizens of the capital before the end of the eighteenth century.

171 *Address to the Electors of the County of Antrim*

By Arthur O'Connor
Pamphlet, published by the *Northern Star*, Belfast, 1796
P. and B. Rowan

This is the pamphlet form of the *Address*, which was originally produced as a broadsheet.

AN

A D D R E S S

TO THE

FREE ELECTORS

OF THE

COUNTY OF ANTRIM.

FELLOW CITIZENS,

THE Post Office is so immediately dependent on the Government, that any anonymous production issuing from thence, must be looked on as coming from the Administration itself; in this light I have viewed the anonymous paper which has been so industriously distributed through the Post Offices of the North, avowedly to deprive me of whatever share of your confidence I might have gained, and in this light I have given it an answer. Had I treated it with silent contempt, I should have hoped that its coming from an Administration which had so deservedly forfeited the confidence of every Irishman, who valued the liberties of his Country, would have insured me from suffering, in your estimation, from the falshood and calumny with which it abounds; but my respect for those invaluable Censors, the Press and the Public Opinion, the conscious integrity of my own heart, and the most perfect reliance on the virtue of the cause I espouse, prompt me to seize any occasion which affords an opportunity of vindicating it or myself from the aspersions of an Administration, whose heaviest charge, in their wretched production, is, that at any time of my life I had been the advocate of them or their measures. As the whole of the work is one continued tissue of misrepresentation and falshood, a plain recital of facts will be the best means of giving it a full refutation. After the

10 Up in Arms, 1798

By 1798, the leaders of the United Irishmen were no longer united. The question of whether or not to wait for another French expedition to arrive before acting and, if so, how long to wait, split the ruling body of the movement. Meanwhile the rank and file became impatient and the loyalists became better organised and better informed. The arrest of most of the Leinster Directory left Lord Edward FitzGerald to lead the plans for a military uprising, till he too was taken. On 23 May the signal was given nevertheless. With no overall leadership, however, the United Irishmen in and around Dublin quickly faded and early successes achieved by surprise in Kildare were soon reversed. Without direction from the capital, most areas hesitated to move as planned. Only in Wexford, least suspected of being well organised, was there a formidable response.

A fortnight later, Antrim and Down followed, but there the movement had been weakened by Lake's earlier disarmament and by news of the recent massacre of Protestants in Wexford. General Nugent's troops were able to defeat the rebels separately at Antrim and Ballynahinch.

The news from Ireland encouraged the French, too late and on too small a scale, to send a hastily assembled force under Humbert to Mayo. After a notable success at Castlebar his army was quickly rounded up. Only then did a somewhat larger force under Hardy arrived off Donegal; defeated at sea, the French got ashore only as prisoners - among them Wolfe Tone, who was found guilty of treason but took his own life.

The fighting in 1798, where it took place, was savage. While military casualties were comparatively light for the numbers engaged, deaths among civilians were high and - to judge by loyalist claims for compensation alone - destruction of property was widespread. In the end the rebels, however numerous and brave, were no match in open battle for even half-trained troops well supplied with muskets and artillery.

172 *John Fitzgibbon, first Earl of Clare, Lord Chancellor of Ireland*

BY GILBERT STUART
OIL ON CANVAS, 108.6 x 67.3 CM
HISTORICAL PORTRAITS LTD, LONDON

Fitzgibbon was born in 1749 near Donnybrook, County Dublin, the son of a Catholic father who had converted to Protestantism in 1731 in order to practise law and who amassed a considerable fortune as a lawyer. Later opponents were to deride Fitzgibbon's modest and Catholic origins as very low and dishonourable, but in fact they appear to have been perfectly respectable. He himself was sensitive about them, however, and resented the fact that he was never fully accepted by the Protestant ascendancy that he defended so stoutly. He reacted against his family origins by completely rejecting his Catholic antecedents and identified wholly with the Protestant interest.

After taking his BA degree at Trinity College in 1762 and an LL.D. three years later, Fitzgibbon went on to take a degree at Oxford and studied law at the Temple in London. Called to the Irish bar in 1772, he made rapid progress. By 1778 his fees amounted to £8,000 a year and by 1798 his earnings were nearly £46,000. Like many a successful and ambitious lawyer, he also went into politics, being elected as a member for Trinity College in 1780 on a fashionably liberal platform.

198

After being appointed attorney-general in 1783, however, he always took the government side, starting with a powerful speech against Flood's reform bill in 1784. Four years later, at the time of the Regency crisis, he aligned himself firmly on the side of Pitt against the Irish Patriots. Lord Westmoreland later wrote, 'He has no god but English government'. The personal animosities generated by politics led to a duel with the liberal lawyer John Philpot Curran in 1789 (someone unkindly remarked that unfortunately both missed). Curran was later to claim that Fitzgibbon's vindictiveness against him had cost him £30,000 in lost fees.

In 1789 Fitzgibbon was appointed lord chancellor of Ireland, an appointment that usually went to an Englishman and a recognition of his considerable abilities as much as the lack of anyone more suitable. The Irish barony he was elevated to on this occasion was followed soon by a viscountcy (1793), the earldom of Clare (1795) and finally an English peerage (1799). As lord chancellor he occupied a key position in the Dublin Castle administration, consistently opposing reforms such as the Catholic relief acts of 1792 and 1793 and anything smacking of French principles, condemning Fitzwilliam's actions and attitudes during the latter's brief reign as viceroy in 1795 and urging his recall. As vice-chancellor of Dublin University in the later 1790s he was responsible for expelling Robert Emmet and other radical students. In the events surrounding 1798 he played a crucial role as the hammer of the United Irishmen, who, as one historian has recently written, 'embraced every element he most hated in Irish society and in Irish political life: feckless, irresponsible Anglicans with impractical schemes for reform, pushy disaffected Catholics, and "restless, republican" Presbyterians'. After 1798, he was a key figure in promoting the Union and in overcoming opposition to it, not least in the Irish bar, which initially voted against by a large majority.

Though hated by his opponents and despised by many on his own side, Fitzgibbon was entirely consistent in his political views. His assessment of Irish society and politics was essentially realistic. 'The Protestant élite did indeed depend for their political survival on a sound English presence and on a sectarian monopoly. Equally sound was his claim that wholesale enfranchisement of Catholics, reform, or grandiose claims of nationhood carried great risks, given the paucity of Protestant numbers and the raw memories of conquest and dispossession' (Kavanaugh). Of course Fitzgibbon, though tactically right, was strategically wrong, as diehard conservatives often are.

Though imperious in manner and a good hater, Fitzgibbon could be personally kind on occasion, as he was with the relations of Lord Edward FitzGerald (despite a privately expressed wish to see him out of the world via the gallows) and as he was too in helping to save the property of Hamilton Rowan and in ending his exile. He was also an upright judge, and carried through necessary reforms of the legal administration. It could also be said of him that he was kind to his scatterbrained and occasionally adulterous wife and his numerous relations, and a fair landlord to his tenants. None of this, had it been known, would have counted with the mob that flung dead cats on his coffin at his funeral in 1802, when he died at the age of fifty-three. With the death of his grandson in the charge of the Light Brigade at Balaclava in 1854 his honours became extinct.

This portrait, which re-emerged only recently, is a reduced version of Stuart's painting of 1789, probably done for Fitzgibbon's sister Elizabeth, who married William Beresford, first Viscount Decies. It was owned by their descendants until 1960. It is almost certainly the image used by the mezzotint engraver Charles Hodges, who was invited to Dublin by Stuart to do the work.

Sources: *DNB.*
Webb, *Compendium of Irish Biography.*
Ann C. Kavanaugh, 'John FitzGibbon, Earl of Clare', in Dickson, Keogh and Whelan (eds), *The United Irishmen.*

173 *Edward Cooke, Under-Secretary of State for Ireland (1755-1820)*

MEZZOTINT BY WILLIAM WARD THE ELDER, AFTER WILLIAM CUMING, 50 x 31.5 CM
NATIONAL GALLERY OF IRELAND, DUBLIN

Cooke was an Englishman, educated at Eton and Cambridge (King's College, where the provost was his father), who became a government official in Ireland in 1778. He was under-secretary in the Irish military department 1789-95 and in the civil department 1796-1801, sitting as MP for the borough of Leighlin throughout the 1790s. In 1795 he quarrelled with the new viceroy, Lord Fitzwilliam, and was removed from office - one of the reasons for Fitzwilliam's recall. The next viceroy, Camden, reinstated him and made him under-secretary of the civil department. This brought him into close contact with Castlereagh, the chief secretary, in opposing the United Irishmen and suppressing the rebellion.

Afterwards, he published anonymously a pamphlet entitled *Arguments for and against an Union between Great Britain and Ireland considered*, which was taken to express views in the higher reaches of government and occasioned many replies. It rested the case for union on grounds conciliatory to all classes of the Irish people, including large concessions to the Catholics as the natural sequel. Cooke was Castlereagh's intermediary in most of the transactions by which support was obtained for the Act of Union. After its passing, he shared the disappointment of Pitt, Cornwallis and Castlereagh, and like them resigned his post. Writing to the lord chancellor, Clare, he vindicated Catholic claims.

A man of great administrative ability, 'his influence was not that of a subordinate official, he was felt as a governing power', as the writer of the *DNB* entry puts it. Identified at first with the conservative clique in Dublin Castle, he became increasingly liberal in his views on Ireland - a change probably resulting from his close association with Castlereagh. Returning to England, Cooke continued his career in the various departments over which Castlereagh presided - the board of control, the war and colonial department, and the foreign office. He retired in 1817 and died in 1820.

Sources: *DNB.*

174 *3-pounder brass field gun with carriage*

DANISH, LATE EIGHTEENTH CENTURY
ROYAL ARTILLERY MUSEUM, LONDON

Few brass field-pieces of this period survive. This one is mounted on a modern replica of a 'galloper' chassis, authentic as to scale and construction but lacking one of its two ammunition boxes and not painted in the regulation colour of the Royal Artillery of the time.

The possession of artillery by the forces of the crown, and trained gunners to work the guns, was one of the main reasons why the rebels were defeated in spite of their general superiority in numbers and the courage they often displayed. Untrained troops could not easily sustain bombardment by artillery, as at Vinegar Hill and Ballynahinch, without becoming demoralised.

175 *Iron cannon, 4-pounder*

MADE BY J. FULLER, C.1790
LENGTH OF BARREL 132 CM
ULSTER MUSEUM

This gun can be dated to c.1790 by the reinforce on the touch-hole, which was introduced about then, and by the initials of the maker, John Fuller, on the trunnions. The Fuller family of Sussex controlled the largest foundry in England and from the mid-seventeenth to the late-eighteenth century made large numbers of cannon for the governments of England and Ireland (as well as some for Savoy and Naples). By the end of the eighteenth century, however, supplies of charcoal from the Sussex forests were running out; the industry then moved to Carron, near Falkirk in Scotland, where there were abundant supplies of both coal and iron. Carron gave its name to carronades, naval guns of short barrel and large bore.

Sources: Charles ffoulkes, *Arms and Armaments: An Historical Survey of the Weapons of the British Army* (London, 1945).

176 *'Land pattern' flintlock musket, late-eighteenth century*

ULSTER MUSEUM

177 *Two pike heads, c.1798*

ULSTER MUSEUM

178 *Pikes from Sentry Hill, County Antrim, with shafts*

(A) WITH PLAIN SPEAR POINT, TOTAL LENGTH 225 CM
(B) WITH SPEAR POINT AND HOOK, TOTAL LENGTH 207 CM
NEWTOWNABBEY BOROUGH COUNCIL

These crudely-made weapons appear to be the products of a local blacksmith working in a hurry, as such men did in 1798. The shafts are certainly old, and may even be original.

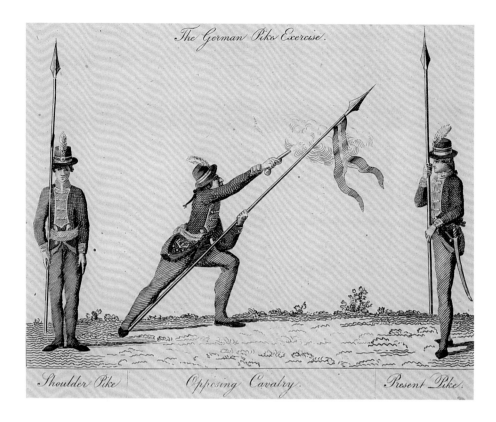

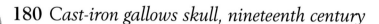

179 'The German Pike Exercise, 1794'

From *The British Military Magazine*, 1800
ULSTER MUSEUM (ARMAGH MUSEUM COLLECTION)
REPRODUCTION

Though the pike had been superseded by the bayonet in most European armies long before 1794, it did not go entirely out of use and could be a formidable weapon at close quarters, even against cavalry, as the rebels of 1798 proved, especially in County Wexford. The Seafield Collection in Fort George, Scotland includes a set of pikes issued to local Fencibles for drilling purposes when muskets were in short supply in the 1790s. In the open field, however, pikemen were very vulnerable to artillery and musket fire if unsupported.

180 *Cast-iron gallows skull, nineteenth century*

ULSTER MUSEUM (ARMAGH MUSEUM COLLECTION)

Public executions in Armagh were carried out at Gallows Hill until 1780; thereafter, until public hangings ceased in 1866, in Gaol Square. The date of this gruesome *memento mori* is uncertain, but it served the same purpose in time of peace as displaying the severed heads of rebels executed by the authorities in 1798.

181, 182, 183 *Three United Irish flags*

ULSTER MUSEUM
REPLICAS

There are several contemporary descriptions and depictions of the standards used by the United Irishmen. The picture of the Battle of Ballynahinch, for example, shows captured standards being brought to General Nugent, and Cruikshank's

illustrations in Maxwell's *Rebellion*, though later in date, were clearly based on contemporary descriptions. Such flags were usually of a simple, home-made kind, with a background of green.

Sources: G.A. Hayes-McCoy, *A History of Irish Flags from Earliest Times* (Dublin, 1979).

184-203 *Items relating to the Scottish Fencible Regiments in Ireland*

NATIONAL MUSEUMS OF SCOTLAND (SCOTTISH UNITED SERVICES MUSEUM), EDINBURGH

The term 'fencible', from the word 'defensible', was used to described individuals or military units formed specifically for home defence during wartime, rather than for foreign service. The fact that it proved comparatively easy to persuade fencible regiments raised in Great Britain to extend their service to Ireland in the 1790s was one of their attractions to a government desperate to meet its military commitments. During the war against France in the period 1797-1802, thirty-four regiments of Fencible Cavalry and fifty-nine battalions of Fencible Infantry were raised. Of these, an extraordinarily high proportion were of Scottish origin, and twenty-five of them were sent to Ireland to make up for Irish soldiers recruited for service abroad and to supplement the Irish Militia and Yeomanry regiments. The Scottish fencibles became the most reliable, if not the largest, element in the Irish government's forces, and on the whole the best-behaved. The Reay Fencibles were particularly well thought of. Some of the highland recruits were Catholic and Gaelic-speaking, most of the lowlanders were Protestant. For some of the latter, service in Ireland confirmed or created a sectarian tendency: the first Orange Lodges in Scotland were composed of ex-fencibles who had joined the Order in Ireland.

184 *Officer's shoulder belt plate of the Midlothian Fencible Cavalry, 1794-1800*

This unusually elaborate design gives a clue to the expense and commitment its colonel, Lord Ancram, was prepared to devote to his regiment. Although originally dressed in red uniform jackets with green facings, the regiment was allowed to adopt blue uniforms in August 1798. This distinction was supposedly sanctioned in recognition of the regiment's 'spirited conduct' during the rebellion.

185 *William Kerr, Earl of Ancram (1763-1824), Colonel of the Midlothian Fencible Cavalry*

The regiment was raised by Lord Ancram and served in Ireland from 1797. It was disbanded at Drogheda in September 1800.

   This pencil and wash sketch by Henry Edridge (1769-1821) is actually dated 1802 - two years after the Midlothian Fencibles were disbanded, although Ancram is still wearing his regimental uniform.

186 *Guidon of the Midlothian Fencible Cavalry, 1794-1800*

As a regiment of light dragoons, the Midlothian Fencibles would have been organised into six troops, each of around fifty men. This complement meant that the regiment actually carried three guidons. This is probably the first, or King's, guidon. During the rebellion, the Midlothian Fencibles took part in the defence of the town of New Ross and were present at the Battle of Vinegar Hill, where their performance was singled out for praise by General Lake. However, it is worth noting that the regiment's small number of casualties for this battle (one officer and one trooper being wounded) gives an idea of just how one-sided the action actually was.

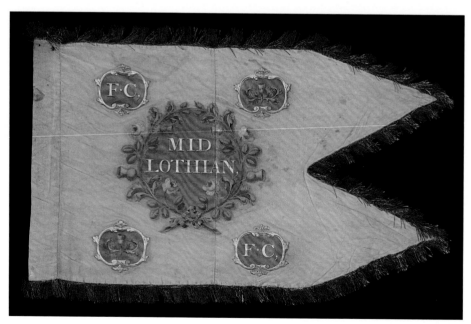

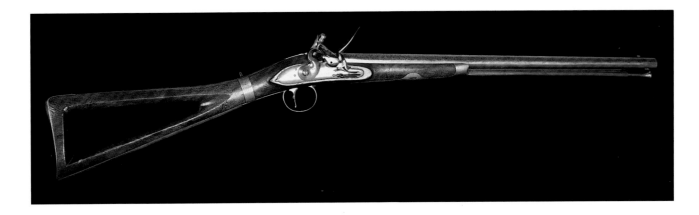

187 *Experimental cavalry carbine designed by the Earl of Ancram and made in Ireland in 1797*

Ancram was a Fellow of the Royal Society of Edinburgh, a highly-regarded organisation established to encourage advances in science and philosophy. Colonel Lord Ancram set out the advantages of his innovative design in a published letter to Lord Cornwallis in December 1798. The carbine was shorter, and therefore lighter, than the standard design used by the Army but had the same range. Because of the excavated butt, it could also be carried and handled more easily. Because of the special design of the breech, the carbine was also 'self-priming': this meant that it was unnecessary to place a separate quantity of powder into the pan; it was filled instead automatically through the touch hole from the main charge rammed down into the breech. The weapon could therefore 'be loaded on horseback at speed, or in the dark, or in windy weather and under the cloak when it rains'. It could also be fired, according to Ancram, five times a minute.

It is obvious that this design, and other suggested modifications to the equipment of light dragoons, was closely based on Colonel Ancram's personal experiences and experiment with his regiment in Ireland.

The carbine was made in Drogheda by a local gunsmith named Obadiah Wisdom in July 1797. It cost £3.11s.6d (Irish). The lock, however, was made in Dublin by Thomas Fowler.

188 *Cavalry sabre with folding guard associated with the Earl of Ancram*

Both Ancram's father and grandfather had been cavalry officers in the British Army. In fact, while the Midlothian Fencibles were in Ireland, the fifth Marquess of Lothian became Colonel of the 11th Light Dragoons, although he actually held the rank of general in the army.

The blade of this sabre is of German manufacture and is of a style inspired by the Hungarian irregular light cavalry troops, known as hussars, recruited into the Austrian army in the early eighteenth century.

The folding sprung guard was a common feature of light cavalry officers' swords of the late eighteenth century. The design gave protection to the hand but also meant that the sword was less cumbersome when the guard was folded away. Ancram bought two sabres with sprung hilts in September 1797, although it is unclear if this is one of these or an earlier one which may originally have belonged to his father.

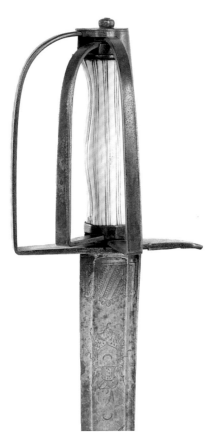

189 & 190 *King's and Regimental colours of the Glengarry Fencibles, c.1801*

This set of colours incorporates the modified union flag adopted after the Act of Union between Britain and Ireland of 1800. The central device on the Regimental Colour is sprigs of heather, inspired by the traditional clan badge of the Macdonalds - the regiment was raised by Colonel Alexander Macdonnell of Glengarry, largely from amongst his tenants and their families.

The regimental title of 1st British Fencible Regiment was granted in recognition of the fact that the Glengarry Fencibles were the first of the fencible regiments recruited to serve throughout Britain, rather than in Scotland alone.

The regiment was unusual in other respects in that it recruited heavily from highlanders who had been drawn to the expanding industrial area in and around Glasgow during the pre-war boom in the textile industry. The general slump which followed the outbreak of war meant that many of these highlanders were then out of work and destitute. Many of these men came from the Glengarry area and the majority were Roman Catholics. A solution to these men's plight was to allow for the creation of a fencible regiment - one in which the men could openly enlist as Catholics and which had provision for its own priest. Both these factors were radical departures for the British Army of the period, still largely governed by rules aimed at preserving the Protestant succession at all costs.

Whilst serving in the Channel Islands, the Glengarry Fencibles were rushed to Ireland in June 1798. They arrived at Waterford and saw action against the rebels at Lacken Hill, Hacketstown and New Ross.

Following the defeat of the rebel army at Vinegar Hill, the Glengarry Fencibles, in common with other highland units, were deployed against small bands of rebels who had taken refuge in the mountains of Wicklow. It was during these operations that the regiment, which had acquired the soubriquet of 'the Devil's Bloodhounds', cornered the celebrated rebel leader Michael Dwyer in a remote farmhouse. In the skirmish which followed, Dwyer managed to escape.

The regiment seems to have had a good reputation in its dealings with the local population. The constant presence and ceaseless activity of its remarkable priest, and one of its founders, Father Alexander Macdonnell, was a great influence

206

both in reassuring the ordinary people and in attempting to prevent the excesses of other units.

The regiment was disbanded in 1802, and, after much lobbying by Father Macdonnell of the Government, which was at that time opposed to highland emigration, the majority of the men and their families were permitted to emigrate to Canada. Their priest went with them and eventually became Bishop of Upper Canada.

191 *Other rank's shoulder belt plate of the 2nd Battalion Breadalbane Fencibles*

These cast brass plates were worn on the shoulder belt which supported the soldier's bayonet.

The Breadalbane Fencibles were one of the first fencible regiments raised in Scotland during the War against Revolutionary France. By 1795, the regiment numbered three battalions, although the actual conditions of enlistment varied between them. In the first and second battalions, raised in 1793, the men were enlisted for service in Scotland alone but could be moved to England in the event of an invasion. However, as the government's priorities changed with the increasing need for troops for service in Ireland, fencible units raised after 1794 were to be liable for service anywhere in Britain or Ireland. By 1799, the government's need for maximum flexibility, balanced with the reduced threat of invasion, meant that an ultimatum was presented to the men of all the fencible regiments either to extend their service to Europe or be individually discharged. If enough men within a single unit refused to extend their service, then the entire battalion would be disbanded. Many Scottish units, including the first and second battalions of the Breadalbane Fencibles, chose to be disbanded. The third battalion, however, elected to extend its service and so remained in existence until 1802, when all fencible regiments were disbanded at the Peace of Amiens.

192 & 196 *Officer's dirk and silver shoulder belt plate of the Reay Fencibles, 1794-1802*

By this period, the highland dirk had virtually lost its practical function as a weapon and had become another element in the elaborate military costume of the highland officer. This dirk is silver mounted, as are the miniature knife and fork carried in the sheath. These recall the dirk's origins and dual function as a piece of hunting equipment as well as an offensive weapon.

The Reay Fencibles were raised in 1794 in the far north-west corner of Scotland, largely under the auspices of Clan Mackay. As it was one of the 'second generation' of fencible regiments raised in the 1790s, it was liable for service in Ireland. In November 1794, the regiment became part of the garrison of Belfast, where it remained until May 1798, when it was moved south to Cavan so as to be able to reinforce Dublin in case of rebellion.

When rebellion broke out on 23 May, the regiment was en route for Dublin. On the 26th, they took a major part in the defeat of a rebel force which had gathered on the Hill of Tara. After this, the Reays continued on to Dublin, where they stayed until they joined General Needham's brigade for the attack on the rebel forces in Wexford. Although not present at Vinegar Hill, the regiment was part of the force involved in the rounding-up of the defeated rebels.

In August, the Reay Fencibles took part in the operations against the French and were present at their surrender at Ballinamuck. Throughout their service in Ireland, the Reays appear to have maintained a high reputation for discipline - a

rare quality in the army at the time which was appreciated both by senior commanders and the local population.

Like all regiments which recruited from the highlands, the majority of the men had Scottish Gaelic as their first language. It is said that several soldiers of the Reay Fencibles first learnt English whilst they were in Ireland and when they spoke it afterwards it was always with an Irish accent.

192

193 *Other rank's shoulder belt plate of the Rothesay and Caithness Fencibles 1794-1802*

This regiment, which was composed of two battalions, was raised by Sir John Sinclair of Ulbster, a remarkable man of many and varied achievements. As well as being a large landowner and an active Member of Parliament, he is best remembered as the creator of *The Statistical Account of Scotland*, a twenty-one volume economic survey of Scotland.

The second battalion of the regiment, often referred to simply as the Caithness Highlanders, served in Ireland from 1795 onwards. Like many of the other highland regiments which served in Ireland, the Caithness Fencibles had a high reputation for discipline and good behaviour. An officer of the regiment wrote in 1798, 'The Lord Lieutenant (Lord Cornwallis) told me he admired the appearance of the men, and that what he liked better, he heard the best report of their good behaviour on every occasion, and from every general under whom they served'.

The title 'Flodden Field', borne on the belt-plate, is perhaps characteristic of Sir John Sinclair - a man with his own very keen sense of history. It commemorates the last time the men of his county, Caithness, had been mustered for national defence - the Battle of Flodden in 1513. The fact that this battle was against the English and resulted in a crushing defeat for the Scots did not, in his view, make it any less worthy of commemoration.

193

194 *Other rank's shoulder belt plate of the Dumbarton Fencibles, 1794-1802 (on loan from Royal Irish Academy)*

As the handwritten label records, this belt plate was taken from an Irish rebel killed at the Battle of Vinegar Hill. As this plate was worn on the front of a shoulder belt that crossed the upper body of the wearer, the projectile which penetrated the plate would have almost certainly caused a fatal chest wound. Given the thickness of the brass plate, it is doubtful that a lead musket ball could have penetrated it, even if fired at close range. Therefore, the hole may have been made by a piece of round iron shot fired from a cannon. Small balls of this diameter could be fired either as 'grape shot' - i.e. loaded together in a cloth bag which burst as it emerged either from the cannon's muzzle so scattering the shot, or as 'canister shot' - loaded in a tin case and fired to similar effect.

In early June 1798, the Dumbarton Fencibles had been involved in actions around Gorey and Arklow, so it is likely that the belt and its plate were captured by the rebels then, probably from the body of a wounded or dead fencible soldier.

195 *Officer's gorget of the Dumbarton Fencibles, 1794*

Made in London and hallmarked for 1794, this gorget is the work of Francis Thurkle, a metalworker who principally produced sword hilts. The gorget was worn at the throat, suspended from two ribbons attached to buttons on the collar of the officer's coat. The gorget was only worn when an officer was actually on duty and its origins

195

can be traced back to the piece of armour which protected the neck and throat.

The Dumbarton Fencibles were raised in 1794, and served in Ireland from 1797 until 1802. In May 1798, when the rebellion broke out, the regiment was part of the Dublin garrison. It was a detachment of eight Dumbarton Fencibles that accompanied the officers who arrested Lord Edward Fitzgerald.

Like many regiments attempting to recruit in the highlands in the 1790s, the Dumbarton Fencibles encountered serious difficulties in attracting sufficient men. At one point in 1795, the principal tenants of the estate of the regiment's lieutenant-colonel, Murdoch Maclaine of Lochbuie on Mull, refused to co-operate in the raising of recruits. Things were so bad that the regiment's colonel, Colin Campbell of Stonefield, seriously considered trying to draft around four hundred captured deserters from the Prussian Army into the regiment, if they could be brought to Britain. Not surprisingly, nothing came of this enterprising suggestion. Ironically, in late 1798 a detachment of the Dumbarton Fencibles was sent to Prussia, Britain's ally at the time, as escorts for a group of four hundred Irish rebel prisoners who were being handed over to the Prussians for enforced military service.

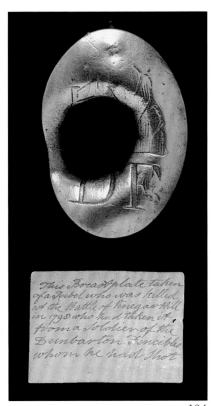

194

197 *Steel 'ramshorn' style pistol of a type popular in the highlands of Scotland in the seventeenth and early eighteenth century*

This example has been engraved with the badge of the 1st Battalion Breadalbane Fencibles and was therefore probably carried by an officer of the regiment. Although such pistols had been carried by earlier highland regiments, by the 1790s they had really become an accessory to a parade uniform and were therefore rarely carried. This pistol possibly dates from earlier in the eighteenth century and may have been taken back into use, and the badge added, when this battalion was raised in the highlands in 1793. Although the first battalion did not actually serve in Ireland, it sent a considerable number of men to the Third Battalion which was there between 1795 and 1802.

198 *All-metal pistol carried by an officer of the Rothesay and Caithness Fencibles, c.1795*

Similar in design to the pistol carried by an officer of 1st Bn Breadalbane Fencibles, this weapon is, however, of a much higher quality. It was made by the Edinburgh gunsmiths Innes and Wallace. Inlaid in silver on the grip is the crest of the Prince of Wales, a personal friend of the regiment's colonel, Sir John Sinclair of Ulbster. As a special distinction, Sir John was allowed to include the title 'Rothesay', the principal town of the Island of Bute, in the regiment's name, even though it did not recruit in that part of Scotland.

199 *Officer's jacket of the Perthshire Fencible Light Dragoons c.1798*

Although this particular regiment did not actually serve in Ireland, this style of uniform was very similar to that worn by those fencible cavalry regiments and yeomanry units which did. The design of the elaborate metal scale shoulder pieces is of Indian origin and was originally intended to protect the wearer from downward sword cuts.

Unlike most fencible regiments, the Perthshire Fencible Light Dragoons were not raised by a single well-placed individual. Instead, the major landowners of the county each subscribed a certain amount of money which was used to pay the enlistment bounties of the recruits. However, it is likely that the Duke of Atholl, as the county's lord lieutenant, would have had a large say in the selection of the officers. This jacket belonged to Cornet James Stirling of Garden, who joined the regiment in 1798.

The deployment in Ireland of mounted units similar to this regiment was a decisive factor in the open fighting of the 1798 Rebellion. The rebels' total deficiency of cavalry gave the government forces a distinct advantage. This imbalance was especially important as the inadequacies in training and reliability of much of the government's infantry were such that the normal tactical superiority of a constituted army over an insurgent force was seriously weakened.

200 *Proclamation of loyalty drawn up by the NCOs and men of the Elgin Fencibles, Cork, June 1797*

In Ireland, the activities of the United Irishmen and the Defenders were seen as a serious threat to the loyalty of the government's forces. The locally recruited Irish Militia, in particular, was widely believed to have been infiltrated and its loyalty therefore compromised. The fencibles were seen as less of a risk, but were not immune. One means the government hit upon to help secure their loyalty was simply to increase their pay. On 16 June 1797 a General Order was issued from Dublin to the effect that the daily pay of all troops in Ireland - regulars, militia and fencibles - was to be brought up to the higher rate paid in mainland Britain. Prior to the Union of 1800, the Dublin government had overall control of the pay and administration of military units stationed in Ireland.

Such public proclamations of loyalty were common in fencible regiments. On the 18th of June, the men of the Midlothian Fencible Cavalry produced a similar, if rather more aggressively worded, document. It warns of the results if any of the 'infamous and dastardly scoundrels who call themselves United Irishmen ... presume to tamper with us, or in our presence to use expressions prejudicial to our most Gracious King and our Constitution, that before we deliver them into the hands of justice we will make such an example of their person, as to convince them that the Midlothian Regiment did not come to this country to be trifled with'.

201 & 202 *Soldier's knapsack and cartridge pouch of the 97th (Inverness-shire) Regiment of Foot, c. 1795*

The 97th was an infantry regiment of the regular army raised in 1794 by Sir James Grant of Grant, a major landowner and political figure in the north-east of Scotland. In 1793, he had also raised one of the first fencible regiments of the war, the Strathspey Fencibles.

The basic items of equipment are similar to those which would have been carried by fencible troops in Ireland in the 1790s. The knapsack is made of painted canvas and was carried on the soldier's back. This design was gradually replacing a slightly more expensive goatskin pattern which was still carried by some units in Ireland. The knapsack was used to carry the soldier's spare shoes and clothing, together with his washing and cleaning kit. During this period, soldiers had to contribute to the cost of much of their clothing and equipment. These articles were termed 'necessaries'. A new knapsack of the correct pattern would cost a soldier around one shilling and it was expected that it would last for six years. In 1794, the actual cost of a canvas knapsack was seven shillings and threepence.

The leather ammunition or cartridge pouch was supplied to the soldier at the expense of the government and was one of the few items of equipment that was actually produced to a universal design. It was carried over the left shoulder and was designed to hold thirty-two cartridges - paper tubes containing a measure of gunpowder and a lead musket ball. These were made up within the regiment by the 'ackward (sic) men as do not make a good appearance in the field'.

On occasions when contact with the enemy was expected, extra ammunition would be issued to the men. In June 1798, each man of the Reay Fencibles, then in Dublin, was ordered to be issued with two extra 'magazine' pouches, each holding thirty cartridges. These were carried on the waistbelt which supported the purse or sporran. Apart from increasing the weight of the soldier's kit to between 50 and 60 lb, the risk of accidental injury through carrying so much ammunition was very serious.

201

203 *Grenadier's fur cap of the 97th (Inverness-shire) Regiment of Foot, c.1795*

An infantry regiment in the 1790s was organised into one or more battalions. Each battalion was divided into ten companies, of which two were designated as 'flank' companies. One of these was specially trained and equipped as a light infantry unit. The other was termed the Grenadier Company and was regarded as the senior company of the battalion. The term 'grenadier' is derived from the earlier practice of certain soldiers being specially trained in the handling of grenades for deployment as assault troops. This élite status led to the adoption of certain distinctive items of dress and equipment, many of which continued in use long past the point when the grenade had lost its tactical importance. The tall 'mitre'-shaped cap, either of embroidered cloth or of fur, was one such item. Being awkward to wear and expensive to replace, these caps were generally only worn on more formal occasions such as reviews and inspections.

The frontlet plate of the cap bears the Royal Crest with a motto associated with the House of Hanover which translates as 'Difficulties do not dismay us'.

204

205

204 *United Irishmen in Training*

By J[ame]s G[illra]y
Coloured aquatint, 18 x 25.4 cm, published in London 13 June 1798 by H. Humphrey
National Army Museum, London

205 *United Irishmen upon Duty*

By J[ame]s G[illra]y
Coloured aquatint, 18 x 25.4 cm, published in London 12 June 1798 by H. Humphrey
National Army Museum, London

These two companion pieces characterise events in Ireland in the summer of 1798 with a typical mixture of horror and derision. The military preparations of the rebels are shown as absurdly incompetent and shambolic, their actions in the field as entirely motivated by malice and plunder in the style of the French Revolution. Though the Rebellion did indeed in some places lead to plundering and worse, on the whole it appears to have been government forces - notably the militia and the yeomanry - that were chiefly responsible for the enormous loss of life and property among the civilian population in those parts of the country where fighting took place (or where disarming of suspected rebels was carried out).

206-216 *Illustrations by George Cruikshank*

George Cruikshank (1792-1878) was one of the best-known caricaturists in nineteenth-century England. His frequently-reproduced etchings of 1798 were first published during the 1840s, although they are often misdated as contemporaneous with the rebellion. Favourably reviewed when first published, these striking, if lurid, images of conflict continue to fascinate.

As in other contemporary images of the Irish in satirical journals such as *Punch* (established in 1841), Cruikshank's rebels had prognathous features, i.e. with projecting ape-like jaws. Such pictures of the Irish only became widespread during

207

208

213

209

212

this decade. Thomas Wright has, however, noted its origins during 1798 itself, when the rebels portrayed in James Gillray's caricatures had 'large, grizzled jaws, bulging eyes, and wide margin between snub nose and thick upper lip.'

Cruikshank's father, Isaac, and his brother, Robert, were also satirical artists. His father's caricatures on the French Revolution and the Act of Union influenced his son's attitude towards Ireland.

The England of Cruikshank's youth was dominated by fears of French invasion. The admiration he retained from childhood for parading militia, drummers and fifers was later drawn upon for his engravings of the 1798 Rebellion. His father was a member of the Bloomsbury Volunteers and Cruikshank himself briefly served

214

213

214

in the Loyal North Britons. He once commented that his response to being drawn for the Militia was to draw the Militia.

After 1825, he worked mostly as a book illustrator. Some of his most successful work, including the illustrations for an 1838 edition of Charles Dickens's *Oliver Twist*, first appeared in part works published by *Bentley's Miscellany* and other pictorial periodicals.

Cruikshank's most popular Irish caricatures illustrated the text of William Hamilton Maxwell's *History of the Irish Rebellion in 1798*. A Newry-born novelist and army officer who had served at Waterloo before taking holy orders, Maxwell was the same age as Cruikshank. His account of the rebellion was written as a corrective to R.R. Madden's *Lives of the United Irishmen* (1842). Maxwell's history

215

was serialised in twelve parts by the London publisher, A.H. Baily & Co., during 1844. The first part appeared in January 1844. The single volume was published in 1845.

The most enduring aspect of Maxwell's history (reprinted several times during the nineteenth century) remains the twenty-one etchings by Cruikshank, which chiefly depict the fighting in Leinster. There are no scenes from the northern theatre of the rebellion and only one from Connaught. Fourteen of the etchings are included in this exhibition.

His simian and marauding peasants contrast strongly with the trim and resolute soldiers and civilians under attack. To the prognathous aspect of the rebels as earlier depicted by Gillray, Cruikshank added bloated cheeks and flaring nostrils. His illustrations also stress the leadership of Catholic clergy and the participation of women and children in the rebellion, chiefly as looters, cooks and appreciative witnesses to pikings.

Sources: A.M. Cohn, *George Cruikshank, A Catalogue Raisonné of the Work executed during the years 1806-77* (London, 1924).
L.P. Curtis, *Apes and Angels. The Irish in Victorian Caricature* (Newton Abbot, 1971).
B. Jerrold, *The Life of George Cruikshank In Two Epochs* (London, 1882).
T. Wright, *The Works of James Gillray, the Caricaturist* (London, n.d.).

206 *Surprise of the Barrack of Prosperous*

BY GEORGE CRUIKSHANK, FROM MAXWELL'S REBELLION
ULSTER MUSEUM
REPRODUCTION

In the early hours of 24 May 1798, a rebel force attacked and successfully captured the barracks in the small Kildare town of Prosperous. The garrison commander, Captain Swayne, a much-hated figure, was killed. Afterwards his body was burned in a tar barrel. The capture of Prosperous was led by John Esmonde, a local doctor and yeomanry officer, who was later hanged for treason. As the garrison fled the burning building they were piked. It was the rebels' most successful action in a number of clashes with crown forces in the South Dublin and Kildare region.

216

207 *The Loyal Little Drummer*

BY GEORGE CRUIKSHANK, FROM MAXWELL'S *REBELLION*
MRS A. JARDINE

On 4 June 1798, a party of Antrim Militia was successfully ambushed near Gorey. One of those taken prisoner was a drummer boy named Hunter. When taken into Gorey, he was ordered to play for the rebels' entertainment. This scene records his defiant response and subsequent fate. Instead of playing a tune, he stamped upon his drum, crying aloud that 'the King's drum shall not be beaten for the Rebels.' He was instantly piked to death. As with later depictions of British deaths during the Indian Mutiny of 1857, Cruikshank's interpretation of this confrontation stressed its David and Goliath-like scale. Its pathos exerted a powerful appeal on the Victorian imagination.

208 *Carousal and Plunder at the Palace of the Bishop of Ferns*

BY GEORGE CRUIKSHANK, FROM MAXWELL'S *REBELLION*
MRS A. JARDINE

This scene of rebels feasting and looting the contents of Dr Eusebius Cleaver's residence in Ferns, County Wexford, is reminiscent of French revolutionaries enjoying the cellars and larders of the aristocracy. In this crowded dining room, toasts are drunk, food is consumed, bagpipes are played, clay pipes are smoked, furniture is wrecked and sacks filled with looted communion plate. Those killed during the rebel occupation of Ferns in late May 1798 included the vicar, parish clerk and sexton.

209 *Destruction of the Church at Enniscorthy*

BY GEORGE CRUIKSHANK, FROM MAXWELL'S *REBELLION*
MRS A. JARDINE

Following a street battle on 28 May 1798, the garrison at Enniscorthy retreated to Wexford. In the looting of the town that followed, the interior of the Church of Ireland was destroyed. Cruikshank records the removal of its pulpit, pews, bell and Bible. One folk memory of the plundering of Enniscorthy parish church was that the sexton was forced to put the Bible on a donkey cart and transport it to Vinegar Hill, where it was burnt. As with other Cruikshank scenes, rebel flags are prominently flown.

210 *The Camp on Vinegar Hill*

BY GEORGE CRUIKSHANK, FROM MAXWELL'S *REBELLION*
ULSTER MUSEUM
REPRODUCTION

This scene of the rebel encampment on Vinegar Hill, near Wexford Town, shows a remarkably well equipped and provisioned, if chaotically organised, force on the eve of General Lake's attack on 21 June 1798.

Some of the trophies captured in earlier incidents now decorate the camp, including the bell from Enniscorthy church. As prisoners are executed, Masses are said, crucifixes and crosses paraded through the camp, flags flying, tents struck, music played and meals are prepared.

217

211 *Battle of Ross. 'Come on Boys her mouth's stapt'*

BY GEORGE CRUIKSHANK, FROM MAXWELL'S *REBELLION*
ULSTER MUSEUM
REPRODUCTION

This incident occurred during the closely-fought battle of New Ross in County-Wexford on 5 June 1798. Maxwell's own text provides a colourful and patronising account: 'one rebel, emboldened by fanaticism and drunkenness, advanced before his comrades, seized a gun, crammed his hat and wig into it, and cried out "Come on, boys! her mouth is stopped". At that instant the gunner laid the match to the gun, and blew the unfortunate savage to atoms.'

212 *Massacre at Scullabogue*

BY GEORGE CRUIKSHANK, FROM MAXWELL'S *REBELLION*
MRS A. JARDINE

When separately exhibited by Cruikshank, this etching was captioned *Irish Rebellion - Burning the Barn Full of People*. It graphically depicts one of the most infamous episodes of the rebellion in Wexford. On 5 June 1798, more than one hundred Protestant civilian prisoners, and a few Catholics associated with them, were burnt alive in a barn attached to Captain King's house at Scullabogue near Carrickbyrne. As with earlier folk memory of the drownings of Protestants in the River Bann in 1641, Scullabogue retained a strong emotive significance for loyalists throughout the nineteenth and twentieth centuries.

213 *The Defeat Of the Rebels At Vinegar Hill*

BY GEORGE CRUIKSHANK, FROM MAXWELL'S *REBELLION*
MRS A. JARDINE

On 21 June 1798, General Lake's army captured Vinegar Hill near Enniscorthy, defeating a force of some 20,000 rebels led by Father Philip Roche. Several hundred rebels were killed during two hours of combat. In depicting this closely-fought battle, Cruikshank contrasts the chaotic and congested deployment of the rebels with the orderly advance of the crown troops. In fact, the failure to close the ring of troops around Vinegar Hill enabled a large force of rebels to retreat into Wicklow. This is the only Cruikshank print that includes the flags carried by the crown forces.

214 *The Rebels executing their Prisoners on the Bridge at Wexford*

BY GEORGE CRUIKSHANK, FROM MAXWELL'S *REBELLION*
MRS A. JARDINE

On 20 June 1798, some ninety civilian prisoners were executed on Wexford Bridge. As with Scullabogue, the memory of this massacre reinforced loyalist fears throughout the next century about their likely treatment under a nationalist state. One victim is being ceremoniously (if acrobatically) piked aloft as exultant women dance and cheer. Loyalist testimonies made after the rebellion claimed that the initials MWS on the flag stood for 'Murder Without Sin', the status allegedly ascribed by Catholic clergy to the killing of Protestants.

215 *Father Murphy and the heretic bullets*

By George Cruikshank, from Maxwell's *Rebellion*
Mrs A. Jardine

Most loyalist narratives and visual depictions of the rebellion stressed the central role of Catholic clergy. This scene shows Fr John Murphy of Boolavogue rallying his forces at Arklow on 9 June 1798. Fr Murphy in fact arrived late in the day, just in time to lead the last charge, in which he was killed. The flag shown is the one associated with him.

216 *The Capture of Colclough and Harvey*

By George Cruikshank, from Maxwell's *Rebellion*
Ulster Museum
Reproduction

Disillusioned by the defeat at New Ross and by the massacre at Scullabogue, one of the principal Wexford leaders of the rebellion, Bagenal Harvey, resigned his command. Accompanied by another prominent rebel, John Henry Colclough, and by Colclough's wife, he fled to the Saltee Islands off the Wexford coast. This print shows their arrest in June 1798. Colclough and Harvey were afterwards hanged on Wexford Bridge.

217 *A Map of New Ross and A Map of part of the Country round Ross, to illustrate the battle of New Ross, 5 June 1798.*

From Musgrave's *Rebellions*, vol. 1
Ulster Museum
Reproduction

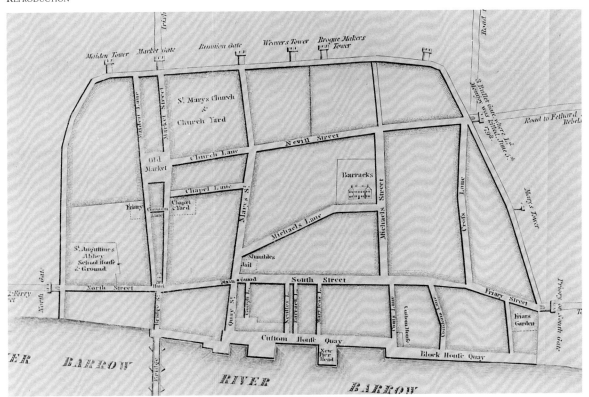

218 *Major-General Henry Johnson*

Mezzotint by Robert Dunbarton after Robert Woodburn, 50.7 x 35.1 cm
National Gallery of Ireland, Dublin

Henry Johnson was born in Dublin in 1748 and entered the army in 1761 as a career officer. During the American War of Independence he commanded a battalion of light infantry, was severely wounded in the fighting and in 1770, when lieutenant-colonel of the 17th Regiment, was surrounded and captured with all his men at Stoney Point. In 1782 he married an American wife and became a full colonel nevertheless, returning to England at the end of the war. When war with France broke out in 1793 he was promoted major-general and spent the next five years organising the recruitment of Irish soldiers to British regiments.

In 1798, recalled to active service, Johnson found himself in command of the garrison of New Ross, County Wexford, when the town was attacked in overwhelming force by the victorious rebel army under the (nominal) command of Bagenal Harvey. At a total of 2,678 men, including local yeomanry, his was the largest garrison in Ireland outside Dublin and Belfast, but the attacking force was twenty times larger and the fortifications of New Ross were in a ruinous state. The garrison had artillery, however, and trained gunners and both Johnson and his aide Colonel Craufurd (later famous for his exploits in the Peninsular War) believed that disciplined troops, well-led and supported by artillery, would defeat any number of irregulars. If New Ross fell, the rebellion was likely to spread throughout the south of Ireland. Failure to take it was to confine the Wexford rebels to Wexford.

The battle of New Ross is famous for the reckless bravery of the rebels, who actually drove most of their opponents out of the town and across the bridge into County Kilkenny. Lack of military knowledge and leadership prevented them from taking advantage of their success, however, and permitted the fleeing garrison to regroup and win the day. Johnson himself behaved with conspicuous courage; he had three horses shot under him. The rebel casualties were very heavy - at least

2,500 killed in the fierce fighting in the narrow streets - while 91 of the garrison were killed and total casualties numbered about 230. When the fighting was over, the victorious troops ran amok and sacked the town, making no distinction between the property (or persons) of friend and foe.

Cornwallis's verdict at the time was this : 'Johnson, although a wrong-headed blockhead, is adored for his defence of New Ross, and considered as the saviour of the south'. Johnson was given a baronetcy in 1818 and died in 1837.

Sources: *DNB.*
A. Webb, *Compendium of Irish Biography.*
T. Pakenham, *The Year of Liberty* (London, 1969).

219 *Plan of the Town of Arklow with part of the circumjacent Country to illustrate the account of the Attack on the Rebels on that Town June 9th 1798.*

FROM MUSGRAVE'S *REBELLIONS*, VOL. 1
ULSTER MUSEUM
REPRODUCTION

220 *'The Battle of Arklow', 1798*

FROM A DRAWING BY CAPTAIN HOLMES, LOYAL DURHAM FENCIBLES
COLOURED ENGRAVING, 15 X 30 CM
NATIONAL ARMY MUSEUM, LONDON

This hand-coloured version of the frontispiece to Jones's *Narrative* shows the town of Arklow, County Wicklow as seen from the north bank of the River Avoca with the bridge and Dublin road in the foreground to left; beyond (to left), the Fishery; the barrack, ravine and Coolgreany (Gorey) road to right; the Yellow Lane on the skyline (centre); and Arklow Rock and the Little Rock in the distance to left. The battle of Arklow, one of the most important engagements of the Wexford rising and of the whole rebellion, was fought on 9 June 1798.

Following the defeat of Colonel Walpole's force at Tubberneering and the death of its commander, the demoralised gove rnment forces retreated northwards into Wicklow. The only troops left on the road between Wexford and Dublin itself were a small force of Antrim Militia in the town of Wicklow, and, at Arklow, fewer than eighty men of the same regiment. Fleeing through Gorey, one group of fugitives from Tubberneering, under the command of Sir Watkin Williams Wynne of the Ancient Britons, paused at Arklow only to requisition some carts for the footsore and to add the garrison to his strength before pushing on to Wicklow, leaving the town defenceless.

When this alarming news reached Dublin, General Lake at once took steps to get together what troops could be spared from the capital itself and appointed General Francis Needham - an old soldier who had seen service in America - to command them. Needham reached Wicklow on the evening of 5 June, bringing with him 360 men of the Cavan Militia and a party of the Reay Fencibles, who were rushed to the front in commandeered carriages. With the troops already there he had a force of something over 1,000. With these he entered Arklow the following day. Fifty dragoons arrived on 7 June, to be followed two days later by 300 Loyal Durham Fencibles (one of whom was Captain Holmes, the author of this sketch) and 128 Dumbarton Fencibles, who arrived in carriages and jaunting cars just in time to face the enemy. By the time the battle was fought, Needham had an army of about 1,500, of which 460 were cavalry. Fortunately for the government, the rebels had delayed advancing long enough to give Needham a chance to check their progress.

When they reached Arklow, their huge numbers - more than 20,000, it is estimated - were a formidable sight to the defenders. Only a tenth of them had firearms, however, and 3,000 or so had pikes. The rest had whatever weapons they could lay hands on or improvise; many must have been camp followers rather than combatants. There appears to have been no proper chain of command in the rebel host. Most prominent among its leaders were Anthony Perry of Inch, a former yeoman who had been tortured by the North Cork Militia until he revealed the names of the leading United Irishmen; Billy Byrne of Ballymanus, County Wicklow; Esmond Kyan, a former artilleryman; Edward Fitzgerald of Newpark and, very late in the day, Father Michael Murphy of Ballycanew. On the other hand the rebels not only had overwhelming numbers but also two or three pieces of artillery, with a good supply of ammunition and some trained gunners; and Arklow was not a good defensive position.

Advancing in two main columns, the insurgents approached from the Gorey road and the road from the Rocks. By six o'clock in the evening the whole area from the south bank of the river above the town to its mouth beyond the Fishery was occupied by a crescent-shaped line of attackers. An eye-witness on the government side saw 'in a moment thousands appear on the tops of ditches, forming one great and regular circular line from the Gorey road through the fields round to the sand banks next the sea, as thick as they could stand'. They all 'put their hats on their pikes, and gave most dreadful yells'. Needham, his back to the river, had to hold his line and the narrow bridge that was his only line of retreat or be overwhelmed. Successive rushes failed to break the line, though Needham was to admit, in a part of his report that was not published, that 'the perseverance of the enemy was surprising' and 'their efforts to possess themselves of the guns on my right were most daring, advancing even to the muzzles, where they fell in great numbers'. There was also fierce fighting at the Fishery, but here too artillery and musket fire proved too much for the attackers. Their own guns at one point seemed to be getting the better of the artillery duel, until Kyan was seriously wounded and had to be carried away. Unable to get their pikemen to close quarters, and running out of ammunition just before their opponents did so, the rebel gunners and musketeers began to draw back after eight o'clock. Father Murphy, arriving late, was killed leading a final charge. According to reports, his body was subjected to indignities by the Ancient Britons. Needham, expecting the attack to be renewed next day, made no attempt to pursue and kept his troops on the alert, but in the event that was the end of the fighting.

Considering the numbers engaged and the severity of the contest, the casualties were surprisingly light. Officially, Needham lost only eighteen killed and twenty-eight wounded; in reality, perhaps seventy-five in all. Perhaps 500 of the 5,000 rebels engaged were casualties. Like New Ross, Arklow was a crucial victory for the government, confining the Wexford revolt - the most serious outbreak of the whole rebellion - largely to the county itself.

Sources: 'Arklow, 1798', in G.A. Hayes-McCoy, *Irish Battles* (1969).

221 *Battle of Vinegar Hill, June 21st 1798*

COLOURED DRAWING BY LIEUT. CAREY, 17TH LT. DRAGOONS; ENGRAVED BY H. BROCAS, DUBLIN.
PUBLISHED BY W. ALLEN, 32 DAME ST.
NATIONAL ARMY MUSEUM, LONDON

222 *Queen's Own Royal Dublin Militia Going into Action at Vinegar Hill the light company Advancing and Firing covering the Road*

'Original Pen Sketch by Sadler, 1879'
National Library of Ireland, Dublin
Reproduction

A pencilled note below the title reads: 'Mr Sadler's Uncle and Mr Read were Lieutenants in this action. Mr Sadler was shot in the groin in a duel by Lieut. Noble'.

223 *Lord Lake*

Line engraving, 24.6 x 14.1 cm
Published in *The Military Chronicle*, 1812
Ulster Museum

224 *A Plan of the Town of Wexford, 1800*

By Peter Fannin, 'Master in the Navy'
From Musgrave's *Rebellions*, vol. 1
Ulster Museum
Reproduction

225 *General Sir John Moore (1761-1809)*

By Sir Thomas Lawrence
Oil on canvas, 75 x 68 cm
National Portrait Gallery, London

John Moore was the son of a Scottish physician and man of letters. He entered the Army as a career officer in 1776, serving first in the American war. By 1790 he had reached the rank of lieutenant-colonel. After service in Corsica against the French he was sent to the West Indies in 1796, where he saw action under Sir Ralph Abercromby. When Abercromby was appointed commander-in-chief in Ireland he asked for Moore, who was at that time convalescing in England from an attack of yellow fever; they arrived in Dublin together at the start of December 1797. In January 1798 Moore was made a major-general and appointed colonel of the 9th West India regiment. His command in Ireland consisted of a mixed force of regulars and militia, based at Bandon, County Cork. From there he was first engaged in disarming the United Irishmen in south Cork before the rebellion broke out, later assisting in its suppression in Wexford. When ordered to disarm the people of South Cork he decided, as he puts it in his diary, 'to excite terror, and by that means obtain an end speedily. I thought this better than to act mildly, and be obliged to continue for any time the real oppression, and as I was present everywhere myself I has no doubt of being able to prevent any great abuse by the troops'. A humane man and a good soldier himself, Moore was appalled by the unnecessarily brutal approach of some of his fellow officers and the indiscipline of their troops. As for the Protestant gentry of the area, he said he had only met two 'who acted with liberality or manliness'; the rest seemed 'actuated by the meanest motives'. While the disarming campaign brought results - in three weeks 800 pikes and 3,400 guns were handed in - Moore thought the pike would soon appear again if the gentry did not change their ways.

In the later stages of the rebellion in the south-east, Moore advanced from Cork into Wexford with a force consisting mainly of raw militia. Approaching Wexford town, he was faced at Foulksmills with one of the main rebel armies (Roche's), much superior in numbers though less well armed. In a sharp engagement, in which he had to rally his wavering troops twice, he held the field, losing 55 men killed or wounded. Twice Moore headed the charge, first on foot, then on horseback. Of the second occasion he wrote: 'I took off my hat, put my horse into a trot, gave a huzza and got them to make a push. The tide immediately turned; we drove the rebels before us, and killed a great many'. Lake had instructed Moore to halt well short of Wexford but, realising the danger of a massacre of loyalist prisoners, he decided to take the risk of advancing at once and entered the town on 21 June. He was just in time to save most of the prisoners, but too late for those killed on the bridge. His work that day, he reflected, had been 'one of the most pleasing services that could fall to the lot of an officer'. Lake arrived the next day, following his victory at Vinegar Hill. In the aftermath of the rebellion, Moore was again notable for his humane treatment of the defeated rebels, to the disgust of the vengeful loyalists even allowing deserters from the yeomanry to take advantage of a general amnesty. He was reported to have received repentant insurgents with 'plenty of food, pipers and whiskey punch'.

Moore's subsequent military career - in Holland, Egypt, Portugal and Spain - was a distinguished one, in the course of which he was dangerously wounded several times. His outstanding achievements were the new system of infantry drill and manoeuvre he introduced, and the historic midwinter retreat to Corunna which saved his army in Spain and led to his own death and elevation to the status of national hero. Despite some criticism of his achievements, he was an intelligent and humane professional soldier, which distinguished him from most of his fellow generals. Napoleon, whom he had thwarted in Spain, said of him: 'His talents and firmness alone saved the British army from destruction; he was a brave soldier, an excellent officer, and a man of talent'.

The artist who painted this portrait of Moore, Thomas Lawrence (1769-1830), was a child prodigy who by the age of ten was supporting his family by drawing portraits of fashionable people at Bath. In 1787 he entered the schools of the Royal Academy for formal training. With the patronage of the court his career thrived: in 1792 he painted George III and was appointed by the King as principal portrait painter. He became an RA two years later. Knighted in 1815, he was sent to the Congress of Aix-la-Chapelle in that year to paint the assembled sovereigns of Europe. President of the Royal Academy in 1820, his portraits were distinguished by their elegance. When he died in 1830 he was buried in St Paul's Cathedral.

Sources: *DNB.*
                Thomas Pakenham, *The Year of Liberty.*

226 *'Battle of Wexford Fought 20th June 1798'.*

ENGRAVING PUBLISHED IN LONDON, AUGUST 1798, BY G. THOMPSON.
NATIONAL ARMY MUSEUM, LONDON
REPRODUCTION

There was no Battle of Wexford fought on 20 June, 1798; the reference is presumably to the engagement at Foulksmills between royal troops under Moore and Roche's United Irishmen. Nor was the Battle of Vinegar Hill fought on 21 July 1798. In fact, although this image was printed in August 1798, only two months after the rebellion in County Wexford had petered out, it would appear to be a cock-eyed representation in the one print of a number of scenes from the final days of the insurrection there. There are also grounds for believing that the scene is basically composed of battle scenes sketched at the time of the American War of Independence.

In fact, the print represents the combined stories of three separate engagements in quite different locations - Wexford town, Enniscorthy and Vinegar Hill.

226

Portrait of an Irish Chief; drawn from Life at Wexford.

Most curious of all, perhaps, is the reference (at 'Q') to 'The Lovely and accomplished Miss Redmond, a Leader of the Rebels, on her Hunter, she is ever fighting where the battle is most violent'. 'Miss Redmond', whoever she was, does not feature in any of the many accounts of the tempestuous events in County Wexford during the months of May and June 1798, though her surname is a Wexford one.

227 *Portrait of an Irish Chief; drawn from life at Wexford*

BY [GILLRAY]
AQUATINT, 32.7 x 22.6 CM (36.2 x 25.3 WITH BORDER), PUBLISHED IN LONDON 10 JULY 1798
BY H. HUMPHREY
BRITISH MUSEUM, LONDON

An Irishman, with coarse features and the cropped hair of a rebel, is shown standing on a rounded hill with arm raised, in the style of an orator, saying *No Union, Erin go Brach!* He wears a round hat tilted to one side, with a tuft or plume, a double-breasted coat with looped-up skirts, pantaloons and half-boots, and a long sabre. In the plain below are tiny fugitives, burning buildings and clouds of smoke.

Though the portrait bears little or no resemblance to the Irish orator Henry Grattan, it is supposed to be he, in typical oratorial pose. Grattan was accused of being a member of the United Irishmen and was dismissed from the Irish privy council in October 1798. He certainly played no part in the rebellion - he spent the summer in England - but the statement of James Hope that he had indeed at one stage joined the movement is hard to overlook entirely.

Sources: *BM Catalogue*, VII, no. 9236.

228 *Edward Fitzgerald of New Park, County Wexford (c.1770-1807)*

MEZZOTINT BY W.T. ANNIS AFTER THOMAS NUGENT, 38 x 27.6 CM
NATIONAL GALLERY OF IRELAND, DUBLIN

228

Fitzgerald was one of the leaders of the United Irishmen in Wexford. Coming from a well-to-do Catholic family which had acquired land near Wexford town, he had adopted radical political views and had become one of the 'colonels' of the secret movement in the county. Along with Bagenal Harvey and John Colclough (his brother-in-law) he was arrested and imprisoned in Wexford gaol just before the outbreak of the rebellion. The authorities in Wexford persuaded Fitzgerald and Colclough to go as envoys to the victorious rebels at Enniscorthy to urge them to disperse, whereupon Fitzgerald was detained by the United Irishmen as a suspected traitor to the cause.

After the fall of Wexford he rejoined the rebels and in the latter stages of the rebellion was one of their most active leaders. At Gorey he is said to have saved some prisoners from the fury of the mob. He took part in the attack on Arklow in County Wicklow and in the desperate ten-hour attack on the barracks at Hacketstown, then went north again to try, for the second time, to link up with the United Irishmen in Kildare. By the time they made contact, at the latter's camp in the Bog of Allen, these men were ready to surrender if promised their lives. Fitzgerald threw in his lot with them. Late in July, the camp at Timahoe was surrendered. Fitzgerald, along with William Aylmer and others, was taken by carriage to Dublin Castle to be examined, the first captured leaders to avoid the gallows. After a period of imprisonment he was allowed to go to England in 1799. Rearrested there in March 1800, he was imprisoned again for a short time before being exiled to Hamburg, where he died in 1807.

229 *'Antient Brittons Cut to Pieces near Carnew by the Insurgents 1798'*

BY WILLIAM SADLER (FL. 1868-80), 1868
NATIONAL LIBRARY OF IRELAND, DUBLIN
REPRODUCTION

230 *Merit medal of the Ancient Britons Light Dragoons, 1798*

SILVER, 6.2 X 4.8 CM OVAL
NATIONAL MUSEUM OF WALES, CARDIFF

INSCRIBED ON OBVERSE: *ANCIENT BRITONS LIGHT DRAGOONS*, IN EXERGUE *1798*
INSCRIBED ON REVERSE   *REWARD OF MERIT J.A. SPARKS*

REPRODUCTION

Obverse

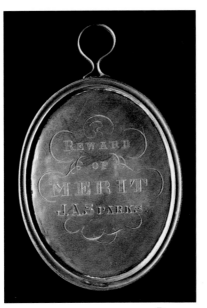

Reverse

The Ancient British Fencible Cavalry, also styled The North Wales Regiment of Fencible Cavalry and, unofficially, The Denbighshire Light Horse, was raised in North Wales in 1794 by Sir Watkin Williams Wynne of Wynnestay, who also commanded it as Colonel. Recruiting took place in Denbighshire, Shropshire and neighbouring counties. From its base at Wrexham the regiment went first to Brighton, thereafter to Aylesbury, Sheffield, Darlington and Carlisle. Early in 1797 it was at Haddington in Scotland, whence it was ordered to go to Ireland. When it landed in Belfast in April, the regiment's strength was 282 men and 192 horses.

In Ireland, the Ancient Britons earned an unenviable reputation for ruthlessness and cruelty, reflected in the nicknames 'Bloody Britons' and 'Sir Watkin's Lambs'. A later writer said of them, 'Like Hessians [German mercenaries], they exceeded other troops in the business of depredation'. They adopted 'Croppies Lie Down' as their regimental song and march. When stationed at Newry they arrested the local radicals and when they discovered pikes and treasonable papers under the floorboards of the group's secretary paraded the man through the town with pike-heads tied around his neck; a number of other suspects wisely fled. Early in May 1797, the *Hereford Journal* reported an encounter between the Britons and 800 local Defenders 'which terminated in the total defeat of the "Defenders" - a great many of them being killed and a considerable number taken prisoner'. In July, a detachment of the regiment dispersed an unlawful assembly at Rathfriland. But it was in the south of Ireland in 1798 that the Ancient Britons really made their name and earned their nicknames - first in County Kildare, then in Wicklow and Wexford. The only major action in which substantial numbers of the regiment took part was the battle of Arklow. Later, along with some 5th Dragoons, the Britons were caught in an ambush by retreating rebels at Ballyellis and badly mauled: between them the two detachments lost nearly forty officers and men before breaking through the pikemen to escape. This is the scene that Sadler recreated many years later, in a watercolour that makes up in visual vigour what it lacks in historical accuracy (the headgear of the soldiers, for example, was Tarleton helmets rather than bicorne hats); Sadler's uncle, incidentally, who was in the Dublin Militia, was wounded at the battle of Vinegar Hill.

The Ancient Britons left Ireland in November 1799 and were disbanded the following year. Their colonel subsequently defended their conduct in Ireland, in particular denying reports of an horrific incident after the battle of Arklow. In a letter to the editor of the *Salopian Journal* he wrote:

> Having lately read a publication entitled 'A History of the Rebellion in Ireland in the year 1798', etc., by the Reverend J. Gordon which contains among other misinterpretations and in-accuracies the following paragraph in p.212, viz:
>> 'Some Soldiers of the Ancient British Regiment cut open the body of Father Michael Murphy after the Battle of Arklow, took out his heart and roasted the body and oiled their boots with the grease that dripped from it'
> I feel that I should be wanting in gratitude to those brave men whom I once had the honour to command and with whom I personally served during the Battle of Arklow above mentioned, did I not take the earliest opportunity of

231 OBV.

231 REV.

declaring that no soldier of the Ancient British Fencible Cavalry ever touched any part of the remains of Father Michael Murphy, consequently the whole of the above anecdote is a gross calumny, totally destitute of any foundation.

Hardly anything in the way of historical relics of the Ancient British Cavalry survives. Flags, uniforms and weapons which had been deposited at Wynnestay when the regiment was disbanded were all destroyed in a great fire in 1858. A possible exception is this Merit Medal in the National Museum of Wales, which, however, puzzlingly calls the regiment the 'Ancient Britons Light Dragoons' and rather too prominently displays the date 1798.

Sources: B. Owen, 'The Ancient British Fencible Cavalry', in *Bulletin of the Military Historical Society*, Nov. 1981 issue.

231 *Silver medal awarded to soldiers of the Antrim Militia for their defence of Hacketstown, County Carlow in 1798.*

INSCRIBED ON OBVERSE: PROTECTORS OF HACKETSTOWN / MAY 25 1798
AND ON REVERSE: SUPPRESSORS OF REBELLION / KING & COUNTRY

ULSTER MUSEUM

There were two engagements at Hacketstown during the Rebellion. The first, on 25 May, was a skirmish in which the rebels were driven off with considerable loss - about 300, according to the report of the local rector, the Rev. James McGhee. The second took place exactly a month later, on 25 June, when the garrison was besieged for ten hours in the barracks before the attackers retreated.

232 *Michael Dwyer, United Irishman*

MEZZOTINT, BY JAMES PETRIE, 21.5 x 12.6 CM
NATIONAL GALLERY OF IRELAND, DUBLIN

Michael Dwyer, the son of a farmer in Glen Imaal, County Wicklow became one of the folk-heroes of the 1798 rebellion. This was not so much because he figured prominently in the main events of the rising in the south-east - though he probably took part in the battle of Arklow and he certainly fought at Hacketstown (25 June) and Ballyellis (30 June) - as because of his exploits afterwards in the Wicklow Mountains. The humane and sensible policy of the new lord lieutenant, Cornwallis, was to encourage the rank and file rebels to return to their homes and surrender under official 'protections'. At the local level, however, the enraged yeomanry sometimes ignored the protections and took summary revenge on their defeated, and now defenceless, enemies. Nowhere was this more so than in Wicklow. Dwyer, who knew he was a marked man, took to the hills with a small band of followers and for five years evaded all the attempts of the authorities to capture him, hoping that the French would come again as they had in 1798.

In 1803 Robert Emmet made contact with Dwyer through James Hope, the northern United Irishman. Hope provided Dwyer and his three closest companions (Byrne, Mernagh and Burke) with new blunderbusses and pistols. In preparations for the planned rising in Dublin, they were also provided with officers' uniforms - that of a colonel (green with large epaulettes) for Dwyer, captains' uniforms for the others. Dwyer was sceptical about Emmet's strategy and the likelihood of success, and was prepared to join the rising only if the rebel flag could be seen flying above Dublin Castle. 'He was resolved', he said, 'not to draw his friends wildly in to be slaughtered without some sign of success, or at least a good fight for it'. In the event, his caution was justified. Emmet's failure, the end of any hope of a French invasion and the state to which himself and his followers were reduced in wintry weather in the high mountains, at last led Dwyer to approach the authorities through the person of William Hoare Hume, of Humewood Castle, an MP and yeomanry commander, whom he trusted. Hume agreed that Dwyer and his family and his companions should be pardoned and allowed to go the the USA. This may not have been so clearly agreed by Dublin Castle, however. In any event, Dwyer surrendered himself to Hume on 14 December 1803 and was conveyed to Dublin in Hume's coach under escort.

After questioning and a period of imprisonment in Kilmainham he and his companions were banished (as free settlers) to Australia, where they arrived in February 1806. In August of that year, the famous Captain Bligh of the *Bounty* became governor of the colony. Convinced that the new arrivals were a serious threat to government, Bligh had them arrested and, though a court acquitted them, sent them to the penal settlement on Norfolk Island, 800 miles away. Bligh exercised his authority as governor so harshly that the commander of the garrison, a Major Johnston, arrested and imprisoned him. The acting governor thereupon brought the prisoners back to New South Wales. (Bligh was imprisoned till 1810, after which he returned to England and ended his extraordinary career as an admiral. Johnston was tried for mutiny and cashiered from the Army). Dwyer, who was eventually joined in Australia by all his family, acquired a 100-acre farm at Liverpool, near Sydney, where he settled down for the rest of his life. He even became a district constable. There he died on 23 August 1825 at the age of fifty-three. His wife survived him till 1861. Dwyer's appearance when in his prime is minutely described in the proclamation offering a reward for his capture:

> Michael Dwyer, about thirty-one years, five feet nine or ten inches high, very straight in the back, short neck, square shoulders, a little in-kneed, rather long legged, with a little rise on the shin bone, very long feet, black hair and complexion, broad across the eyes, which are black, short cocked nose, wide mouth, thin lips, even teeth, but stand separate, very long from nose to the end of the chin, full breasted and rather full faced, born in Imale. Five hundred guineas for taking him.

James Petrie, a Dublin portrait painter, was the father of the much more celebrated George Petrie.

Sources: Charles Dickson, *Life of Michael Dwyer* (Dublin, 1944).

233 a-d   *Some accounts of the Rebellion*

233(a) *Rev. James Gordon, History of the Rebellion in Ireland in the year 1798, second edition (London and Dublin, 1803*

ULSTER MUSEUM

233(b) *A History of the Rise, Progress, and Suppression of the Rebellion in the County of Wexford, in the year 1798*

BY GEORGE TAYLOR
A NEW EDITION CORRECTED, DUBLIN, 1829
ULSTER MUSEUM

Title page and frontispiece *View of the Massacre on Wexford Bridge, June 20th. 1798.*

A HISTORY
OF THE
RISE, PROGRESS, AND SUPPRESSION
OF THE
REBELLION
IN
THE COUNTY OF WEXFORD,
IN THE YEAR 1798.

TO WHICH IS ANNEXED
THE AUTHOR'S ACCOUNT OF HIS CAPTIVITY,
AND MERCIFUL DELIVERANCE.

BY GEORGE TAYLOR.

A NEW EDITION CORRECTED.

DUBLIN :
WILLIAM CURRY, JUN. AND CO.
9, UPPER SACKVILLE STREET.
1829.

233 (B)

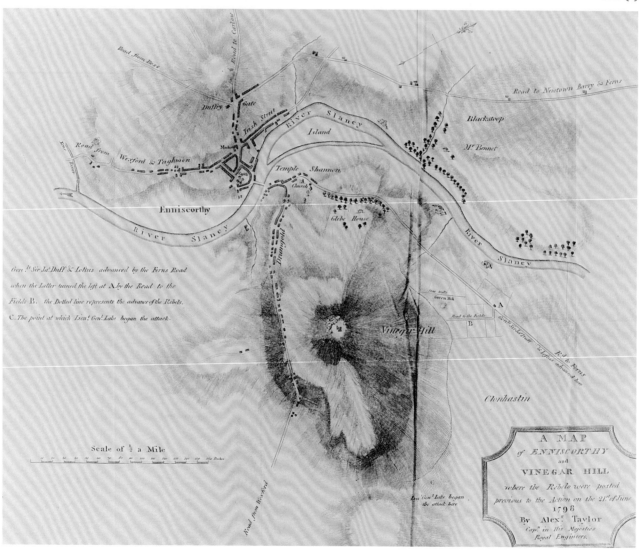

233 (C)

233(c) *Sir Richard Musgrave, Memoirs of the Different Rebellions in Ireland (Dublin, 3rd edition, 1802), vol. 1, displaying A Map of Enniscorthy and Vinegar Hill, by Alexr. Taylor.*

ULSTER MUSEUM

233(d) *W.H. Maxwell History of the Rebellion in Ireland in the year 1798. (London, 1844), Part 1.*

First edition, in parts; illustrated by George Cruikshank, cover design by Cruikshank

P. AND B. ROWAN

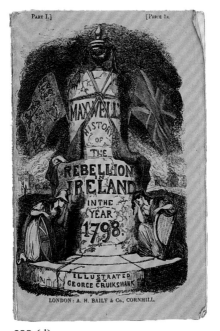

233 (d)

234 *Lieut.-General Sir George Nugent Bt*

ENGRAVING BY R. WOODMAN AFTER J. DOWNMAN A.R.A., 44 × 29 CM
NATIONAL ARMY MUSEUM, LONDON

George Nugent was born on 10 June 1757, the natural son of a lieutenant-colonel in the Foot Guards who died unmarried in 1771. He joined the Army as an ensign in the 39th Regiment of Foot in 1773. In 1777 he was sent to New York as a lieutenant in the 7th Royal Fusiliers and by the end of the American War he had become a lieutenant-colonel. After a period on half-pay, in 1787 he became aide-de-camp to his kinsman George Nugent Temple Grenville, first Marquess of Buckingham, then lord lieutenant of Ireland. At the outbreak of war with France he was sent with the Guards to Holland. A period in Ireland was followed by service with the Duke of York in the Netherlands in 1794. He was then appointed to the Irish staff. Family influence, combined with military talent, ensured that promotion continued; in 1796 he became a major-general.

In Ireland, he served first in the south, before succeeding Lake as general commanding the northern district. He remained in charge at Belfast throughout the 1798 rebellion, personally commanding his troops at the battle of Ballynahinch, which practically ended the insurrection in the north. Nugent had proceeded carefully and cautiously, well aware that the loss of a major engagement would have brought out many more United Irishmen than had at first appeared in arms; one disastrous afternoon could have lost the north. His policy of concentrating his forces and dealing separately with the risings in Antrim and Down was rendered effective by intelligence from well-placed informers in the movement.

In Belfast in 1797 he married Maria Skinner, daughter of a former attorney-general of the state of New Jersey. The Nugents were well-known and well-liked members of Belfast society. A prudent and humane man, he earned the good opinion even of Mrs McTier, who in 1797 wrote to her brother, William Drennan: 'General Nugent is much liked, and always was in this town; and I believe in my soul will act with all the forebearance the nature and difficulty of his station will allow'. She was sufficiently confident in his good intentions to remain in her house after the royal victory at Ballynahinch, when many others fled. Nugent's tolerance, or ability to show clemency, had its limits, however: he refused to receive Henry Joy McCracken's mother when she went to plead for his sentence to be commuted to banishment, and he rejected the plea of the Rev. James Porter's wife.

From 1799 to 1801, Nugent held the post of adjutant-general in Ireland. During

this time he also sat in the last Irish parliament as MP for Charleville, County Cork - like Lake (MP for Armagh), in order to swell the supporters of government in the Union debates. Thereafter he was appointed lieutenant-governor of Jamaica (1801-06) and, again like Lake, commander-in-chief in India (1811-13); in the process he was promoted to full general and became a baronet. When nearly ninety he was made a field-marshal, dying in March 1849 at the age of ninety-two.

Sources: *DNB.*
            A.T.Q. Stewart, *The Summer Soldiers.*

235 *Handbill, dated 28 May 1798, issued in Belfast by General Nugent; and supporting appeal, dated 29 May, by 150 citizens*

PUBLIC RECORD OFFICE OF NORTHERN IRELAND

Five days earlier, news of rebellion breaking out in Leinster increased the likelihood that the rebel forces known to be organised in Counties Antrim and Down would be mobilised. The object of the appeal was to identify and trace the whereabouts of six brass cannon provided originally for the Volunteer companies in the 1780s by the government. One, hidden under a pew in Templepatrick Presbyterian Church, was used by the rebels at the Battle of Antrim ten days later.

The list of names supporting the appeal for information about the field pieces included many who had originally been identified with radical politics when first the Society of the United Irishmen had been established but who now felt the need to distance themselves from their former colleagues who were about to engage in rebellion.

Sources: George Chambers, 'Divided Loyalties in the Business Community of Belfast in 1798', in *Familia*, vol. 10 (1994).

236 *John O'Neill, first Viscount O'Neill of Shane's Castle, c.1780*

BY FRANCIS WHEATLEY
ULSTER MUSEUM
REPRODUCTION

O'Neill was born on 16 January 1740, the eldest son of Charles O'Neill, of Shane's Castle, Randalstown, County Antrim. He was educated in Dublin and Oxford. From 1761 to 1783 he represented the borough of Randalstown in the Irish House of Commons and for the next ten years was one of the MPs for County Antrim. A prominent member of the Patriot party and a supporter of reform both in and out of Parliament, he was an enthusiastic Volunteer and was one of the five delegates chosen to represent County Antrim at the National Convention of Volunteers held in Dungannon in September 1783. An advocate of parliamentary reform and Catholic emancipation, but no radical, he was one of the original members of the Dublin Whig Club in 1789. In 1793 he was ennobled, in the peerage of Ireland, as Baron O'Neill; two years later he was made a viscount.

O'Neill opposed the United Irishmen and as governor of County Antrim did what he could to prevent the spread of their ideas and organisation in an area where both were strong. The date he chose for a meeting in Antrim of the county's magistrates to consider the imminent threat of insurrection decided Henry Joy McCracken to attack the town on that day in order to secure them as hostages. O'Neill had been in Dublin and, hurrying home, had not stopped at Lisburn, when General Nugent had left a warning for him. At any rate, he turned up in the thick of the battle in the main street, and in the melée was piked by 'a man in a grey frieze coat', who may have been one of his own disgruntled tenants, though he was a popular landlord. He lingered, against all expectation, until 18 June, dying in Antrim Castle.

This half-length portrait, until 1984 ascribed to an unknown artist, is now known to be by Francis Wheatley. O'Neill appears prominently in Wheatley's great painting of the Irish House of Commons in 1780, for which this may have been a preparatory study. An identical version is in the collection of the present Lord O'Neill.

Sources: Eileen Black, *Irish Oil Paintings, 1572-c.1830*.
A.T.Q. Stewart, *The Summer Soldiers*.

237 *A Map of the Town of Antrim, with key, to illustrate the account of the battle of Antrim, 7 June 1798*

Displayed in Musgrave's *Rebellions*, vol. 2
Ulster Museum

EXPLANATION OF THE PLATE.

No. 1. Where the rebel columns from Ballyclare and Templepatrick joined.

2. The rebels in close column with a six-pounder in front, when the curricle guns under lieutenant Neville opened their fire on them.

3. Lieutenant Neville, with two six-pounders, flanked by the yeomanry and dragoons under colonel Lumley firing on the rebels.

4. Colonel Lumley charging the rebels after passing the church-yard.

5. The church-yard lined with rebels, who are represented by the dotted lines, firing on the dragoons, charging as they passed, and among whom they did great execution.

6. The guns under lieutenant Neville, after retreating from No. 3, firing on the second column of the rebels advancing up Bow-lane.

7. The second rebel column.

8. The dragoons, after charging, drawn up under the dead wall of lord Massareene's garden, and covered on their left flank by a demi bastion.

9. The yeomanry firing over the wall on the rebels who attempted to get possession of the guns at No. 6, after the artillery had abandoned them, and the dragoons had retreated across the river.

10. The watering-place over which the dragoons retreated.

11. The entrance to lord Massareene's court: The dotted lines from it represent the road the yeomanry retreated to take post in the garden where they could only be attacked by the narrow walk through which they got in.

12. Lord Massareene's castle.

13. Lord Massareene's domain.

14. Lord Massareene's walled garden.

15. The Six-mile water.

16. Colonel Durham with the Monaghan militia, and captain Coulson of the artillery, firing on the rebels retreating by the Ballymena road.

17. The light battalion from Blaris camp under colonel Clavering drawn up.

18. Distillery.

19. Barracks.

20. Doctor Macartney's.

21. Flour-mills.

22. Market-house with the prisoners.

23. Little guard-house, behind which lord O'Neil was killed.

24. The rebel column under colonel Orr.

THE

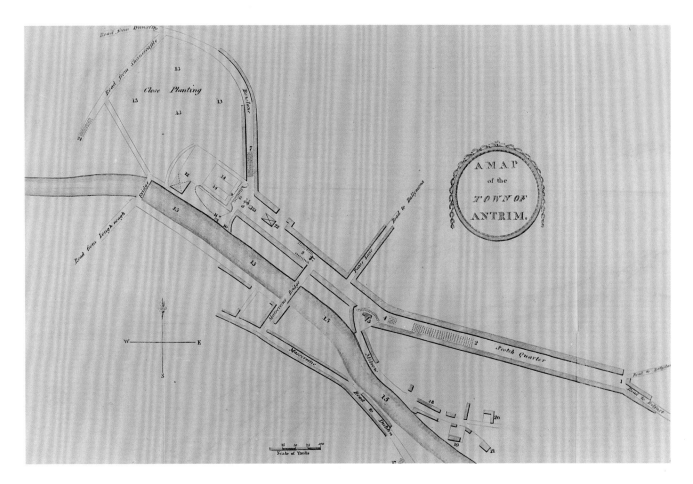

240

238

238 *Henry Joy McCracken*

BY SARAH CECILIA HARRISON (1863-1941)
OIL ON CANVAS, 63.5 X 56.2 CM, SIGNED AND DATED 1926
ULSTER MUSEUM

Henry Joy McCracken was the fifth child of Captain John McCracken, a Belfast shipowner and ropemaker, and his wife Ann Joy, a daughter of the founder of the *Belfast News-Letter*. Between them, his parents represented two of the most respectable Presbyterian families in the town. Henry Joy (as he was always known) was born at 39 High Street on 31 August 1767. Brought up to earn his living in the textile trade, he was at age twenty-two appointed manager of a cotton mill in the Falls on the outskirts of Belfast, in which his father was a partner. As an employer he showed himself unusually sensitive to the hard life of the working poor, as did his favourite sister Mary. The two of them helped to establish the first Sunday School in the town, to teach reading and writing to poor boys and girls. This humanitarian venture was closed down by the Anglican vicar of Belfast, Dr Bristow, a pillar of the local establishment who later occupied the office of sovereign (mayor) of the corporation. McCracken lived near his mill until 1795, when his father withdrew from the partnership and he himself returned home. By that time he was deeply engaged in radical politics, as the friend and confidant of Russell, Tone and Neilson and as an active member of the Society of United Irishmen. His sister and two of his brothers, Francis and William, shared his views.

McCracken's business as a buyer in the textile trade provided good cover for his political activities, but he soon became known to the authorities as a dangerous radical and when the leading figures among the United Irishmen were arrested in September 1796 McCracken was among them. He was sent to Kilmainham gaol in Dublin, where he was later joined by his brother William. They both remained there until released on bail, without trial, in December 1797. Kilmainham was an unhealthy place. Like Neilson, with whom he quarrelled seriously whilst in prison, he contracted severe rheumatism there, and was very ill when he got home to Belfast. Restored to health, he at once resumed his activities, becoming a member of the Ulster executive of the United Irishmen and one of its delegates appointed to make contact with the national executive in Dublin. In Dublin, he and Neilson (now reconciled) escaped the arrest of the Leinster leaders at Oliver Bond's house in March, remaining at large to make plans with Lord Edward FitzGerald for an uprising in May.

Returning to Belfast in mid-May, McCracken found the leadership of the movement in Ulster confused and uncertain about what to do. When the signal for the north to rise came with the stopping of the Dublin mail coach at Santry, there was at first no response. Though on paper formidable, the United Irishmen and their Defender allies in Ulster had been severely affected, in morale and military material, by the disarming of the province by General Lake's troops the year before. Fewer than 4,000 of the 26,000 nominal rebel soldiers in County Antrim possessed muskets, and they had virtually no artillery. Robert Simms, who had been chosen as adjutant-general for Antrim, was at first dilatory about calling his men out and then - when obliged by McCracken, Hope and others to call a meeting - resigned his command. McCracken was eventually, and unexpectedly, obliged to take his place and also to become in effect commander-in-chief of all the United Irish forces in the north.

His plan was to launch simultaneous attacks at Randalstown and Antrim with himself leading the attack on Antrim, where a meeting of magistrates, planned for 7 June, provided a useful objective; in County Down, it was assumed, there would be similar activity, with Ballynahinch, Saintfield, Newtownards and Portaferry as particular targets. These plans soon became known to General Nugent in Belfast through informers, so that he was able to concentrate his forces and deal first with the rising in Antrim, then with the one in Down. On 6 June, McCracken issued his proclamation: 'Army of Ulster, to-morrow we march on Antrim - drive the garrison of Randalstown before you, and haste to form a junction with the Commander-in-Chief'. It was signed with his name and dated, in French revolutionary style, '1st year of liberty, 6th day of June, 1798'.

Early on the following morning, McCracken planted a green flag at Craigarogan fort, a Norman mound between Glengormley and Templepatrick. As rebel commander, McCracken wore a 'coat of green' as his uniform. One of the cannons belonging to the former Belfast Blue Battalion of Volunteers, which had been hidden in 1793 when the Volunteers were disbanded and subsequently secreted - unknown to the minister - under the floorboards of Templepatrick Presbyterian meeting-house, was brought out and mounted on a makeshift carriage, in the charge of a deserter from the Royal Irish Artillery who, unusually for a Presbyterian, was a sworn member of both the United Irishmen and the Defenders.

The main assembly point for the rebels in south Antrim was the hill of Donegore. Some of the 7,000 or 8,000 who made their way there were extremely reluctant when it came to the point of risking their lives. When McCracken's force went off to attack Antrim, most of those who had turned out remained in reserve at Donegore and later dispersed to their homes without taking part in the fighting.

The battle of Antrim took place during the afternoon of 7 June. To begin with, the forces of the crown consisted of only one troop of the 22nd Dragoons, a company of the Antrim Yeomanry and about forty armed civilians, but General Nugent had despatched help from Belfast and Lisburn which was soon to increase that number. At 2.45 p.m. the rebels advanced, 'in good order', as James Hope later reported, 'until our front arrived opposite the Presbyterian meeting house'. The fighting that followed took place in the main street which, then as now, ended at the market house and the high wall of Lord Massareene's demesne and was overlooked in its lower course by the parish church and graveyard. The soldiery held the demesne wall, the rebels in the course of the fighting occupied the churchyard. The arrival of fresh rebel columns from Randalstown and elsewhere might have settled the outcome if they had not misunderstood the situation and fled in panic, for a charge up the street by dragoons just arrived from Lisburn had been successfully repulsed by McCracken and his men. In the confused fighting that followed, Lord O'Neill, the governor of County Antrim, was caught near the markethouse and piked. The advance of the main relief force from Belfast - McCracken in his inexperience appears to have employed no roadblocks or other delaying devices on the road behind him - eventually forced the rebels to quit the field, James Hope and his 'Spartan band' in the churchyard helping to cover the retreat, which then became a rout. The Monaghan Militia then went through the houses and gardens in the Scotch Quarter to cut off fugitives. The troops made little distinction between friend and foe. Their commanding officer, Colonel Durham, later wrote: 'When out of my sight they killed every man they could get at. My order of cease firing was not obeyed, nor could I carry it into effect although riding among them and with my sword throwing up their firelocks'. Later, some of the houses were burned, and all were thoroughly sacked. Later still, the local yeomen combed the town looking for any remaining rebels.

McCracken, along with Hope and others, retreated northwards towards Ballymena, where the United Irishmen had taken over the town and ran it through a short-lived Committee of Public Safety on the French model. The camp at Donegore Hill melted away, and McCracken found temporary safety for himself and about a hundred followers on Slemish mountain. Dislodged from there by approaching troops, some moved north, but McCracken and a dwindling band made their way across country towards County Down, where he still hoped for action. Near Derriaghy he heard the bad news from Ballynahinch and turned back to hide in the mountains above Belfast. There his sister Mary made contact with him and arranged for him to have money, a change of clothing, a forged pass and passage on a foreign vessel from a secluded spot on the Belfast Lough. In a letter to her during this period he ascribed his failure to treachery, quoting the famous line from Thomas Paine's American pamphlet, 'These are the times that try men's souls' and averring that 'the rich always betray the poor'. The shock of defeat was all the greater because, as he told her, 'on Friday the 8th June all the county was in the hands of the people, Antrim, Belfast and Carrickfergus excepted'.

Having spent the night of 7 July in a safe house at Greencastle on the lough shore, McCracken - disguised as a workman and carrying a bag of tools - set out to walk towards Carrickfergus with two companions. They had the bad luck to meet a party of yeomen, one of whom knew McCracken from having had business dealings with him. Having almost agreed to accept a bribe to let the rebels escape, the yeomen then turned them in and McCracken was lodged in Carrickfergus Castle. He was brought to Belfast on 16 July, tried by court martial the following day and hanged outside the market house in High Street the same evening. General Nugent allowed the body to be handed over to Mary on condition that it was buried before dark. The head was not to be severed and publicly exposed, as had happened in other cases, and Mary made arrangements to try to revive the corpse, but to no avail. The body was buried in St George's churchyard. Some years later, when part of the ground was sold off, some of the graves were disturbed. What were thought to be McCracken's remains were reburied in the cemetery at Clifton Street, where a memorial was erected.

Sarah Cecilia Harrison (1863-1941) was born in Holywood, County Down. She spent her early life in London, where she attended the Slade School of Art and won many awards. In 1880 she moved to Dublin. During the 1890s she spent some time painting in Brittany, exhibiting regularly at the Royal Hibernian Academy. An ardent nationalist and champion of women's rights, she was the first woman member of Dublin City Council. She was a great-grand niece of Henry Joy McCracken.

This portrait of him, which she painted in 1926 and presented to the Belfast Museum and Art Gallery the following year, was based on a miniature which once had belonged to his sister Mary. The well-known lithograph by J.H. Lynch, published in Madden's *United Irishmen*, was also copied from the miniature.

Sources: A.T.Q. Stewart, *The Summer Soldiers*.
             Edna Fitzhenry, *Henry Joy McCracken* (1936).
             R.R. Madden, *The United Irishmen*, second series, vol.2.

239 *Coat of Henry Joy McCraken, c.1789*

ULSTER MUSEUM

Reputedly part of the 'suit of green' he wore as commander of the United Irishmen at the battle of Antrim, 7 June 1798, this coat was donated to the Belfast Museum & Art Gallery by descendants of the McCracken family.

240 *The Battle of Antrim*

BY J.W. CAREY (1859-1937)
PEN DRAWING, 21.1 x 25.9 CM, SIGNED AND DATED 1895
ULSTER MUSEUM

Joseph William Carey was a well-known Belfast artist and illustrator. He and his brother John, sometimes in collaboration, produced a number of imagined scenes from local history. This is Joseph Carey's reconstruction of the battle in the main street of Antrim in June 1798, done at a time when the approaching centenary of the rebellion was arousing a great deal of interest.

241 *Henry Munro, Chief of the Irish Rebels*

ETCHING BY THOMAS ROWLANDSON, 29 X 35 CM
NATIONAL GALLERY OF IRELAND, DUBLIN

Munro, on horseback and heavily armed with sabre, pistols, musket with bayonet fixed and pike, is shown leading an army of yokels. The caption describes him as having

> Commanded on the 13th of June 1798 an Army of about 7000 Rebels, on the high ground behind Lord Moira's house, near Ballynahinch was after the defeat of his Army taken prisoner the 15th Inst. skulking in the fields near Castlewellan with a few of his followers, on Saturday the 16th he was tried by a Court Martial at Lisburn (where he had been a Shopkeeper) and on the Evidence of his own Adherents was found guilty of High Treason and Executed before his own door at 4 o clock of the same Day his Head was afterwards removed from his body, and fixed on a Pike on the Market House'.

Like Henry Joy McCracken in County Antrim, Henry Munro became commander of the army of the United Irishmen in County Down by having the position thrust upon him at the last moment in June 1798, in his case following the arrest of the Rev. William Steel Dickson. He joined the rebels at their camp near Saintfield, after their success there against Colonel Stapylton and his force of York Fencibles and local yeomanry, who had been ambushed and forced to retreat after suffering heavy casualties. As a person of some standing in the movement, Munro was at once appointed to command, though his sister-in-law was later to claim that he had joined the rebels 'more from impulse than reflection'. At any rate, according to James Hope, his appearance was unexpected.

Born in 1758, Munro was a linen draper from Lisburn. Like McCracken, he

had found excellent cover for his clandestine political activity in the travelling around the country that his trade required. He too had been an enthusiastic Volunteer and a Freemason, adopting radical views on reform and Catholic emancipation. He had become a United Irishman in 1795 after (it is said) seeing a member of his Masonic lodge publicly flogged in Lisburn as a suspected rebel. Unlike most of the northern rebel leaders he was a member of the established church rather than a Presbyterian, though he had Presbyterian ancestors and was in fact descended from the Scottish General Munro who had been defeated by Owen Roe O'Neill at Benburb in 1646.

As soon as he took command, Munro hurriedly did what he could to drill and train his men. Next day, Monday 11 June, he sent his adjutant, a probationer Presbyterian minister named Townsend, to occupy Ballynahinch. Royal forces consisting of Argyle Fencibles along with cavalry and artillery from Lisburn, under the command of Lieutenant-Colonel Stewart, had passed through on their way to secure Downpatrick, leaving a small garrison. These troops retreated as soon as the much larger rebel force appeared. Townsend occupied Windmill Hill, which overlooked the town from the east. Munro, arriving later the same day, set up his main camp on Ednavady Hill, to the south-east, in Lord Moira's demesne of Montalto, from where he sent out recruiting parties (who found the response disappointing); he also issued proclamations declaring that henceforth no rent was to be paid to landlords, 'as such rent is confiscated to the use of the National Liberty War'. General Nugent and his forces arrived the following day, and on Wednesday 13 June the battle of Ballynahinch was fought.

When the day was lost and it was every man for himself, Munro and a companion (a former clerk in the office of the *Northern Star*) made for the slopes of Slieve Croob, where they found shelter with a farmer named Holmes. Holmes betrayed them to the authorities and they were arrested in the pig house where they had been concealed, taken to Dromore and put in the charge of a local loyalist landowner, who escorted them to Lisburn and handed them over to the army. Munro's companion later escaped, but Munro was tried by court martial on 16 June and sentenced to death. His dignified and courageous behaviour made a good impression on the officers who tried him. Later in the same day, after receiving communion at the house of the local rector, the Rev. Snowden Cupples, he was hanged on the gallows erected in Market Square, close to his own house; afterwards, in accordance with the sentence of the court, his head was severed and exhibited on the market house. His last words were 'Tell my country I have deserved better of her'.

Sources: A.T.Q. Stewart, *The Summer Soldiers.*

242 *Jug presented to Masonic Lodge No. 193, Lisburn, County Antrim, by Henry Monro, c.1794*

CREAMWARE, TRANSFER-PRINTED, 36 CM HIGH
IRISH LINEN CENTRE & LISBURN MUSEUM

This is one of two jugs presented to Lodge 193 by Monro. The Lodge was originally founded in 1749 but had petered out by c.1790. Monro revived it in 1794 with himself as Master. It declined after 1798 and was suppressed in 1817. To judge by the membership, it was probably a cover for United Irish activity during the years 1794-98; apart from Monro himself, it was joined by his friends Bartholomew Teeling (1795) and Samuel Neilson (1796).

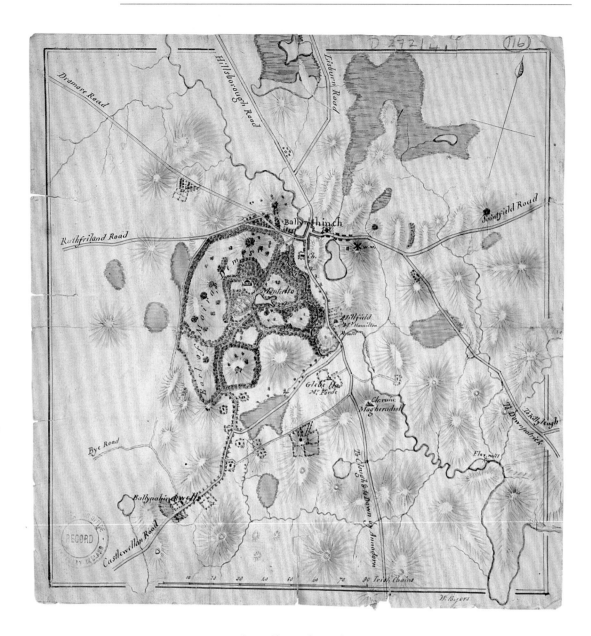

243 *MS Map of Ballynahinch area, c. 1798*

BY W. BYERS
PEN AND WATERCOLOUR ON PAPER, 27 X 26.5 CM; SCALE 0-80 IRISH CHAINS; SIGNED
PUBLIC RECORD OFFICE OF NORTHERN IRELAND

William Byers (fl.1788-98) served as an assistant to Lt. Col. Charles Vallancey on the military survey of Ireland in the 1790s. His private survey work that survives, or is known about, was done mostly in County Down - a map of the county, for the grand jury, never finished, and some estate maps for Lord Downshire - with some also in Wicklow.

This map of Ballynahinch and its immediate neighbourhood was probably done for the Earl of Moira, whose demesne of Montalto is the central feature. It does not appear to have been produced specifically in order to show the battle in 1798, but it is undoubtedly of about that date and does in fact illustrate the main features of the battlefield - Windmill Hill (* 'W.M.'), Ednavady Hill ('Montalto'), the parish church ('Ch.'), the old Church of Magheradroll, the streets of the town and the roads leading to it from all directions.

Sources: J.H. Andrews, *Plantation Acres*.
             Peter Eden (ed.), *Dictionary of Land Surveyors and Local Cartographers of Great Britain and Ireland 1550-1850*, 3 parts, (Folkestone, 1975), pt 1.

244 *Six-pounder cannon ball, found at Windmill Hill, Ballynahinch*

ULSTER MUSEUM

245 *The Battle of Ballynahinch, 1798*

BY THOMAS ROBINSON (d. 1810)
OIL ON CANVAS, 161 x 238 CM
OFFICE OF PUBLIC WORKS, DUBLIN

After their heartening success at Saintfield, in which they inflicted heavy casualties on a force of York Fencibles and local yeomanry, the rebel forces of County Down, now under the command of Henry Munro, concentrated at Ballynahinch and prepared to do battle with the army of Major-General Nugent. On the morning of Tuesday 12 June 1798 Nugent set out from Belfast to march to Ballynahinch with a force consisting of the Monaghan Militia, the Fifeshire Fencibles, dragoons of the 22nd (Irish) Regiment, local yeomanry and a detachment of the Royal Artillery with six six-pounder guns and two howitzers. He left behind General Goldie from Blaris camp near Lisburn with some Breadalbane Fencibles, as a reserve, supplemented by some Belfast Yeomanry, 'to prevent the inhabitants of Belfast from rising in the absence of the troops'. A prominent inhabitant later recalled 'the death-like silence which pervaded the streets when the counties of Down and Antrim resounded with the noise and tumult of battle'; and indeed the sound of the artillery at Ballynahinch could be clearly heard. Panic prevailed among the inhabitants, many of whom fled the town. Large numbers of women and children made for Scotland, Nugent's wife among them. The uncertainty of the outcome, and the anxiety to get away while there was still time, are vividly recorded in the diary of Lady Roden, from Tollymore. The coal boat in which she and her party were lucky enough to obtain passage ran aground in the Lagan. 'All confidence being entirely lost in our countrymen, there was no security that this was not intended', she wrote. On that day, Saturday 9 June, 'There was an engagement near Saintfield, in which our troops were driven back, and this day, Sunday, 10th of June, the ladies upon the deck had the misery of seeing the York Fencibles flying over the bridge of Belfast, to which, as we lay a-ground, we were very near indeed'. They eventually got away to Portpatrick on the Monday, after a second grounding.

A young eye-witness at Ballynahinch, James Thomson, whose uncle was Lord Moira's gardener at Montalto, visited the rebel encampment on Ednavady Hill and many years later set down his recollection of what he had seen: men without uniforms but dressed in their Sunday go-to-meeting clothes, all wearing some article of green, or green and yellow. Many sported patriotic decorations, the most common of which featured harps (without the crown), shamrock, caps of liberty and inscriptions such as 'Liberty or Death', or 'Freedom to Ireland'. Most were armed with pikes, some only had pitchforks, relatively few had muskets or other guns (these no doubt included some of the wildfowlers from the shore of Strangford Lough, whose long pieces had done notable execution in the fight at Saintfield a few days earlier).

Colonel Stewart, summoned from Downpatrick, arrived in position on the southern approaches to Ballynahinch a couple of hours before Nugent himself - his route marked by burning farmsteads - appeared from the north. In a combined

The Battle of Ballynahinch

move they first drove the rebels from Windmill Hill, where the general established his headquarters. From there his artillery bombarded the town and the demesne until night fell. The Monaghan Militia, which then occupied the town, plundered and looted it, setting fire to some of the houses. The traditional story is that Munro, when urged by one of his lieutenants, a local doctor, to attack the drunken enemy under cover of darkness, was too chivalrous to do so, whereupon his Catholic Defender allies withdrew in disgust. It is highly unlikely that the rebel commander was so foolish, but it is true that, for reasons still obscure, both United Irishmen and Defenders from south Down were conspicuous by their absence when the main battle was fought next day; many, of course, could not stand their first taste of being bombarded by artillery and melted away when darkness fell. Most of the insurgents who remained came from north Down - Bangor, Hollywood, Donaghadee, the Ards and Castlereagh, possibly Killyleagh (though James Hope says the Killyleagh men decamped in a body).

The artillery opened up again at three o'clock in the morning. Munro's main body advanced from the demesne gate up Bridge Street (now Dromore Street) and into the town in the face of artillery fire from two six-pounders, while a force from his right advanced through the demesne to cross the river at Mill Bridge on the Clough road, with the intention of proceeding across the Mill Fields to attack Nugent's position on Windmill Hill from the flank. To forestall this latter move, Stewart advanced down the Mill Fields and up Crabtree Hill towards the ruins of the old church of Magheradroll, from where his six-pounder and howitzer could fire into the grounds of Montalto. At the Mill Bridge, where fighting was heavy, the rebels could make no headway against this artillery and the steady musketry of the Argyle Fencibles and their Yeomanry allies. Stewart later advanced into the demesne and took possession of Ednavady Hill, 'where he found their eight guns with a great quantity of ammunition, their Colours, Cars, Provisions, etc. etc.'. A large number of the defeated rebels concealed in the plantations about Montalto House were killed there when found.

The main battle, however, was fought in the streets of the town itself. Here the Monaghan Militia, despite their superior firepower, were driven back by the sheer ferocity of the rebel attack, in which the two field guns commanding Bridge Street were captured. The army was driven back from Church Street as far as Market Square and then, by pike and bayonet, into Meeting House Street (now Windmill Street) and towards Nugent's own position. When a cavalry charge failed to dislodge the rebels, the general ordered a general retreat from the town. The United Irishmen, mistaking the bugle signal as a sign that government reinforcements had arrived, now also began to retreat. The more experienced military recovered first from this situation and, returning to the attack, drove their opponents back through the town. When the troops were fired upon from some of the houses, half the town was set on fire. The fleeing fugitives were cut down by the cavalry. Most of the casualties, and the worst of the atrocities, occurred during this operation. General Nugent claimed to have killed 300 in the fighting itself and a further 200 in the pursuit, numbers which were almost certainly exaggerated. He said he lost only one captain and five other ranks, with a lieutenant and sixteen others wounded, not counting yeomen; his actual losses may have been about forty . Most of the indiscriminate atrocities carried out by the soldiers were ascribed to the 22nd Dragoons, though it was men of the Hillsborough Yeoman Cavalry who were held responsible for the one that lingered longest in popular memory - the murder of Elizabeth (Betsy) Gray, who had gone to Ballynahinch with her brother and her fiancé and shared their fate. Though long since a famous figure of local folklore, Betsy does seem to have existed; she was probably the daughter of a Presbyterian farmer named Hans Gray, from Gransha, in north Down. A hundred years later, a monument erected to mark the place where the three victims were buried became a source of contention between Home Rule pilgrims and local loyalists, both claiming Betsy for their own; the stone was smashed by the indignant loyalists, some of whose ancestors, like her, would have been rebels in 1798.

The battle of Ballynahinch effectively ended the rebellion in the north. The shock of defeat, and the harsh punishment of the defeated, combined with news of the sectarian nature of the rising in Wexford - a view assiduously promoted by government propaganda - dismayed and disillusioned all but the stoutest of the rebels. This became clearly apparent in 1803, when Thomas Russell singularly failed to rouse United Irish sympathisers in County Down to action in support of Emmet's rising.

Thomas Robinson painted his picture, which he originally entitled *Combat Between the King's Troops and the Peasantry at Ballynahinch*, not long after the battle. Bishop Percy of Dromore was writing to his wife in August 1798 to say, 'Robinson the painter now lives with his family at Lisburn and is painting the Battle of Ballynahinch in a good style somewhat in the manner of [Benjamin West's] Death of Wolfe'. The painting is indeed a set piece in the manner of West, but more realistic in that portraits of real people were used in it; the bishop reported in December that Lord Hertford, who had acquired the picture by winning the raffle for it, was to hang it at his house in Lisburn 'to be viewed ... by all who were at the Battle of Ballynahinch, many of whom have their portraits drawn in it'. Robinson produced a key to the identity of these people, possibly in the form of an Indian ink design for *The Death of Captain Evatt at Ballynahinch*, which was exhibited in Dublin in 1809, but it has unfortunately disappeared. Some can be identified, however: the central expiring figure is certainly that of Captain Henry Evatt, of the Monaghan Militia, who was shot during the street-fighting in the town; the two mounted staff officers to the right, with their backs to the viewer, are almost certainly (left) Colonel Stewart and (right, in cocked hat) General Nugent; the captured United Irishmen to left is probably one Hugh McCullough, a grocer from Bangor, who was hanged on Windmill Hill. The foreground of the picture is Windmill Hill, Nugent's command post, which overlooks the spire of the parish church (centre) and (to right) the town on fire, with Lord Moira's house and demesne beyond. Based, as it must have been, on eye-witness reports, the general picture is likely to have been accurate, as the uniforms and accoutrements of the military, such as the yeoman infantry and cavalry to left, certainly are. The two captured rebel flags being brought by the dragoons on the right, also presumably correct, are thought to be the only contemporary representation of such things in colour.

Altogether, the painting is a unique contemporary work. When finished it was exhibited at the Exchange in Belfast in November 1798. In an advertisement in the *Belfast News-Letter* on 6 November, Robinson claimed: 'The Picture contains many *original Portraits*, and is a faithful representation of the Field of Battle and its events'. Admission to the show was one shilling for spectators, but free to those who subscribed a guinea to enter the raffle for the picture; sixty tickets were sold. Oddly enough, *The Battle of Ballynahinch* was to be the subject of another raffle. As reported in the *Northern Whig* on 23 May 1938 the picture, correctly attributed to Robinson but said to depict 'the death of Lord Mountjoy at the Battle of New Ross, Wexford, when the rebels under the unhappy Beauchamp Bagenal Harvey were put to rout', was won by a Brighton dealer for only 24 guineas. Later in the same year it was acquired by a Dublin man, who offered it for sale to the Belfast Museum and Art Gallery. Negotiations were interrupted by the Second World War - Belfast in the Blitz would have been no place for such a large new acquisition - and when correspondence resumed in 1944 the Director of the Museum found that the painting had been disposed of six months earlier.

Sources: A.T.Q. Stewart, *The Summer Soldiers.*
Anne Crookshank and The Knight of Glin, *Irish Portraits 1660-1860* (catalogue of an exhibition, 1969).
Diary of Anne, Countess Dowager of Roden (Dublin, 1870).

246 *James Thomson (1786-1849)*

PHOTOGRAPH, C.1845
ULSTER MUSEUM (KELVIN COLLECTION)
REPRODUCTION

In 1798, as a boy of twelve, James Thomson was an eye-witness of Munro's army of United Irishmen just before the battle of Ballynahinch was fought. James's uncle was a gardener, employed at Montalto, the demesne of Lord Moira, which became the rebels' main encampment. When Munro issued a proclamation calling for support from local people, including the supply of provisions for his army, the Thomson women, 'and such others as could be procured to assist in preparing oaten cakes and boiling large portions of salted beef and bacon', got to work. Three of them then set off for Montalto, accompanied by James, who was thought to be too young to come to any harm among the rebel host. Many years later, in 1825, he set down his recollections.

Having handed over their contribution, the Thomsons were taken round the camp in front of Montalto House by two or three young men who had offered their services as guides:

> Everything was explained with minuteness: pikes of different constructions were pointed out and their uses explained, the cannon and ammunition were shown ... The leaders were also pointed out ... The eye was presented with a mixed and motley multitude.... They wore no uniforms; yet they represented a tolerably decent appearance, being dressed no doubt in their 'Sunday clothes'.

The only common feature was the wearing of some article or decoration of green. Most of them were armed with pikes, some had old swords, some only pitchforks; only the 'higher class' had guns.

The Thomsons hurriedly left the field when soldiers could be seen approaching along the road from Downpatrick and the camp began to prepare for action.

James Thomson was to become a notable mathematician. After taking his degree at Glasgow University in 1812 he was appointed professor of mathematics three years later at the Academical Institution in Belfast, was awarded an honorary doctorate by Glasgow in 1829 and in 1832 was made professor there. His son William, Lord Kelvin, became a famous scientist.

Sources: *DNB.*
[James Thomson], 'An eye-witness by "Iota"', in *Belfast Magazine*, vol. 1, no. 1 (1825).
A.T.Q. Stewart, *The Summer Soldiers.*

247 *'Prisoners' Names in the Donegall Arms, Belfast', late 1798*

PUBLIC RECORD OFFICE OF NORTHERN IRELAND

The Donegall Arms, Belfast's principal hostelry in the 1790s and one of the town's best-known meeting places - it was the last point of arrival of the mail coach - was used in 1798 for the detention of individuals suspected of involvement in the planned rebellion.

The list of thirty-one names given here contains not only well-known figures in the Society of the United Irishmen but also in Belfast's merchant and professional classes. Robert Hunter was a successful shipbroker as well as having been a prominent United Irishman who earlier in the year had been chosen along with Henry Joy McCracken to represent the Ulster Executive with the National Executive in Dublin.

Robert Simms had until shortly before the outbreak of Rebellion been the leader of the County Antrim rebels, a position he resigned just before the rising.

Of the other leading names, perhaps the most notable is that of William Tennent, who is recorded as 'lying ill ... of a broken leg'. According to William Steel Dickson's *Narrative*, Tennent broke it while exercising in an attempt to keep warm during his period of detention at the end of 1798 on the prison ship in Belfast Lough.

All three - Hunter, Simms and Tennent - were among the twenty United Irish leaders sent in 1799 to Fort George.

248 *The Hanging of Henry Joy McCracken*

By John Carey
From R.M. Young (ed.), *Historical Notices of Old Belfast* (Belfast, 1896)
Ulster Museum
Reproduction

Carey's imagined scene of the execution of McCracken on the gallows erected outside the old Market House in Belfast, though clearly inaccurate so far as the costume of some of the spectators is concerned, gives some idea of how the place might have looked. The heads of some of the rebels executed earlier were displayed above the Market House, as the Rev. James Porter's young son vividly remembered; McCracken's family, who were among the most prominent and respected people in Belfast, were spared that final indignity.

249 *Gold memorial ring of Henry Joy McCracken containing a lock of his hair, 1798*

ULSTER MUSEUM

In his cell just before his execution, McCracken's sister Mary cut off a lock of his hair as a keepsake. The authorities were concerned about the use to which such relics might be put, and on this occasion Major Fox insisted on making her give up the packet she had put in her dress. It must have been returned to her later, however, for it is still preserved among the Madden papers in Trinity College, Dublin.

This ring bearing McCracken's initials was given to the Belfast Museum by his great-grand-nephew, Henry Harrison.

250 *THE ALLIED REPUBLICS OF FRANCE AND IRELAND LIBERTY AND EQUALITY*

BY ? SANSOM
ENGRAVING, IN A CIRCLE (22.9 CM DIAM.) INSET IN A SQUARE, WITH VERSES BELOW
(PL. 32.5 x 23.2 CM), PUBLISHED IN LONDON 17 OCT. 1798 BY S.W. FORES.
BRITISH MUSEUM, LONDON

The design inside the circle, entitled ERIN GO BRAY, shows a French soldier, in ragged uniform and wearing a cap of liberty with cockade, riding an ass, which tramples underfoot the symbols of monarchy and church (crown, sceptre, mitre). The soldier carries a drawn sabre inscribed *Fraternité*. The ass, which is branded on the flank with the mark of an Irish harp with the standard and cap of liberty, is laden with plunder - *Usquebaugh, Beef and Pork, Linen, Potatoes* - and is prodded onward by the spear of a devil, to right. In the background to left, across a bridge, is a castle and buildings in flames. In the background to right, two bodies hang from a high gibbet and a ragged French soldier tries to ravish a woman.

The verses below, written in pidgin English, are as follows:

[1]
From Brest in de Bay of Biskey
me come for de very fine Whiskey
to make de Jacobin friskey
While Erin may go bray
    While Erin may go bray
    While Erin may go bray
Me have got de mealy Pattato
From de Irish Democrato
To make de Jacobin fat o
    While Erin may go bray

[2]
I get by de Guillotine Axes
De Wheats & de Oats & de Flaxes
De Rents & de Tides [tithes] & de Taxes
While Erin may go bray
    While Erin may go bray
    While Erin may go bray
I put into Requisition
De Girl of ev'ry condition
For Jacobin Coalition
    And Erin may go bray

[3]
De linen I get in de Scuffle
Will made de fine Shirt to my ruffle
While Pat may go starve in his Hovel
And Erin may go bray
    And Erin may go bray
    And Erin may go bray
De Beef is good for my Belly
De Calf make very fine Jelly
For me to kiss Nora & Nelly
    And Erin may go bray

[4]
Fitzgerald & Artur o Conner
To Erin have done de great Honor
To put me astride upon her
For which she does now bray
    For which she now does bray
    For which she now does bray
She may fidget & Caper & kick o
But by de good help of old nick o
De Jacobin ever will stick o
    And Erin may go bray

It was popularly supposed that Frenchmen wore ruffles but no shirts. France's revolutionary armies were notorious for their rapaciousness in the countries they 'liberated'. We know from his diaries that Wolfe Tone was seriously concerned about the possible behaviour of a French army in Ireland and the temptation for the French government, if successful, to treat Ireland as a subject province. In his negotiations with the Directory he tried to ensure that Irish liberty and property would be respected.

Sources: *BM Catalogue*, VII, no. 9254.

251 *The French in Killala Bay*

BY WILLIAM SADLER
OIL ON PANEL, 12 x 19 CM
NATIONAL GALLERY OF IRELAND, DUBLIN

Painted long after the event, this picture shows an imagined scene on the beach at Killala, with the bishop's palace - General Humbert's headquarters - above.

252 *General Humbert (1755-1823)*

COLOURED ENGRAVING, 34 x 24 CM
NATIONAL ARMY MUSEUM, LONDON

Jean Joseph Amable Humbert was born of humble parents at Saint-Nabaud in the Vosges on 22 August 1767. His military career began at the Revolution, in the National Guard of Lyon in 1789. He transferred to the regular army in 1792, rising rapidly through the officer ranks to general of brigade by April 1794. He campaigned in the west of France in 1795, before joining the Army of the Rhine and Moselle in 1796. Courageous, impetuous, ambitious for glory in the service of the Republic, Humbert was available for service when an Irish expedition was hastily prepared in 1798. When he left Rochefort in August with his flotilla of three frigates and a brig carrying just over 1,000 men, it was intended that his would be only the advance party of a larger force under the command of General Hardy, not an independent command. As it turned out, Humbert alone succeeded in landing in Ireland, and was to make his mark there.

Arriving off the north coast of Mayo on 22 August, the French landed near Killala next day and occupied the town. Humbert was accompanied by two United

HUMBERT

Général des Armées de la République f.se tel qu'il étoit à la Bataille de Castlebar

EN IRLANDE.

A Paris chez Basset M.d d'Estampes et Fabriquant de Papiers peints, rue Jacques au coin de celle des mathurins. 670

Irishmen, Matthew Tone (Wolfe Tone's brother) and Bartholomew Teeling. Proclamations were issued and large numbers of the local peasantry flocked in to be drilled and armed (not to mention clothed). The French officers made the Church of Ireland bishop's house, where the recently-appointed Bishop Stock and his family were in residence, their headquarters, behaving with great correctness. The anti-clerical invaders, who had been misinformed as to the situation in Ireland, were amazed and amused at the devout Catholicism of their new allies and disappointed that the Protestant gentry did not welcome them. The French ships sailed away on 27 August. Humbert proceeded to occupy Ballina and then, instead of waiting till larger forces arrived, marched on Castlebar, where he won a notable success against the army of General Lake, who had arrived just in time to take charge of an inexperienced and unreliable mixture of units, mainly militia and fencibles. Hearing the news, Cornwallis set off from Dublin with powerful reinforcements, while Humbert - disappointed that his victory had not, as he had expected, roused the whole countryside - moved towards Sligo with Lake and Cornwallis in pursuit. Checked at Collooney, despite getting the better of a sharp fight there, Humbert turned into Leitrim and then south into Longford, closely pursued. On 8 September he was forced to make a stand at Ballinamuck. After a short battle, in which only a small part of his army was engaged, Humbert and his French (96 officers and 746 men) surrendered and became prisoners of war. Their wretched Irish allies were hunted down without mercy and a reign of terror ensued as the frightened local loyalists and despised militia took their revenge.

Humbert and his officers were received in Dublin with courtesy as prisoners of war - all except Tone and Teeling, who were hanged as traitors. Humbert himself was exchanged soon afterwards.

The Irish expedition was the summit of Humbert's career. Much was made in the French press of his victory at Castlebar, the inspiration for this print. The general disaster of France's effort in Ireland, however, soon overlaid Humbert's unexpected success. He was later employed in the West Indies, where his conduct led to his dismissal. In 1812 he was allowed to transfer to the service of the United States, subsequently taking part in the Mexican War. He stayed on in America, dying, down and out, in New Orleans in 1823.

Sources: Webb, *Compendium of Irish Biography.*
Tulard, Fayard and Fierro, *Histoire et Dictionnaire de la Révolution Française.*

253 *MS Journal of Joseph Stock, Bishop of Killala, 23 Aug. -15 Sept. 1798*

TRINITY COLLEGE, DUBLIN

The journal kept by Bishop Joseph Stock of events in the west of Ireland, from the first landing in Killala Bay, County Mayo of the 1,000 troops led by General Jean Joseph Amable Humbert provides a striking account of the long-awaited arrival of the French. Thinking they are English men of war, his sons row out to greet the French ships and are captured. While the bishop is entertaining a 'visitation' in his palace, Humbert's troops come ashore. After scattering the local yeomanry, killing two of them, they present themselves at the palace [castle] with one of the sons (brought because he can speak French) and ask for 'Monsieur L'Eveque'. In the rest of the journal, Stock's eye-witness descriptions of incidents as they unfolded around him are all the more gripping for his economic and factual style. The journal begins:

> Killala Aug. 23 1798

> Lord guard us! here come the French sure enough. [Army has?] taken Killala and are in the house at the moment I am writing to you. It is the will of God and we must not murmur at it. Yesterday morning we descried 3 very large vessels in our Bay so near the shore that we could plainly see them carrying English colours. This tempted my two sons Edwin and Arthur to throw themselves into a fishing boat together with the Post Surveyor and set off for what they longed to see, English Men of War. They were made prisoner and Arthur and the Surveyor are still in their hands. Edwin they brought ashore with them possibly because he spoke French.

254 *[Joseph Stock], Narrative of What Passed at Killala in the Summer of 1798. By an Eyewitness (Dublin, 1799)*

P. AND B. ROWAN

The *DNB* entry for Stock remarks: 'this little work is the most authentic record extant of the episode it describes, and is written with a rare impartiality'.

255 *Proclamation headed LIBERTY, EQUALITY, FRATERNITY, UNION, issued by General Humbert on arrival at Killala Bay, County Mayo, 22 August 1798.*

NATIONAL LIBRARY OF IRELAND, DUBLIN (REPRODUCTION)

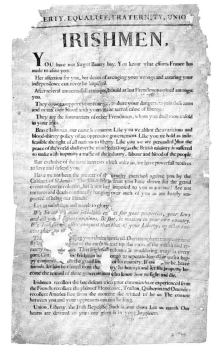

'You have not forgot Bantry Bay' claims the first line of the proclamation, a reference to the abortive mission in December 1796. As had been the case in 1796, however, the expedition had been bedevilled by delay and poor co-ordination. On this occasion, a second and larger fleet from Brest, scheduled to supplement Humbert's three frigates and corvette, which sailed from Rochefort, was delayed by nearly two weeks. 'If the Brest and Rochefort divisions could have landed their troops', wrote a soldier, Jean-Baptiste Thomas, who served in Ireland with Humbert, 'we might have hoped to succeed in spite of the vast number of the English army. We would have formed [an army of] 5 or 6 thousand men'.

256 *Bartholomew Teeling (1774-98)*

FRENCH SCHOOL, C.1796 / J.H. LYNCH
LITHOGRAPH, 11.9 x 8.3 CM
NATIONAL GALLERY OF IRELAND, DUBLIN

Bartholomew Teeling was born at Lisburn, County Antrim into a well-to-do Catholic merchant family. His father Luke was an active radical and was to be arrested in 1798 and kept in prison until 1802. His younger brother Charles was also a United Irishman. A friend of Lord Edward FitzGerald, Teeling was one of a younger generation of United Irishmen from the north of Ireland who in the mid-1790s were pressing for a rising without waiting for a substantial invasion force from France. He fled from Ireland in 1796 to escape arrest and took part in Hoche's expedition to Ireland under the name of Biron. In 1798, under the name of Veron, he served as a captain in the expedition under Humbert which landed at Killala in August. As a soldier he behaved with notable courage. He was also conspicuous in protecting the lives and property of the Protestant gentry in the west from the hands of the Irish peasants who joined Humbert's army. When Humbert was surrounded and forced to surrender at Ballinamuck, Teeling was identified as a British subject and sent to Dublin for trial. His claim to be a French officer was in vain, despite Humbert's efforts to have him treated as such. He was tried by court martial and hanged on 24 September 1798, along with Wolfe Tone's brother Matthew. This portrait shows him wearing his French uniform.

257 *David McAnally, surgeon of the Armagh Militia 1793-1818*

FROM A MINIATURE
ULSTER MUSEUM PHOTOGRAPH

David McAnally was born about 1765, probably at Lambeg, County Down. He

studied medicine at Edinburgh from 1781 to 1785, qualifying in surgery and midwifery. After a brief period in practice in Lisburn, he moved to Markethill in County Armagh and was appointed surgeon to the Armagh Militia when the regiment was embodied in November 1793. He held the post, along with a commission as lieutenant, until he died in 1818.

The services of both 'surgeon and man midwife', as he had advertised himself, were required in his military post, for large numbers of wives and children followed the regiment: in garrison at Clonmel in 1809 there were 228 women and 313 children. While treatment of wounds received in action was his essential function, the regimental surgeon more routinely inspected recruits and supervised the ferocious floggings that were handed out as punishments to the rank and file. In the Armagh Militia in 1807 desertion drew 600-900 lashes, riotous conduct 200-800, drunkenness 200-600. The surgeon's role was to feel the victim's pulse and stop the flogging if the man seemed likely to expire.

Sources: Henry McAnally, *An Irish Militia Surgeon: David McAnally, 1765-1818* (Dundalk, no date).

258 *Set of surgical instruments, mid-nineteenth century*

IN FITTED MAHOGANY BOX, BRASS-BOUND
ULSTER MUSEUM

These instruments are not essentially different from those an army surgeon would have had in 1798, though possibly the steelwork is of finer manufacture. There

was nothing new about such elaborately presented collections, however. A set captured by the French at Castlebar in 1798, and which had probably belonged to the surgeon of either the Longford or the Kilkenny Militia, was described as being a complete collection including midwifery instruments, in a mahogany case, with locks and fittings in silver, the contents wholly or partly embellished in gold, silver, ebony, ivory, mother-of-pearl and shellwork.

This set was presented by Lord Londonderry, colonel of the Royal North Down Rifles, to John S. Armstrong, the regimental surgeon, in 1855.

Sources: Henry McAnally, *An Irish Militia Surgeon.*

259 *Heroic conduct of the Highland Sentinel*

BY GEORGE CRUIKSHANK, FROM MAXWELL'S *REBELLION*
ULSTER MUSEUM
REPRODUCTION

This is the only Cruikshank illustration from one of the rebellion's other theatres, the West of Ireland. It depicts the last stand of a sentry of the Fraser Fencibles. When posted outside the new gaol in Castlebar on 27 August 1798, he refused to retreat with his comrades. He is said to have killed five French soldiers before being overcome by superior numbers. The steadfastness of the sentinel contrasts with the widespread desertion by the militia in the face of the French attack. Humbert's victory over Lake was thus christened 'the Races of Castlebar'.

260-262 *French battle plans, 1798*

BY J.-B. THOMAS
SERVICE HISTORIQUE DE L'ARMÉE DE TERRE, CHÂTEAU DE VINCENNES
REPRODUCTIONS

These plans of the three principal engagements of General Humbert's campaign in the west of Ireland were drawn by an officer in his army, Jean-Baptiste Thomas. They accompanied Thomas's 'Souvenirs' of his military service 1794-1810, written in the late 1820s. His recollection of the rout of British troops at Castlebar seems to confirm that they were indeed 'the Castlebar races' ... 'the enemy, driven from all their positions, abandoned their artillery and the greater part of their baggage [and] were hotly pursued for the space of two leagues'.

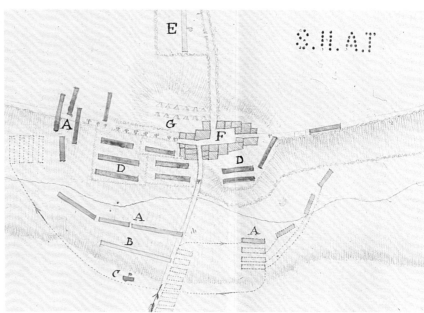

260 *Bataille de Castlebar ... le 27 aôut en Irlande*

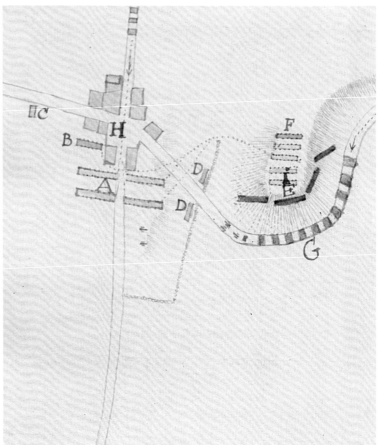

261 *Bataille de Cloon ... en Irlande*

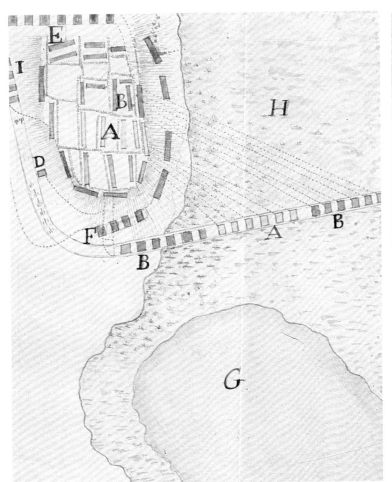

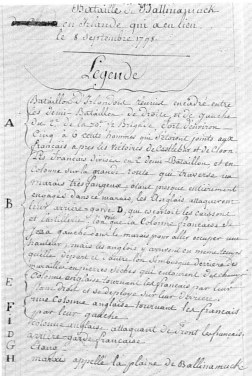

262 *Bataille de Ballinamuck ... le 8 septembre 1798*

263 *French regimental colour, 1798*

SILK, 193 x 193 CM FRAMED
ARMAGH PUBLIC LIBRARY, ARMAGH

This colour of the 2nd battalion of the 70th Demi-Brigade of the French Revolutionary Army was captured by the 8th or Armagh Militia at the battle of Ballinamuck, 8 September 1798, when Humbert's army surrendered to the overwhelming forces of Cornwallis and Lake. The flag, which is in remarkably good condition, is of (now) cream-coloured silk with, in the centre, painted decoration depicting a red cap of liberty surmounting the fasces (bundles of rods and axes, symbols of the magistrates in the Roman Republic, which were used as emblems of the French Republic), above a wreath of oak leaves. *Republiqué* and *Française* are painted in gold letters on a white ground, above and below this device; the number *70* appears large at top and bottom left, next to the pole sleeve, and, middle right, the number *2*. The painting is the same on the back, except that *Discipline Et Soumission/Aux Loix Militaires* replaces *Republique/Francaise* and *Bon* [Battalion] replaces *2*. This is almost certainly what was described at the time as 'a large flag of white silk, or substance like silk, having in the centre "Republique Francaise" embroidered within a wreath of laurel'.

After the battle the standard was kept, along with the Armagh Militia's colours, at Gosford Castle, County Armagh. In 1891 it was transferred to the north aisle of

259

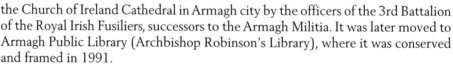

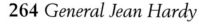

the Church of Ireland Cathedral in Armagh city by the officers of the 3rd Battalion of the Royal Irish Fusiliers, successors to the Armagh Militia. It was later moved to Armagh Public Library (Archbishop Robinson's Library), where it was conserved and framed in 1991.

Sources: W.H. Maxwell, *History of the Irish Rebellion in 1798*.
             G.A. Hayes-McCoy, *Irish Flags*.

264 *General Jean Hardy*

MEZZOTINT
BIBLIOTHÈQUE NATIONALE, PARIS

Hardy was the unfortunate French general who commanded the expedition which left Brest in September 1798 for Ireland. Embarking on 14 August with 2,300 men, Hardy was accompanied on the 74-gun flagship *Hoche* by Wolfe Tone; the rest of the naval force consisted of eight frigates (one of them the ill-fated *Fraternité*, whose delay in reaching Bantry Bay had scuppered Hoche's expedition in 1796) and a schooner. Delayed by the wait for a favourable wind and dogged by the attentions of the British ships blockading Brest, the fleet sallied out on 6 September and finally got clear ten day later. Since Humbert's even smaller force, which had departed from Rochfort earlier, had by this time surrendered, the expedition was suicidal. Intercepted off the coast of Donegal by Admiral Warren, Hardy and his men got ashore only as prisoners. When he heard that Tone was being treated as a British traitor rather than a French officer, Hardy wrote at once to the viceroy,

Cornwallis: 'I will not touch on the question of grievances you may have against this officer; but he is a French citizen, member of the French army, prisoner of war, and for each of these reasons he should be treated with consideration and respect ... Adjutant General Wolfe Tone is a good citizen; his courage and spirited behaviour have gained for him the confidence of the French Government and the esteem of all honourable soldiers ... I was astonished to learn that you were treating him like a criminal'. Hardy's protests were in vain.

The West Indies, earlier in the 1790s, had been Hardy's most successful theatre of operations, a fact which is reflected in the background to this portrait of him.

265 *Attack of the French Squadron under Mons. Bompart Chef d'Escadre upon the Coast of Ireland by a Detachment of His Majesty's Ships under Command of Sir J.B. Warren, Oct. 12, 1798*

By Nicholas Pocock (1740-1821)
Oil on canvas, 69.4 x 99.5cm ; signed and dated 1799
Ulster Museum

This contemporary painting shows the encounter between the French admiral Bompart in his flagship, the 74-gun *Hoche*, and some of Admiral Sir John Borlase Warren's fleet off the coast of Donegal, in which the French were defeated and Wolfe Tone was among the prisoners taken.

Nicholas Pocock was a former merchant captain, who in 1780 took up painting sea-pictures in oils. In 1789 he settled in London, where he became a very successful painter of naval engagements. In 1804 he helped to establish the Water-Colour Society. There and at the Royal Academy he exhibited nearly 300 works in all. This picture has a companion piece, another scene from the same action. Both were donated to the Museum by a descendant of the artist.

Sources: *DNB.*

266 *Sir John Borlase Warren (1753-1822)*

By John Opie (1761-1807)
Oil on canvas, 76.2 x 62.8 cm
Ulster Museum

Warren was the English naval officer who in 1798 commanded the squadron which intercepted a French expedition carrying troops under General Hardy to invade Ireland, among them Wolfe Tone, off the coast of Donegal. With his comparatively much superior fleet of three ships of the line, five powerful frigates and some smaller vessels, Warren caught up with the French under Bompard, who had one ship of 74 guns, the *Hoche*, eight frigates (mostly smaller than those of the English) and a schooner. After a running fight on 12 October the *Hoche*, dismasted, its sails in tatters and with 200 casualties, surrendered along with three of the frigates. The others escaped, but three more were captured within a few days. Only two frigates and the schooner got back to France. Warren's own flagship, the *Canada*, was not engaged but he got the credit for the success of the action which, after the anxiety of the rebellion and Humbert's landing, put paid to any further fear of a French invasion of Ireland that year. The relief felt in official quarters and by loyalists in general was evident in the vote of thanks Warren received from both the British and the Irish parliaments and the gold medals which were awarded to him and his officers. The *Hoche*, renamed the *Donegal*, later formed part of the British fleet which triumphed under Nelson at Trafalgar in 1805.

John Borlase Warren, born in Nottingham, was the fourth son of a country gentleman. Intended for the church, he studied at Emmanuel College, Cambridge from 1769 to 1771. Then the deaths of his elder brothers altered his prospects and his profession. For a time he seems to have divided his time between the navy and his studies, graduating in 1773. Elected to Parliament in 1774, he inherited a baronetcy the following year. He bought Lundy Island and a yacht in which to amuse himself in the Bristol Channel, before joining the navy in earnest in 1777. Retired on half-pay after 1783, he was given command again in 1793 as captain of a 36-gun ship. In 1794 he was made commodore of a frigate squadron on the coast of France, to look for French frigates which were harrying British merchantmen. He caught up with them in April and captured three of the four. Rewarded with a KB, he had further successes, and destroyed a large number of French coasting vessels. In the frigate *Pomone* he took part in the disastrous Quiberon expedition in 1795. In 1796 he destroyed or captured no fewer than 220 French ships, including thirty-seven armed vessels, and was presented with a sword of honour. In 1797 he was appointed to command the 74-gun *Canada*, and was fortunate to be at sea when the mutinies at Spithead and the Nore broke out.

Promoted to rear-admiral in 1799, Warren was made a privy councillor in 1802 and sent to St Petersburg on a mission to the czar. He became a vice-admiral in 1805 and a full admiral five years later. In 1815, when the Order of the Bath was extended and reorganised, his KB was replaced by the new GCB (Grand Cross). His naval service ceased in that year. He died suddenly at Greenwich in 1822.

Warren's defects as a professional sailor were compensated for by his courage, activity and good luck. As shown here, he appears to have been a handsome man of fashionable appearance, and that was his reputation.

John Opie, the son of a Cornish carpenter, came to London when he was nineteen and was introduced to the court, where he became fashionable as 'the Cornish wonder'. George III gave him a commission and he painted many of the ladies of the court. He exhibited at the Royal Academy from 1782, became an RA in 1787 and later lectured there as professor of painting. He is said to have died of overwork, and was buried in St Paul's. Among his sitters were Dr Johnson (whom he painted three times), Fox, Burke and Southey. His portrait of Warren, dated 1794 and presumably commissioned to mark the award of the KB in that year, shows the sitter proudly wearing the Star and Sash of the Order of the Bath. It is a fine example of Opie's work. It was exhibited in 1867 at the South Kensington Exhibition. It was donated to the Belfast Museum and Art Gallery in 1915.

Sources: *DNB.*
            Seamus Brady, 'Wolfe Tone and Donegal', in *Donegal Annual*,
            vol. 1, no. 2 (1948).

267 *Medals commemorating victory of Admiral Warren, September 1798*

(a) Copper gilt medal, engraved by J.G. Hancock, to commemorate the defeat of the French fleet off Tory Island. Bust of Sir J.B. Warren on obverse and on the reverse a design showing a seated Hibernia (unusually playing her harp), skilfully holding up a sprig of olive at the same time, whilst seated on a cannon and a pile of cannon balls. In the background the stern of a ship, flying an indistinguishable flag. It may be that this is intended to represent a French ship fleeing the Irish shores.

(b) Copper medal by an anonymous engraver, showing an almost-facing bust of Admiral Warren and a naval battle scene on the reverse. The legend *The Sister Country once again Rescued from Invasion* probably refers to the abortive French attempt to land at Bantry Bay in 1796. It is difficult to render portraits on medals other than in profile. This medal relates to (and is sometimes muled with) another piece commemorating Nelson's victory at the Nile. The style of portraiture may ultimately relate to a series of seventeenth-century Dutch medals celebrating naval successes.

268 *The Londonderry Journal and Donegal and Tyrone Advertiser, 6 Nov. 1798*

Bound volume no. 5
The Library, University of Ulster at Magee, Londonderry

By the time General Hardy's fleet, intended to support Humbert's invasion in the west, set off from Brest on 14 September 1798, Humbert's small force had already surrendered at Ballinamuck. The expedition of nine ships was attacked off Lough Swilly by a superior British squadron commanded by Sir John Warren. The 84-gun *Hoche*, with Wolfe Tone on board, was one of three ships captured. After a three-week delay, due to bad weather, the prisoners from the *Hoche* landed at Buncrana on 3 November.

The Londonderry Journal carried on 6 November 1798 an account of the arrival and disembarkation of ... 'the celebrated Wolfe Tone ... now with the rank of Adjutant-General in the French army... On landing, he was immediately recognised by many of his College and bar acquaintance'. Tone was the first officer to step ashore, where he was met by Sir George Hill, MP for Londonderry and with whom he had been at Trinity College, Dublin. 'He recognised me and addressed me initially with as much *sang froid* as you might expect from his character', wrote Hill.

On arrival at Derry jail, Tone was put immediately in irons. He wrote directly to Lord Cavan, area military commander at Buncrana. 'I do protest in ... the strongest manner against the indignity intended against the honour of the French army in my person'. Cavan's reply was to the point: 'The motive ... for your being put in irons was ... that you have proved yourself a traitor and rebel to your Sovereign and native country and as such you shall be treated by me'.

Sources: Frank MacDermot, *Theobald Wolfe Tone.*
                Marianne Elliott, *Wolfe Tone.*

269 *'The Unfortunate' Theobald Wolfe Tone, 1798*

ANONYMOUS LINE ENGRAVING, 17.6 X 10.8 CM
NATIONAL GALLERY OF IRELAND, DUBLIN

This print, from a drawing done at his trial by court martial, shows Tone in the French officer's uniform he insisted upon wearing for the occasion. Despite his claim to be a French soldier, he was inevitably found guilty of treason to George III and sentenced to death by hanging, instead of the military death by firing squad that he asked for.

270 *Death mask of Wolfe Tone, 1798*

PLASTER CAST, 21 CM HIGH
NATIONAL GALLERY OF IRELAND, DUBLIN

Following Tone's death from a self-inflicted wound on 19 November 1798 and a coroner's inquest later the same day, Lord Castlereagh gave permission for the body to be delivered to the friends of the deceased, 'but on the express condition that no assemblage of people shall be permitted and that it be interred in the most private manner'. Next day the body was taken to 52 High Street, the house of relatives named Dunbavin, where Tone's parents were living at the time. There the corpse was laid out on the second floor and a plaster cast was taken of his face. During the next two days crowds of mourners called to pay their respects.

The death mask was later used to produce busts, two of which are known to have survived - one in Trinity College, Dublin, the other in the Irish-American Historical Library, New York. Several copies of the cast were made, of which this is one. Tone's remains were buried quietly in the family plot at Bodenstown, County Kildare on 21 November.

Sources: Marianne Elliott, *Wolfe Tone.*

271 *Napper Tandy - Taken from Life in Newgate, Novemr 2nd 1799*

BY J[AMES] GILLRAY
COLOURED ENGRAVING, 19.4 x 16.2 CM, PUBLISHED IN LONDON 8 NOV. 1799 BY H. HUMPHREY
BRITISH MUSEUM, LONDON

In Gillray's portrait, taken from life in his cell in London's Newgate prison, Tandy wears French uniform. Following his abortive expedition to Ireland in the French ship *Anacreon* in 1798, when he briefly landed on Rutland Island off the coast of Donegal, he had escaped to Norway and thence to Hamburg. The Hamburg authorities eventually gave way to British pressure and extradited him to England, where he arrived on 27 October 1799 en route to his trial in Ireland, which took place at Lifford, County Donegal. He was convicted but not executed because there were doubts about the legality of his arrest and the French government made forceful representations. In the end these were successful and led to his release when the Anglo-French war ended with the treaty of Amiens in 1802. (It was said that Napoleon had threatened to break off negotiations for a treaty unless Tandy's release was guaranteed). Tandy landed at Bordeaux, where he received a hero's welcome. He died there in 1803. His wife, who would not follow him to France, died in Ireland in 1820. In her absence he took up with his French housekeeper, fathered a son by her, and bequeathed to her his estate in France. His wife and son James contested the will. Having supported Napper Tandy throughout his radical career they subsequently suffered considerably from the connection. James narrowly escaped assassination in Dublin, presumably by a disgruntled loyalist. He was then arrested, interrogated by the privy council and imprisoned in Kilmainham for almost a year, on a charge of treasonable practices. Both his health and his business suffered. Mrs Tandy too was shot at, and was later scarred by a missile flung through her window.

Though it looks like a caricature, Gillray's picture of Tandy was by all accounts an accurate portrait of the veteran revolutionary as he looked in 1799 (he was nearly sixty by then, and much the worse from hardship and hard drinking). Though he had long been among the leading figures of the radical cause in Ireland, he owed his posthumous immortality more to the fact that he featured in a contemporary ballad which was to become an anthem of Irish nationalism, 'The Wearing of the Green'.

NAPPER TANDY.
— *Taken from Life in Newgate. Novem.r 2.d 1799.*

> I met with Napper Tandy,
> And he took me by the hand,
> Saying: How is poor old Ireland,
> And how does she stand?
> She's the most distressful country
> That ever yet was seen;
> They are hanging men and women
> For the wearing of the green!

Sources: *DNB.*
        Rupert J. Coughlan, *Napper Tandy* (Dublin, 1976).

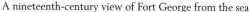
A nineteenth-century view of Fort George from the sea

272 *Aerial view of Fort George, near Inverness*

HISTORIC SCOTLAND
REPRODUCTION

Fort George was built on a promontory overlooking the Moray Firth in the years after the defeat of the Jacobite clans at nearby Culloden. It was intended to be an impregnable obstacle to any future French invasion and was therefore constructed to a scale and specification equal to those of the great fortifications of the Continent. Its impregnability was never tested in battle, however. Instead it has survived, externally almost unchanged, as a perfect - and highly impressive - example of an eighteenth-century artillery fort.

This remote and wild spot was chosen in the late 1790s as the place of incarceration for the Irish state prisoners. Originally they were to be banished to America, but, the government of the United States at that time refusing to accept such political refugees and the British government not wishing to let them loose in Europe whilst war with France continued, they were instead interned for the duration in Fort George in 1799 and released in 1802 when the war ended. Under a humane governor they were physically well treated, though the winters were severe.

The prisoners, who included Arthur O'Connor, MacNeven, Thomas Addis Emmet, Russell, Neilson and William Tennent, were housed on the top floor of a barrack block close to the main magazine. The Rev. William Steel Dickson relates the panic among them on one occasion when there was a chimney fire.

Sources: Dickson, *Narrative.*
            Iain MacIvor, *Fort George* (Historic Scotland guidebook, 1995).

273 *A Narrative of the Confinement and Exile of William Steel Dickson D.D.*

BY WILLIAM STEEL DICKSON; SECOND EDITION (BELFAST, 1812)
ULSTER MUSEUM

William Steel Dickson was one of a number of suspected leaders of the United Irishmen detained without charge in the weeks immediately prior to the outbreak of rebellion in the early summer of 1798. He was initially held in the Donegall Arms, in the company of others arrested at the same time. In August 1798 he was removed to a prison ship in Belfast Lough and in March 1799 was sent with nineteen other very prominent United Irish figures to Fort George, Invernesshire, in the north of Scotland, where they were to spend three years until their release in 1802.

Dickson's *Narrative* is our main source of information about the journey of the prisoners, heavily escorted, to Fort George and their life there. They were well treated by a humane governor and the food was excellent - 'very fine salmon twice or thrice a week ... wine, porter, and ale uniformly good' etc.

Early in 1802, Dickson was released along with Robert Simms, William Tennent, Robert Hunter and William Dowdall, who all signed recognisances guaranteeing their future good conduct. They were allowed to return to Belfast and to resume their former careers. The remaining fifteen prisoners, who refused to give similar undertakings, were in due course escorted to Hamburg, where they were released.

This copy of the *Narrative* bears the bookplate of James Plunkett, Earl of Fingall, a Catholic peer who had been a leading figure in the Catholic Committee in the early 1790s.

274 *Brevet d'honneur, c.1804*

PARCHMENT, 34 x 43 CM, SIGNED BY BONAPARTE AS FIRST CONSUL
MR NEVILLE WHITTLEY

A *brevet d'honneur* was the official citation marking recognition by the French Republic of noteworthy service. It was accompanied in this instance by the award of a sabre to its military recipient. It is signed by Napoleon Bonaparte in his capacity as First Consul (head of state) of the Republic, the title he held before he proclaimed himself Emperor in 1805. It is dated *an onze* (Year II) by the French Republican calendar, which reckoned from 1792. Only 209 were issued.

275 *Nécessaire or campaign kit*

BY MAIRE OF PARIS, C. 1790
BRASS-BOUND WOODEN CASE WITH FITTINGS, 30 X 16 X 10 CM
MR NEVILLE WHITTLEY

This fine example of a nécessaire or personal campaign kit was apparently made by the noted Parisian maker Maire. Both of the razor blades are marked with his name, and a label of his is fixed to the case of the razor strop (though it is possible that the label was a later addition). The very compact design accommodates a wide range of personal toilet accessories and useful articles: a shaving mirror (of later style and therefore apparently a replacement), a pair of shaving brushes, several glass bottles with silver tops, two ivory or bone-handled razors, a bone-handled penknife, a pair of scissors, a folding bone ruler marked in inches (a possible clue to date this, since France adopted the metric system officially in 1799), a pair of metal boot-jacks, a boot hook (for buttoned boots or spats), a corkscrew, a watch key with a variety of sockets, a tortoiseshell comb, an instrument with toothpicks and a scoop for removing ear wax, a steel for flint, small implements possibly used for removing fragments of shot and de-scaling teeth, a toothbrush, a folding jacknife, a razor strop with sheath, and a small clothes hook (?). The case has a double-turn lock.

In two places, the red leather interior bears the arms of the Spanish Bourbons stamped in gold. This device consists of the personal arms of King Carlos III (1764-88) with the chain of the Order of Carlos III which he instituted in 1771; the arms are identical with those on some of his coinage. Together with the bone ruler mentioned above, this suggests a date in the 1780s or early 1790s.

According to the label, Maire carried on his business in the rue de Rivoli. He worked for Louis XVI before the Revolution, for some of the revolutionary leaders

in the 1790s (one surviving example of his work is a magnificent picnic or campaign set of plates, cutlery etc., made for Paul Barras, one of the Directors) and in the early 1800s for Napoleon.

276 *Double-barrelled flintlock sporting gun presented by the Emperor Napoleon I to Marshal Davoust, 1812*

BY LE PAGE OF PARIS
LENGTH 120 CM
MR NEVILLE WHITTLEY

According to the old, partly-legible label on the stock, which has been varnished over to preserve it, this splendid piece was a present from Napoleon to Marshal Davoust, *Cadeau de Napoleon I^{ier} à Maréchal Davoust ...*, in 1812.

The barrels, which are proof-marked, carry the inscription *Le Page à Paris* and are complete with ramrod. The gun has silver mounts, hallmarked on the butt, all lavishly decorated with hunting scenes and French symbols (the republican fasces, a cockerel, an eagle). The stock is of carved walnut or similar dark wood. The stock has a cheek-pad, originally covered in green velvet.

Davoust accompanied Napoleon to Russia in 1812, on the ill-fated campaign that helped to break his power in Europe. The flamboyant style of this sporting weapon is typical of the best French makers of the period.

277 *Brevet of a Captain Commadant [sic] in Madgett's Legion, 1798*

P. AND B. ROWAN

Headed *Erin Go Brah! Liberty. Equality.* the brevet is signed by Nicholas Madgett and dated at Orleans 10 fructidor, year 6 of the French Republic by the revolutionary calendar (27 August 1798). It reads:

By virtue of the power delegated to me by the secret committee of the Society of united Irishmen of Paris, for raising a military corps, to bear the name of MADGETT'S Legion, said corps to be chiefly composed of such Irishmen, actually in France, as are desirous to rescue their county from the iron yoke of England, I do hereby nominate and appoint *Robert Legentil* to the rank of *Captain of a Company* in said Legion *to Enjoy the rights and Prerogatives of said grade and duty as such* - Earnestly requesting he may be confirmed in said rank or commission with the honour and pay annexed to it, by the sister societies of united Irishmen and by the future government of Ireland. Given under my hand and the seal of the Society.

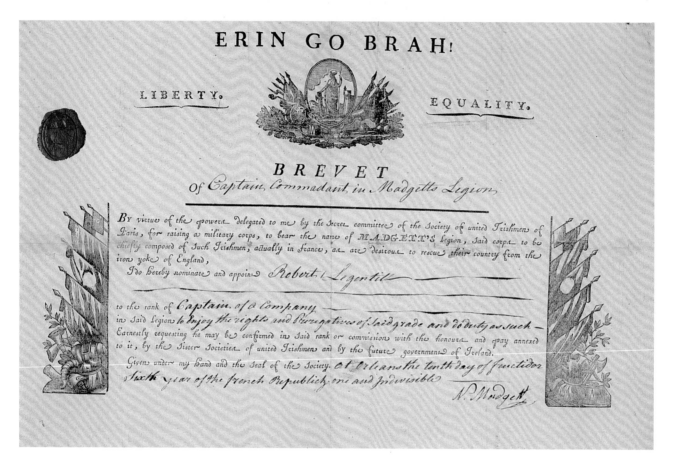

11 The Union

The Rebellion and the circumstances of its suppression made the union of Great Britain and Ireland - by no means a new idea - inevitable. Only within a United Kingdom could the safety of Ireland from foreign invasion and internal subversion be guaranteed and emancipation be safely granted to Irish Catholics - a permanent minority in the United Parliament. The good intentions of Pitt, Cornwallis and Castlereagh in regard to the latter were beyond doubt.

The Irish Parliament had to be persuaded to agree to abolish itself. Being a thoroughly corrupt body, it did so when sufficiently rewarded. The ministers and officials who carried through this necessary but distasteful task simply employed, in a more determined and concentrated (and better-funded) way, the means by which British administrations had always achieved their objectives in Ireland.

The Catholic question, however, was a harder matter. Pitt knew of George III's objections but counted on the opposition of a united cabinet to overcome them. Instead, the King was encouraged by some influential figures at court to believe he would be breaking his solemn coronation oath if he agreed to emancipation. Though Pitt, Cornwallis and Castlereagh all resigned, the Union had got off to a bad start. The King's longevity, and the more urgent needs of the continuing war, thereafter kept the matter on hold.

The turmoil of 1798 was briefly revived in 1803 by Robert Emmet's attempted rising. Was Emmet a romantic young fool and his plan a harebrained and hopeless one, or was it something more serious? The jury, thought to have handed in an adverse verdict long ago, now appears to be reconsidering.

278 *The Right Honble William Pitt*

MEZZOTINT BY GEORGE CLINT, AFTER JOHN HOPPNER; 48 x 35.5 CM
NATIONAL GALLERY OF IRELAND, DUBLIN

In normal circumstances, Pitt was notoriously uninterested in Irish affairs, as Irish viceroys soon discovered. 'I believe as you candidly acknowledged to me before I came hither', wrote Camden, 'that Ireland occupys little of your thoughts'. Camden's predecessor Lord Westmoreland had found the same thing. When faced with serious trouble in Ireland, however, Pitt had to give some thought to the problem of a satisfactory relationship between the two kingdoms. The Regency crisis in 1788, for instance, had been potentially threatening but had blown over with George III's recovery from madness. In 1792 Pitt was stimulated by the continuing Catholic agitation and the deteriorating situation in Europe to look for 'a permanent system which they [Anglo-Irish relations] could stand upon'.

The idea of uniting the two legislatures was not a new one, but from this point onward it began to be considered seriously by Pitt, though at first as a confidential hypothesis. Writing to Westmoreland in November 1792 he said

> The idea ... has long been in my mind ... The admission of Catholics to a share of the suffrage could not then be dangerous - the Protestant interest in point of power, property and Church establishment would be secure because the decided majority of the supreme legislature would necessarily be Protestant.

Westmoreland replied:

> The Protestants frequently declare that they will have an Union rather than give the franchise to the Catholics, and the Catholics that they will have an Union rather than submit to their presentstate of degradation. It is worth turning in your mind how the violence of both parties might be turned on this occasion to the advantage of England.

In the event, Pitt obliged the viceroy to sponsor a bill to give the vote in parliamentary elections to Catholic freeholders, on the same terms as Protestants, and to carry through other reforms. A bill to admit Catholics to Parliament, however, was defeated by 163 votes to 69. The fact that money was provided to build a new House of Commons, to replace the building destroyed by fire in 1792, suggests that at this stage the Union was not being regarded as inevitable. The hopes the reforms of 1793-94 created among liberals were wiped out by the disaster of the Fitzwilliam episode. Thereafter, developments in Ireland - increasingly militant agitation by radicals looking to France, an increasingly reactionary response by the authorities, increasingly sectarian conflict in some rural areas - in the context of the war with France, culminating in the attempted French invasion of 1796 and the rebellion of 1798, made the Union increasingly attractive, not to say essential as a long-term solution. It is only fair to note that at every point along this road Pitt envisaged that outcome as necessarily to be accompanied or followed by Catholic emancipation. When it was not, he resigned.

John Hoppner (1758-1810) was born in London of German parents. He was highly successful portrait painter, exhibiting no fewer than 168 pictures in the Royal Academy between 1780-1809. At his best he was regarded as the main rival to Sir Thomas Lawrence.

George Clint (1770-1854), the engraver who produced this mezzotint from Hoppner's picture, was to be particularly well known for theatrical portraits.

Sources: G.C. Bolton, *The Passing of the Irish Act of Union* (Oxford, 1964).

279 *Charles Cornwallis, first Marquess and second Earl Cornwallis (1738-1805)*

BY JOHN BACON, RA (1740-99)
MARBLE BUST, 75 CM HIGH
ENGLISH HERITAGE

Charles Cornwallis was born on 31 December 1738, the sixth child and eldest son of the first Earl Cornwallis and his wife Elizabeth, daughter of Lord Townshend. He was educated at Eton and at the Military Academy of Turin before entering the Grenadier Guards as an ensign in 1756; his military experience in the Seven Years War which broke out in the same year included the battle of Minden, and he ended the war as a lieutenant-colonel. In 1765 he was appointed a lord of the bedchamber, ADC to the King and colonel of the 33rd Regiment. Having succeeded his father as a peer, he was one of only five who voted against the resolution asserting Britain's right to tax the Americans. Though he was a Whig in politics and the Whigs were detested by George III, Cornwallis was personally trusted by the King, who appointed him constable of the Tower of London and promoted him to major-general. Despite his earlier opposition to the government's treatment of the colonists, Cornwallis loyally accepted a command in the war against them, first under Howe and then under Clinton, achieving some success in his subordinate role, and gaining promotion to lieutenant-general. The overall conduct of the war was so incompetent, however, that Cornwallis sent in his resignation, which George III would not accept. He had some successes in the campaigns he led in the southern colonies but got little support from Clinton and was at last cornered by the Americans and their French allies at Yorktown in Virginia, where he was obliged to surrender in October 1781 with his entire army. Cornwallis was not blamed by anyone for this disaster, which effectively ended the war.

Back home, Cornwallis reluctantly in 1781 accepted appointment as governor-general of India, where British prestige was at a low ebb and corruption among the British officials was rife at all levels. His attempted reforms made no great

impression, but he did break the power of Tippoo Sahib, sultan of Mysore, who in 1792 was forced to give up half his kingdom and pay a huge fine of £3,600,000. Both Cornwallis as commander-in-chief and his commander in the field, General Medows, left their prize money (£47,244 and £14,997 respectively) to be distributed among the army, which made a great impression. Cornwallis was created a marquess for his services. He left India in October 1793. He nearly went back to India in 1797 because of a military crisis there (he was actually sworn in, but gave up the appointment again when the crisis subsided). Instead, he was sent to Ireland as viceroy and commander-in-chief, to the relief of Pitt, who wrote to him: 'You have, in my opinion, conferred the most essential obligation on the public which it can perhaps ever receive from the services of any individual'.

By the time Cornwallis arrived in Dublin, on 20 June 1798, Lake had defeated the Wexford rebels at Vinegar Hill; Moore entered Wexford town the next day. It was therefore the aftermath of the rebellion that Cornwallis had to deal with: preventing it from spreading, mopping up the rebel forces still in the field, curbing the excesses of the military and the vindictiveness of the more extreme Protestants in Parliament and in the country - and, in due course, achieving the union of parliaments that Pitt decided upon as the only answer to the Irish problem. The pacification of the country was complicated by Humbert's landing in Mayo and by his astonishing success at Castlebar. Cautiously assembling a large army, Cornwallis barred the French advance and finally forced Humbert to surrender at Ballinamuck. His own instinct thereafter was to punish the ringleaders of the rebels and spare their followers. He strongly disapproved of the pogroms that occurred in some areas under the cloak of martial law, and made himself deeply unpopular with more extreme loyalists by reprimanding the Earl of Enniskillen, who had presided over one particularly notorious court martial.

So far as the Union was concerned, Cornwallis's main role was to ensure that the Irish secretary, Castlereagh, received all the support he needed to put the measure through. Cornwallis left the sordid details, which he personally detested, to his subordinate. Castlereagh had to buy the support of the necessary majority in the Irish parliament by promises of titles, places and (in the form of compensation for disfranchised boroughs) cash. After the passage of the bill in Dublin, when George III at first declined to fulfil some of these pledges, the lord lieutenant threatened to resign. He strongly believed, with Pitt and Castlereagh, that union should be accompanied by Catholic emancipation. When it was not, he did resign. 'No consideration', he wrote, 'could induce me to take a responsible part with any administration who can be so blind to the interest, and indeed to the immediate security of their country, as to persevere in the old system of proscription and exclusion in Ireland'.

Subsequently, Cornwallis was British plenipotentiary at the negotiations for peace with France, which resulted in the treaty of Amiens in 1802. Since he was not a trained diplomat, had largely forgotten his French, and was faced by cleverer men (one of whom was Talleyrand), this was not one of his successes. In 1805, after three years retirement, he was suddenly asked to go to India again as governor-general and commander-in-chief. Despite his advanced age - he was sixty-six - he felt it to be his duty. Three months after landing at Calcutta he died, on his way up the Ganges to put an end to the fighting that Lake (whom he had superseded as commander-in-chief, as once before in Ireland) had been carrying on with notable success. He was buried where he died. Statues were erected to him in St Paul's Cathedral and at Bombay and Madras. The East India Company's court of directors voted £40,000 to his family.

John Bacon (1740-99) was one of the most successful sculptors of his day. Beginning as an apprentice modeller in a china factory, he became a student of the Royal Academy on its foundation in 1768 and was awarded its first gold medal the following year. Among his best-known works are the monuments to Pitt in Westminster Abbey and to Samuel Johnson in St Paul's Cathedral. This bust of Cornwallis, signed and dated 'Bacon 1798', was one of his last works. It is part of the collection at Audley End, Saffron Walden, Essex.

Sources: *DNB.*

280 *Robert Stewart, Viscount Castlereagh*

By Hugh Douglas Hamilton
Oil on canvas, approx. 80 x 60 cm
Lady Mairi Bury

Robert Stewart was born, probably at Mount Stewart in County Down, on 18 June 1769, the eldest son of Robert Stewart, a landowner of Scottish descent from County Donegal whose father Alexander (d.1781) had bought his County Down estate (which included the town of Newtownards, though not its corporation, which controlled two seats in the Irish parliament) in 1744. Alexander thus became the largest Presbyterian landowner in the county. His son Robert remained a Presbyterian all his life, but *his* son Robert was to change to the established church. In 1789 the elder Robert was raised to the Irish peerage as Baron Stewart of Londonderry, to which were added Viscount Castlereagh (1795), Earl of Londonderry (1796) and eventually Marquess of Londonderry (1816). From 1796, the younger Robert Stewart was known by the courtesy title of Viscount Castlereagh, though for the last few months of his life he was second marquess of Londonderry following the death of his father.

Educated at the Royal School, Armagh and St John's College, Cambridge, Stewart entered public life in 1790 when he was elected to the Irish House of Commons as one of the members for County Down, after a contest with the Downshire family which is said to have cost his father £60,000 (and Downshire £30,000). As a Presbyterian Whig with reforming ideas he was enthusiastically supported by liberals - Samuel Neilson, later a leading United Irishman and editor

of the *Northern Star*, was his election agent, and another partisan was the Rev. Dr William Steel Dickson - and in Parliament supported reforming measures such as the Catholic Relief Act of 1793. In that year he was also appointed lieutenant-colonel of the newly-established Londonderry Militia, having voted for the suppression of the Volunteers. This, from someone who had once presided at a public dinner where a toast to 'Our sovereign lord, the people' was drunk, marked a complete change. His erstwhile friends were shocked, but in fact the excesses of the French Revolution and the growing enthusiasm for radical reform put off a good many moderate reformers. Much worse was the fact that Stewart went on to become a leader of the reactionary party, though it is important to note that he was always in favour of Catholic emancipation. In 1794 Stewart married the youngest daughter of the Earl of Buckingham and was drawn more and more into English political circles. When his brother-in-law Lord Camden was appointed lord lieutenant of Ireland in 1795, following Fitzwilliam's recall, Castlereagh (as he was now known) was made keeper of the privy seal and became, with the illness of the chief secretary Pelham, acting secretary. In 1799, when Pelham at last resigned his post, Castlereagh became secretary in title as well as in effect, Cornwallis breaking the hitherto strictly observed rule that the chief secretary should always be an Englishman. Castlereagh was thus the head of the administration in Dublin Castle throughout the crucial period of the Rebellion and its immediate aftermath and as such was responsible for the arrest of the leaders of the United Irishmen and the suppression of the revolt itself. Afterwards, he was the key figure in bringing about the Act of Union, not shrinking from the dirty business of doing whatever was needed to persuade a majority in the Irish Parliament to vote for its dissolution. All this made his name hated by Irish nationalists, as it was later to be by English radicals. When George III would not agree to follow the Union by the granting of Catholic emancipation, Castlereagh (like Pitt himself, Cornwallis and Cooke) resigned from office. He was barely more than thirty years old.

His subsequent political career in the politics of the United Kingdom, culminating in his long tenure of the office of foreign secretary from 1812 to 1822 when he guided the fate of Europe as well as that of the British Empire, need not detain us here. He was the greatest foreign secretary of modern times, perhaps the greatest ever. Though unimpressive as a speaker - the liberal Lord Brougham wrote that 'His capacity was greatly underrated from the poverty of his discourse: and his ideas passed for much less than they were worth, from the habitual obscurity of his expressions ... incapable of uttering two sentences of anything but the meanest matter in the most wretched language' - he was wonderfully cogent on paper, as any historian who has ever read his letters and despatches can testify. He was also personally incorruptible and extremely hardworking. In fact, overwork and anxiety killed him. In 1822, while disturbed in his mind (there were rumours too about something scandalous in his private life), he cut his throat with a penknife. His funeral in Westminster Abbey attracted an immense crowd, including many who came to jeer rather than to mourn. The poet Shelley's savage lines 'I met Murder in the way - He had a mask like Castlereagh', express the hatred felt by the radicals.

Sources: *DNB.*
             Webb, *Compendium of Irish Biography.*
             H. Montgomery Hyde, *The rise of Castlereagh* (London 1933).

281 *John Thomas Troy, Archbishop of Dublin (1739-1823)*

BY T.C. THOMPSON
OIL ON CANVAS, 74 X 61CM
NATIONAL GALLERY OF IRELAND, DUBLIN

John Thomas Troy was born near Dublin in 1739 and left Ireland at the age of fifteen to pursue his theological studies at Rome, where he joined the Dominican order in 1756. He was rector of St Clement's in Rome when appointed Bishop of Ossory in 1776.

Troy was an exceptionally conservative figure, both in religious matters and in his political views. He opposed any kind of rebellion by Catholics against constituted authority, condemning the Whiteboys and anathematising the United Irishmen and their French-inspired ideas. In this he reflected the official line of the papacy and the hierarchy. He was instrumental in the foundation of Maynooth College in 1795, and later supported proposals for government endowment of the Catholic clergy. After the Rebellion, his was the most influential Catholic voice to approve of the Union scheme, in the belief that emancipation was much more likely to come from a United Parliament than from the Irish Parliament. When emancipation did not follow union, his influence was greatly weakened. This loss was underlined by the fact that the cleric appointed as his coadjutor in 1809, Daniel Murray, held very different views.

The artist Thomas Clement Thompson (c.1780-1857) was born in Belfast and learned to paint at the Dublin Society Schools. He began as a painter of miniatures before establishing himself in Dublin in 1810. He was a founder-member of the Royal Hibernian Academy, though living in London after 1817 and exhibiting at the Royal Academy there as well as in Dublin. His prolific output included many portraits, which have been described as 'solid though uninspired'.

Sources: *DNB.*
              Webb, *Compendium of Irish Biography.*
              Anne Crookshank and The Knight of Glin, *The Painters of Ireland, c.1660-1920.*

282 *AN IRISH UNION!*

BY I[SAAC] C[RUIKSHANK]
ENGRAVING, 22.2 X 33.4 CM, PUBLISHED IN LONDON 30 JAN. 1799 BY S.W. FORES
BRITISH MUSEUM, LONDON

Below the title is an ironic quotation from Shakespeare: 'If there be no great love in the beginning - yet heaven may decrease it upon better acquaintance'.

Pitt joins together the hands of a bemused John Bull and a suspicious Paddy, who is listening to Dundas reading from a *History of Scotland* about the economic advantages that country has enjoyed from its union with Britain *(you will find how many made the siller frae that time to this)*. Pitt says: *'Depend upon it - what that Gentleman says is right - thus I join your hands in Friendship & one Interest - and whom I put together - let no man put asunder.* But Paddy says, *'Now is it Blar[n]eying you are at?'*, while John says: *'This may be Nation good Fun - but dang my buttons if I know what it is about! & cousin Paddy dont seem quite clear in the case neither.* On the left stands a man, possibly Joseph Smith, private secretary to Pitt at the Treasury, who carries blankets marked *Tax on Income* and says *'When you want the Wet Blankets - I have them ready'* - a reference to the likelihood that Pitt's income tax would probably be extended to Ireland after the union.

Sources: *BM Catalogue*, VII, no. 9344.

283 *The Union Coach*

COLOURED ENGRAVING, 23.2 X 37.5 CM, PUBLISHED IN DUBLIN JUNE 1799 BY MCCLEARY, 21 NASSAU STREET
BRITISH MUSEUM, LONDON

Pitt drives the union coach towards Westminster, with Dundas as the guard. Inside it are a greedy crew of Scottish members, anxious not to upset the existing cosy arrangement. In the basket behind are Irish supporters of union, prominent among whom are the lord chancellor (Lord Clare) and John Beresford. They are being

threatened by a stout Irishman with a cudgel, who says, *The Devil Relieve you all I wish I had the Beting of ye I'd make ye remember yr Native Country.*

In a reference to the difficulty in getting the union bill through the Irish Parliament, Pitt is shown complaining: *These Paddy's in the Basket are the most troublesome People I ever Drove aye-aye-its a sign they're not used to such good Travelling ... if they grumble so now what will they say when I lip them the Long Trot over the Flints in Parliament Street.*

This print is a Dublin version of one by Cruikshank published in London early in June. In Cruikshank's, three of the Irish members are shown saying *I dont much relish this Union Coach the Guard told us the back seats were the best, by Shaint Patrick the front ones must be bad enough then!*. Seats in the basket of a coach were notoriously the worst ones, and many travellers of the period - Pastor Moritz in 1782, for example - describe the horrors they suffered there.

Sources: *BM Catalogue*, VII, no. 9395.

284 *Horrors of the Irish-Union; Botheration of poor Pat-or-a Whisper across the Channel*

By J[ame]s Gillray
Coloured engraving, 22.7 x 34.8 cm, published in London 24 Dec. 1798 by H. Humphrey
British Museum, London

A buxom figure of Britannia, with bales of goods and a cornucopia of coins and jewels, sits on one side of the Irish Channel holding a scroll entitled *Union of Security Trade & Liberty* and looking appealingly towards Pat; one foot tramples on the serpent of Discord. In the bushes behind her are Fox, Tierney and Taylor telling Pat to beware. Fox whispers:

'Hip! my old Friend Pat! - hip! - a word in your Ear! take care of yourself Pat! - or you'll be ruin'd past Redemption - dont you see that this damn'd Union is only meant to make a Slave of you! - do but look how that cursed Hag is forging Fetters to bind you, & preparing her knapsack to carry off your Property, & to Ravish your whole Country, Man, Woman & Child! - why you are blind sure! - rouse yourself Man! raise all the

279

Horrors of the IRISH-UNION; — *Botheration of poor Pat:* or — *a Whisper across the Channel*

Lawyers & spur up the Corporations, Fight to the last drop of blood, & part with the last Potatoe to preserve your Property & Independence -'.

Pat, a sturdy fellow in ragged clothes and with his pike broken (a reference to the defeat of the rebellion) says:

Plunder & Knapsacks! & Ravishments, & ruin of little Ireland! - why - by St Patrick, its very odd, now! for the old Girl seems to me, to be offering me her Heart & her Hand, & her Trade & the use of her Shelalee [shillelagh, i.e. physical protection] to defend me into the bargain! - by Jasus! if you was not my old friend, Charley, I should think you meant to bother me with your Whispering to put the old Lady in a passion, that we may not buss one another, or be Friends any more.

The proposals for a union, put forward by Pitt in the wake of the 1798 rebellion, met with opposition on both sides of the 'Irish Channel', hence a propaganda campaign to win over public opinion, as well as political manoeuverings at Westminster and in Dublin.

Sources: *BM Catalogue*, VII, no. 9284.

285 *Last Journals of the Irish House of Commons*

PUBLIC RECORD OFFICE OF NORTHERN IRELAND

Two volumes from a set of *Journals* of the Irish House of Commons bound for John Foster who, from 1785 until it was abolished by the Act of Union, was Speaker of the House.

286 *Union Bill, 1800*

P. AND B. ROWAN

This is a rare survival of a parliamentary working document.

When the question of Union was first debated by the Irish House of Commons, on 22 June 1799, there was a slender majority in favour. Two days later, however, the motion was defeated by five votes. Many members of the Dublin parliament

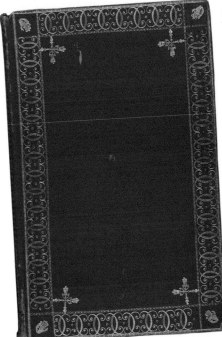

were initially reluctant to give up a lucrative source of income and patronage. During 1799 the Irish government, in close association with the British cabinet, busied itself with amending the terms of the Bill. During this time, too, a greater awareness was evident among the landed class, many of whom held seats in College Green, that union with Britain offered the best means of protection for their estates and families.

The Irish Parliament that was about to be liquidated had 300 members. Representation of Ireland at Westminster was fixed at 100 seats. The plan of union introduced at the beginning of 1800 recommended that the 32 Irish counties, and the cities of Dublin and Cork, should each return two members to the United Parliament in London, making a total of 68. A means had to be found of selecting 32 boroughs which would each return one member, thus making up the 100 seats. The management of this scheme, and the winning of the support of influential parliamentarians, was entrusted to Robert Stewart, Lord Castlereagh, assisted by under-secretary Edward Cooke.

By February 1800, in what was said to have been the largest division in the history of the Irish House of Commons, there was a majority in favour of 158 to 115. A corresponding Bill in the Parliament at Westminster was approved without a division.

Sources: G.C. Bolton, *The Passing of the Act of Union* (1966).
            The Act of Union PRONI Education Facsimiles Nos 41-60 (1970).

287 *The Act of Union, 1800*

P. AND B. ROWAN

This is a copy of the Act by which the Irish Parliament was merged with the Parliament of Great Britain in the Parliament of the United Kingdom. Under its terms, legislative union between Great Britain and Ireland became effective from 1 January 1801. Both Pitt and Castlereagh had intended that the Union would be accompanied by Catholic Emancipation (which was, of course, one of the original aims of the United Irishmen). Local Ascendancy opposition and, crucially, the refusal of the King to countenance such a departure ensured the withdrawal of the relevant clause. A disappointed Pitt then resigned.

ANNO TRICESIMO NONO & QUADRAGESIMO

GEORGII III. REGIS.

C A P. LXVII.

An Act for the Union of *Great Britain* and *Ireland*.
[2d *July* 1800.]

288 *Robert Emmet (1778-1803)*

BY JOHN COMERFORD
MINIATURE, WATERCOLOUR ON IVORY, 6.9 X 5.7 CM
NATIONAL GALLERY OF IRELAND, DUBLIN

Robert Emmet, younger brother of Thomas Addis Emmet, was born in Molesworth Street, Dublin in 1778, shortly before the family moved to Stephen's Green. He entered Trinity College in October 1793. His career there, like his brother's before him, was a brilliant one, especially in mathematics and chemistry. He was an exceptionally eloquent speaker in the debates of the College Historical Society, taking the national side on political motions. This brought him to the attention of the College authorities. When, in April 1798, the lord chancellor, Fitzgibbon, held a formal visitation of the College and summoned Emmet to appear before him, the young radical denounced the proceedings and resigned his place. Little is known about his activities during the next few years. In 1800 he visited his brother in Fort George, before going to the Continent, where he travelled in Belgium, France, Switzerland, Spain, returning by way of Holland and Belgium (where he met his brother, recently released). In the autumn of 1802 he met Napoleon (whom he thought insincere in his promises to make Ireland independent) and Talleyrand,

before returning to Ireland in October.

He at once began to make plans for a revolution in Dublin the following summer, using his own money to buy arms or the materials for his followers to make arms, which were stored at strategically-placed depots around the city. He also hid arms between floors at his parents' country house at Casino, and in a house at Rathfarnham that he rented under an assumed name. The plans included an attack on Dublin Castle, the seat of government, when the viceroy and senior officials were to be seized. The rising was intended for August, but an accidental explosion at the depot in Patrick Street on 16 July - the first inkling the authorities had of the conspiracy - brought it forward to 23 July. Emmet left home and holed up in the depot in Marshalsea Lane. There, says Madden, 'he lay at night on a mattress, surrounded by all the implements of death, devising plans, turning over in his mind all the fearful chances of the intended struggle, well knowing that his life was at the mercy of upwards of forty individuals, who had been or still were employed in the depots; yet confident of success ...'. When the day came, the cautious Michael Dwyer, who had been contacted on Emmet's behalf by James Hope, did not move; others assembled but were given no definite orders. Late in the evening, hearing that the military were on the move, Emmet donned the revolutionary leader's uniform he had had made for the occasion and sallied forth from Marshalsea Lane at the head of about a hundred followers, making for the Castle. In Thomas Street, the stragglers came upon the coach of Lord Kilwarden, chief justice of the King's Bench, travelling with his daughter and a nephew to a meeting of the privy council. Kilwarden, a fair-minded judge who had shown courage in dealing with the military authorities at the trial of Wolfe Tone, was piked along with his nephew, dying of his wounds an hour later. News of the murder reached Emmet, who was horrified and, finding he could no nothing to control the mob, departed for Rathfarnham.

The fighting in Dublin was over the same evening, as troops poured into the city and martial law was proclaimed. In the north too, Emmet's friend Thomas Russell had completely failed to raise the country. After hiding with some of his followers at Rathfarnham for nearly two days, Emmet fled to the Wicklow mountains, where Anne Devlin visited them. Instead of trying to get out of the country immediately, Emmet insisted on returning to Dublin to take leave of his fiancée Sarah Curran, daughter of the liberal John Philpot Curran (who entirely disapproved of the liaison and later disowned her). He was betrayed to the authorities for a reward of £1,000, and arrested on 25 August. The result of the trial was a foregone conclusion, not only because the judge, Lord Norbury, was very hostile but also because Emmet made no attempt to deny his responsibility. He was sentenced to be hanged and beheaded the next day. The trial was remarkable, however, and was to become famous, for Emmet's stirring speech from the dock, which contained the inspirational words: 'Let no man write my epitaph ... When my country takes her place among the nations of the earth, then, and not till then, let my epitaph be written.' What the sword had so signally, and yet again, failed to achieve, the pen eventually redeemed. Emmet was only twenty-four when he died.

John Comerford (c.1770-1832) was an Irish miniature-painter who exhibited in London 1804-09.

Sources: *DNB.*
Webb, *Compendium of Irish Biography.*
Robert Emmet: the insurrection of July 1803, PRONI Education Facsimile (1976).

289 *Thomas Russell (1767-1803)*

ENGRAVED BY J.W. HUFFAM FOR MADDEN'S *LIVES OF THE UNITED IRISHMEN*, 'FROM A SKETCH IN THE HIBERNIAN MAGAZINE OF 1803, CORRECTED BY A FRIEND OF RUSSELL'S'.
ULSTER MUSEUM
REPRODUCTION

Thomas Russell was born on 21 November 1767 in County Cork, the youngest of the five children of Lieutenant John Russell, a soldier who had fought at Dettingen and Fontenoy and a deeply religious man who, in educating young Thomas himself at home, imparted to him a deep sense of religion and morality as well as a sound knowledge of the classics, science and modern languages. Like his father, Russell intended at one point to take holy orders in the Anglican church. Instead, in 1783 he volunteered to serve with the 52nd Regiment (in which his brother Ambrose was a captain) in India. There they took part in one of the campaigns against Tippoo Sahib and his French advisers. On his return to Ireland, Russell got a commission in the 64th Regiment and lived on his half-pay of £28 a year with his father at the Royal Hospital, Kilmainham.

In the summer of 1790 he and Wolfe Tone met by chance in the public gallery of the House of Commons. Their acquaintance soon ripened into the closest of friendships. Writing in Paris in 1796, Tone recalled their meeting as 'a circumstance which I look upon as one of the most fortunate of my life' and went on to remark:

> There cannot be imagined a more perfect harmony, I may say identity, of sentiment, than exists between us; our regard for each other has never suffered a moment's relaxation from the hour of our first acquaintance, and I am sure that it will continue to the end of our lives. I think the better of myself, for being the object of the esteem of such a man as Russell ...

In his journals, Tone usually refers to Russell affectionately as 'P.P.', - from Swift's *Memoirs of P.P. Clerk of This Parish*, a tale of a pious young man led astray by pleasure and women. Russell's complex personality, as documented originally in Tone's journals and confirmed more recently by the publication of his own hitherto largely impenetrable private writings, in fact combined great idealism and high-mindedness with frequent resort to casual sex and drunkenness, followed by self-recrimination.

In 1791 Russell sold his army commission in order to meet the debts of a friend. In his unworldly way, he became so poor that he could scarcely support himself and his much-loved sister in County Fermanagh and became dependent on the charity of others. Mrs McTier wrote of him in 1793: 'he seems very poor, is agreeable, very handsome and well informed and possess'd of most insinuating graceful manners - his dress betrays poverty and he associates with men every way below himself, on some of whom I fear he mostly lives.' He was a true egalitarian, deeply sympathetic to the ordinary people he came across and hostile to the ruling class (though his admiration for everything French was greatly reduced when he came across corruption among republican officials). Almost alone among the United Irish leaders he also believed in the equality of the sexes. For a time he was a magistrate at Dungannon, then resigned because of the prevailing practice on the local bench of 'inquiring what a man's religion was before going into the crime with which a prisoner was accused'. In 1794 his friends in Belfast got him appointed librarian of the Belfast Library (now the Linen Hall Library), which brought a small salary. With Tone and others he founded the Belfast Society of United Irishmen. Nothing like so fluent as Tone, he published little apart from some contributions to the *Northern Star* and a pamphlet on the Catholic claims. Nevertheless, he was one of the major figures in the establishment of Irish republican nationalism, often more advanced in his views than his friend and a powerful influence on him.

Russell was arrested in Belfast in September 1796. For almost six years he was kept in prison, first in Dublin and then at Fort George, thus missing the rebellion of 1798. When released in 1802, however, he rapidly made contact with Robert Emmet in Paris and became his enthusiastic companion in conspiracy. Given the task of rousing the north, he met with little response. When Emmet rose in Dublin in 1803, there was no corresponding turnout in Ulster. Even then, Russell could write to his friend Mary Ann McCracken, 'I hope your spirits are not depressed by a temporary damp, in consequence of the recent failure, ... of ultimate success I am still certain.' Instead of leaving the country he went to Dublin, where he was arrested and despatched to Downpatrick for trial on a charge of high treason. He was found guilty on 19 October and hanged the following day. Mary Ann McCracken paid for a stone slab with the inscription 'The grave of Russell', and for the next eighteen years looked after his sister, who died in 1821. Miss McCracken, who was more than a little in love with him, recalled Russell as 'a model of manly beauty', of 'majestic stature' and 'martial in his gait and demeanour'. Even the order for his arrest in 1803 was couched in complimentary terms.

Sources: Marianne Elliott, *Wolfe Tone.*
                 C.J. Woods (ed.), *Journals and Memoirs of Thomas Russell, 1791-5* (1991).
                 Webb, *Compendium of Irish Biography.*

290 *Emmet preparing for the Insurrection*

BY GEORGE CRUIKSHANK, FROM MAXWELL'S *REBELLION*
ULSTER MUSEUM
REPRODUCTION

This scene is set in a warehouse off Thomas Street in Dublin. It records the fevered preparations for rebellion by Robert Emmet and his associates in the summer of 1803. While instructions are being read out, pikes are forged, uniforms sewn and stores delivered. Elsewhere in the room, less motivated individuals are feasting and drinking. Emmet's rebellion, dogged by misfortune (including an explosion in this depot), was one of the shortest and most easily quelled in Irish history, but very alarming to the authorities because it showed what determined conspirators working in secret could still achieve five years after 1798.

291 *The Murder Of Lord Kilwarden*

By George Cruikshank, from Maxwell's *Rebellion*
Ulster Museum
Reproduction

On the evening of 23 July 1803, a small group of rebels attacked the carriage of the lord chief justice, Arthur Wolfe, 1st Viscount Kilwarden, as it made its way up Thomas Street towards Dublin Castle. Kilwarden had left his home at Rathcoole to seek shelter in the Castle. He and his nephew were pulled from the carriage and piked to death. His daughter Elizabeth was allowed to escape. This attack was the most notorious episode of Emmet's rebellion and evoked memories of similar murders only five years previously. Cruikshank's Dublin pikemen strongly resemble those who killed the loyal little drummer in Wexford in 1798.

12 POSTSCRIPT

This last section consists of biographical glimpses of some of the people concerned in one way or another with the Rebellion who survived it. Beyond that, the essential shape of the history of Ireland during the post-1798 period is characterised by the opposed figures of the Presbyterian political clergyman Henry Cooke and the Catholic politican Daniel O'Connell. The process by which Presbyterians by and large abandoned Irish nationalism and instead joined with other Protestants in supporting the Union created the basis for modern Unionism. O'Connell's rejection of the physical-force route to reform tried by the United Irishmen and his adoption, in the great campaign for Catholic emancipation, of mass democracy based on the active support of the Catholic clergy, created Irish parliamentary nationalism. His failure to achieve repeal of the Union by similar means, however, brought impatient challenge from the Young Irelanders, whose romantic view of the past made them anything but afraid to 'speak of Ninety-Eight'. The essential cast was thus assembled for the continuing drama.

292 *Mrs Tone and two of her children*

ENGRAVING FROM MADDEN'S *Lives of the United Irishmen*
ULSTER MUSEUM

Margaret Tone, shown here with her sons Theobald Wolfe and Matthew, survived all of her children, dying in 1818. Her daughter-in-law Matilda was left a widow with three children at the age of twenty-nine. Two of them died of tuberculosis in their teens. The third, her younger son William, attended the Lycée Imperial before joining Napoleon's army. He was awarded the Légion d'Honneur at Leipzig, and resigned his commission on the defeat of Napoleon. He went with Matilda to the United States after she married Thomas Wilson in Paris (in the British Embassy, curiously) in 1816. William himself married Catherine, daughter of William Sampson, a leading United Irishman and friend of his father's who had been exiled there after the rebellion. He published his father's biography in 1826 but died of the family scourge of tuberculosis in 1828. Matilda died in 1849, aged eighty, making her one of the longest-surviving of the post-1798 exiles.

293 *Life of Theobald Wolfe Tone, founder of the United Irish Society...*

WRITTEN BY HIMSELF AND CONTINUED BY HIS SON ... EDITED BY HIS SON, WILLIAM THEOBALD WOLFE TONE...
(WASHINGTON, 1826). FIRST EDITION, 2 VOLS. MED 8 VO.
P. AND B. ROWAN

This first edition, in addition to Tone's diary and journals, contains his political writings, selections of correspondence between the United Irishmen, data on the Catholic Committee and other appendices. Volume 1 has a frontispiece portrait, from the likeness by Katherine [sic] Sampson Tone, wife of the editor.

Tone's frank and entertaining diaries give us a much greater insight into his true character and thoughts than the memoirs of any other leader of the United Irishmen, while his political writings give depth to his claim to be regarded as a central figure of the movement. These volumes were the foundation on which a cult of Tone as republican hero was developed from the 1840s onward, aided by increasingly selective editing of them. Professor Elliott concludes that the cult

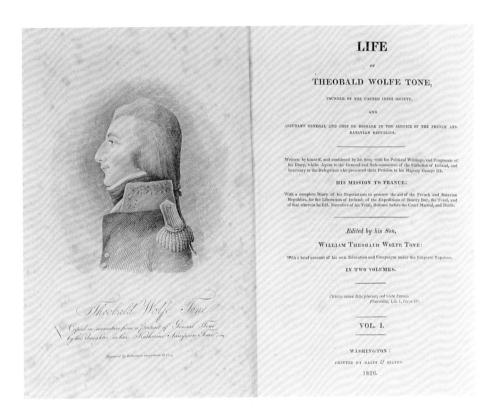

'was not created by the publication of the *Life* in 1826, but it would not have developed as it did without it'.

Sources: Marianne Elliott, *Wolfe Tone*.

294 *Autobiography of Archibald Hamilton Rowan, Esq.*

EDITED BY WILLIAM HAMILTON DRUMMOND, D.D., M.R.I.A.
(DUBLIN, 1840); WITH FRONTISPIECE PORTRAIT
ULSTER MUSEUM

In an introductory letter to his children, dated 1826, Rowan explains that his memoir was begun while he was in America on his own, 'not expecting to return to Europe, and unwilling to solicit my family to rejoin me there'. What he wrote was not intended for publication, but shortly before he died he entrusted the manuscript to a barrister friend, T.K. Lowry. Rowan's daughter subsequently engaged the Rev. Dr Drummond, an old friend of her father's, to prepare the memoir for publication. As Drummond says in his preface, 'Had Mr. Rowan wished to make a romance of his history, he had abundant materials ...'.

295 *Mary Ann McCracken (1770-1866)*

FROM AN ORIGINAL CARTE-DE-VISITE PHOTOGRAPH BY JOHN GIBSON, BELFAST, C.1865.
ULSTER MUSEUM

Mary Ann McCracken - always Mary to her family - was the younger sister of Henry Joy McCracken and his close companion in many activities, including radical politics, an interest in Irish culture and a deep concern for the poor. After her brother's execution in 1798 she devoted herself to business, to the rearing of her brother's illegitimate daughter and to philanthropic causes, especially those concerning women and children. She took a particular interest in the Charitable

Institution (the Poorhouse), acting as secretary of its Ladies' Committee for twenty-five years. During the Famine of the 1840s she was president of a committee for the relief of Irish destitution. A campaigner against slavery and the use of climbing boys as chimney sweeps, and for equality of women, especially in education, she survived with all her wits about her until her mid-nineties.

This portrait of her, by the Belfast photographer John Gibson (flourished c.1865-75), shows an alert old woman. It was taken shortly before her death in 1866.

Sources: Mary McNeill, *The Life and Times of Mary Ann McCracken, 1770-1866* (Dublin, 1960; reprinted Belfast, 1988).

296 *Death mask of James Hope (1764-1847)*

ULSTER MUSEUM

James Hope was one of the most fervent and effective of the United Irishmen and, for a man so notable in the movement, highly unusual in being all his life a plain working man. He was born on 25 August 1764 in the parish of Templepatrick, County Antrim, into a humble Presbyterian family of Covenanter stock. He received scarcely any formal education before starting work as a farm labourer but later, with the help of people who took an interest in him, and in the intervals of working as a weaver, learned to read and write. His reading confirmed his instinct for radical democracy, while his experience and observation of working life made him in effect an early socialist.

As with so many United Irishmen, his connection with politics began in the ranks of the Volunteers, in his case the Roughfort corps. This was in the later stages of the movement, when entry became possible in some units for a working man and when the French Revolution had revived the Volunteers as a vehicle for national reform. Hope recalled the 1792 Bastille Day review in Belfast, when 'the company to which I belonged, marched into the field in coloured clothes, with green cockades. We had a green flag, bearing for a motto, on one side "Our Gallic brother was born July 14, 1789. Alas! we are still in embryo" and on the other side "Superstitious galaxy" [and] "The Irish Bastille - let us unite to destroy it". These stirring words were dictated by Hope himself and painted on the flag by his brother-in-law.

The suppression of the Volunteers in 1793 closed down this channel for radical politics. As Hope later explained: 'My motives for joining the United Irishmen were, to carry out the objects of the Volunteers [that is, parliamentary reform and Catholic emancipation]; my first views were not beyond theirs ...' He added, however, that his views soon became 'more extensive' and he became one of the 'Foreign aid men'. He was sworn into the Mallusk society of United Irishmen. Its members elected him as their delegate to a general committee in Belfast, where he made the acquaintance of Samuel Neilson, Henry Joy McCracken, Thomas Russell, and others who came to admire and trust him. According to his own recollections he 'was employed in 1796, 1797, and the spring of 1798, as an emissary, going from place to place throughout the country, organising the people. I received my orders generally from Russell, Wilson, and McCracken, and communicated with certain persons I was sworn never to name ...

Along with Putnam McCabe, Hope spread the message of the United Irishmen widely, fostering an alliance with the Defenders and creating a network of organised groups wherever he went. His trade as a weaver provided him with useful cover on this mission. News of his activities reached the authorities, of course, who apparently offered him £500 on one occasion, through Lord Downshire, if he would provide evidence to convict Neilson, McCracken and Russell. Though always poor, Hope remained incorruptible. He was later to remark: 'We had traitors in our camp from the beginning to the close of the career of our society'. In his view, renegade United Irishmen who secretly took the Orange oath 'were the cause of more bloodshed in 1798 than the open enemy whom we knew and might avoid'.

In 1798 itself, Hope acted with great coolness and courage, first in escaping from Belfast with munitions and rebel flags to join McCracken in his march on the town of Antrim, then in the battle of Antrim, where his 'Spartan band' played a notable part in the fighting and covered the retreat. After the failure of the rebellion, he made his way to the relative anonymity of Dublin, where he earned his living as a cotton weaver and, later, haberdasher. In 1802 Neilson, released from Fort George and on his way to exile in America, appeared illegally in Dublin intending to visit his family before crossing the Atlantic. At great risk to himself, Hope conducted Neilson to Belfast and back again and saw him safely on his way. By good fortune, Hope was apparently overlooked in the aftermath of 1798, perhaps because, being of humble origin, he appeared a much more subordinate figure than he really was. In fact he still hoped, and worked for, another chance to overthrow the government. This steadfastness of aim, and his discretion and reliability as a conspirator, recommended him to Robert Emmet. It was Hope who made contact with Michael Dwyer and his band on Emmet's behalf in 1803. When the abortive attack on Dublin Castle took place, Hope was in the north with his old friend Russell, vainly trying to rouse the country there.

Afterwards, he worked in and around Dublin till 1806, when his wife petitioned the new British government for a pardon of some sort and he was allowed to return openly to the north. The McCracken family employed him for a while. Thereafter for nine years he worked for an Englishman named Tucker in the neighbourhood of Larne, finally acting as a clerk for Joseph Smyth, a Belfast publisher. His wife died in 1831 and with her much of his own zest for life. He wrote poetry, samples of which can be found in Madden's memoir of him. He died in 1847 at the age of eighty-three and was buried in the graveyard at Mallusk, near where he was born. There the tombstone erected to his memory refers to him as 'an honest man, steadfast in faith, and always hopeful in divine protection, in the best era of his country's history a soldier in her cause, and in the worst of times, still faithful to it ...' Jemmy Hope's name and fame were later made use of by both Catholic nationalists (his portrait appears on the banners of republican clubs) and by Protestant socialists.

Sources: Webb, *Compendium of Irish Biography.*
            Madden, *The United Irishmen,* third series (1846), vol. 1.
            A.T.Q. Stewart, *The Summer Soldiers.*

297 *French passport, issued to William Putnam McCabe in the name of William Lee, 5 December 1807*

38 x 26 CM
BOARD OF TRINITY COLLEGE, DUBLIN

William Putnam McCabe was an important, if elusive, United Irishman. Born in Belfast in 1772, he was the son of Thomas McCabe, a noted watchmaker and part-owner of a cotton mill, a man of radical views and an early member of the Society, who had in 1786 successfully opposed a project of some of the town's merchants to take part in the African slave trade. Young William was trained for the cotton industry in Belfast, Manchester and Glasgow. Being an excellent mimic, he was to put both his profession and experience of provincial accents to good use when he joined the United Irishmen and began to travel the country as an emissary and organiser. He was also a master of disguise, avoiding capture or escaping from

custody in amazing fashion; in fact, he was a real-life Emerald Pimpernel. At one stage he attracted large audiences among rural Presbyterians in the north by advertising himself as 'a converted Papist [who] would preach the Word in —, on ——, and explain how he became convinced of the true doctrines of Presbyterianism' - which turned out, of course, to be those of the United Irishmen. Later, he and James Hope travelled the south establishing units of the new military-based system in Wexford and elsewhere. Professor Cullen's recent judgment is that 'McCabe's role ... was crucial in the United Irishmen. He both promoted organisation in depth, and spearheaded the final stages of structuring the movement, that of converting the civilian structure into military form...'. In this work he constantly covered his tracks by disguises and aliases, appearing variously as a Scottish pedlar, clergymen of various kinds, military officers, even travelling from

London to Dublin on one occasion as a King's Messenger. A Wexford man told Madden, McCabe's biographer, that he had met the man twenty times and never recognised him until he revealed himself.

In May 1798 he was in Dublin, acting as aide-de-camp to Lord Edward FitzGerald and organising the bodyguards who helped the latter move safely about the city despite having a price on his head. On the evening of 18 May, McCabe was one of a party conveying FitzGerald to Magan's house on Usher's Island - in fact a trap, since Magan was an informer - when he was arrested after a scuffle in the street with Major Sirr's men. He therefore took no part in the early stages of the rising itself. By adopting a broad Scottish accent, however, he subsequently persuaded the soldiers (Dumbarton Fencibles, no less) that they had arrested an innocent Scotsman out for an evening stroll. Thereafter he appeared among the rebels in Kildare, and in County Cork, later joining the French in Mayo (he was, or became, a fluent French speaker). In the aftermath of the Rebellion, McCabe appears to have acted as an intermediary for the State Prisoners; he is known to have possessed a copy of the compact they made with the government, at a time when this document was still highly secret. Little is known about his movements during this period, but he left Dublin in December 1798 by the Liverpool packet, en route to London and eventually Paris. Before he and his companion, one George Palmer, reached the Continent at Hamburg, McCabe appears somehow to have made contact with the State Prisoners recently arrived at Fort George in Scotland, where their quarters inside the wall were enclosed by a wooden stockade (the 'invalids' who constituted the garrison perhaps posed no great challenge to his abilities). At any rate, he obtained a letter from the prisoner O'Connor to the French Directory which concealed a message written in invisible ink. It appears that he also contracted a secret marriage in Edinburgh in 1799.

Thereafter, having travelled to Hamburg as an American, he made contact with Pamela FitzGerald and other, more secret characters in the world of intrigue of which Hamburg was the centre, before travelling on to Paris. In 1802 he settled at Rouen in Normandy, where he established a successful cotton mill. The mill building, constructed to his specification, apparently included secret rooms, the exact purpose of which is not known. Since the mill became a focal point for some of the United Irishmen arriving in France, however, one may guess. There McCabe is said to have trained some of the people who were to assist Robert Emmet in preparing the ill-fated rising of 1803.

As a dangerous rebel still at large, McCabe was among those excepted from the general pardon. In 1799 Castlereagh, the Irish Secretary, explained: 'for the past four years McCabe has been employed in organising every part of Ireland. He is mentioned in our Fugitive Bill and is liable to be hanged upon being identified...'. And the head of the Aliens Office in London reckoned that 'next to Lord Edward Fitzgerald, McCabe was the life and soul of the 1798 Rebellion. He organised the whole North of Ireland with the most astonishing speed and talent'. After the failure of the Rebellion in Ireland he was appointed to the new United Irish Directory in Paris, for whom he undertook a number of secret and dangerous missions in England and Ireland, risking death if caught. In 1814 he was at last arrested in Ireland but, with the French war approaching its end, was ultimately deported to Portugal. Three years later, he went to Ireland again, accompanied by his daughter, only to be arrested and lodged in Kilmainham for eighteen months. In 1819 he was arrested in Scotland. When McCabe's friends approached the government for his release, on the plea that he only travelled on his own business, the Home Secretary replied: 'It might be true that Mr McCabe never went to any part of England or Ireland except upon business of his own; but it was very extraordinary that, in whatever part of the King's dominions his own business brought him, some public disturbance was sure to take place'.

As one might expect of a person who at one time had no fewer than twenty-five outstanding indictments for treason against him, there is no known portrait of McCabe. One of the proclamations offering a reward of £500 for his capture describes him as follows: 'height five foot eight inches: well made: walks smart: full face: black or dark eyes: dark hair: whiskers: good complexion: not corpulent but pretty lusty: a great deal of vivacity: wears pantaloons and boots'. This passport describes him as being 1m. 70 (5ft 7ins) in height, with chestnut hair, beard and eyes, a regular forehead and nose, a round chin, oval face and florid complexion.

Issued by the Prefecture of Police of the Department of the Seine in the name of William Lee, manufacturer, a native of Belfast now living in Paris, the document was for a journey to the United States from either Nantes or Bordeaux and was valid for one month. The holder was to be accompanied by his ward, Louise Neville, aged thirteen, his daughter, aged nine, and a maid of forty.

McCabe died in Paris on 6 January 1821 and was buried there in the Vaugirard cemetery.

Sources: John McCabe, 'A United Irish Family', in *Familia: Ulster Genealogical Review*, vol. 13 (1997).
R.R. Madden, *The United Irishman, their Lives and Times*, third series (1846).
L. M. Cullen, 'Politics and Rebellion: Wicklow in the 1790s', in K. Hannigan and W. Nolan (eds), *Wicklow: History and Society* (1994).

298 *General F. R. Chesney (1789-1872)*

By Carl Schmid(?), 1853
Oil on canvas, 92 x 71.3 cm
Ulster Museum

Francis Rawdon Chesney, born near Kilkeel, County Down in 1789, was at the age of nine years the youngest soldier to play any part in the events of 1798 in Ireland. His father, Alexander, who had been a Loyalist in Carolina during the War of Independence, had been obliged to return to Ireland when the colonists were victorious. He became coast officer in the Revenue service at Annalong, County Down. As a government employee and a former captain of militia in America he was an active opponent of the United Irishmen in south Down in the 1790s. He raised a body of yeomanry, called the Mourne Infantry, and in 1798 commissioned his nine-year-old son Francis in this unit as a sub-lieutenant.

In May 1798 young Francis Rawdon (so named in honour of his father's old commander in America, Francis Rawdon Hastings, Earl of Moira) walked the twenty miles from Kilkeel to Newry barefoot to join his regiment, which was reviewed by Lord Cornwallis, the new commander-in-chief, under whom Chesney senior had also served in America years before. Cornwallis somewhat mortified the boy by describing him as 'rather small' for a soldier, but this absurdly early experience of military life settled his choice of career. Though he took the field, there is no evidence that he took part in any fighting during the brief period of the rebellion in the north; south Down remained pretty quiet, despite a great deal of activity there by the United Irishmen earlier.

In 1803 Lord Moira presented Chesney with a cadetship at the Royal Artillery academy at Woolwich, where he did well despite his failure to grow in size. Thereafter, though bursting to see active service, he was employed on garrison duty until the war with Napoleon ended. Chesney's first task after Waterloo was to walk over all Napoleon's main battlefields - a matter of 3,000 miles or more - to improve his knowledge of strategy and tactics. He never got the chance to put this knowledge to use in military action, but was to become famous as an explorer, beginning in 1829 when as a lieutenant of artillery he was sent on a mission to the Middle East to explore possible overland routes to India. In a voyage of three years he travelled from Egypt and Syria to the Euphrates and then descended the river on a raft with a few Arab companions. He reported that a Suez canal would be feasible, as would the overland route from Syria. Parliament put up £20,000 for a second expedition under his command which, setting out in 1835, transported the makings of two small steamboats across the desert to the Euphrates and with them explored the rivers Euphrates and Tigris, going as far as India and returning across the Arabian desert. Chesney arrived back in London in 1837. After various promotions and appointments, including a spell in Hong Kong, he retired from army service to his family estate at Kilkeel in 1851. In 1857 and again in 1863 he visited Constantinople to seek concessions for a projected railway across Turkish territory; he also revisited Syria. In 1849 the first two volumes of his great work on his exploration of the Tigris and Euphrates appeared in print.

Chesney ended his life with the rank of general. His exploring exploits were recognised by scholars and fellow travellers. When he visited Paris in 1869 Ferdinand de Lesseps publicly acknowledged him as 'father of the Suez Canal'. He became a Fellow of the Royal Society and of the Royal Geographical Society, and Oxford University made him a Doctor of Common Law. The physical toughness that he had acquired in boyhood stood him in good stead all his life and survived into old age; he was still striding the Mournes when in his eighties.

This fine portrait of Chesney is dated 1853. It is signed by the artist but since the last part of the signature is unclear it is difficult to be sure which of many German painters named Schmid or Schmidt he may be. The likeliest candidate is Carl Frederich Ludwig Schmid (b.1799), a portrait and genre painter who worked in Aachen, Rome and London and exhibited at the Royal Academy.

Sources: *DNB.*
            Webb, *Compendium of Irish Biography.*
            Article in *National Army Museum Annual Report 1978-1979.*

299 *Sword presented to Lt Col. Chesney, 1837*

WITH PRESENTATION SCABBARD WITH GILT METAL FITTINGS AND VELVET COVER, ALSO A SERVICE SCABBARD; OVERALL LENGTH 97 CM
ULSTER MUSEUM

The inscription on the blade reads:

By permission of His Most Gracious Majesty King William the Fourth, this sword was presented to Lt. Col. Chesney Royal Artillery by the gentlemen of the Chamber of Commerce at Bombay, as a token of their admiration of the manner [in] which he conducted the expedition to the Rivers Euphrates, Karun & Tigris.

The blade, which is stamped with the name of the makers Hunt & Roskell, 156 Bond St, has a pipe back.

300 *The Rev. Henry Cooke, DD (1788-1868)*

BY SIR DANIEL MACNEE
OIL ON CANVAS, 127.3 x 88.9 CM
ULSTER MUSEUM

Henry Cooke, one of the most influential Irish Presbyterian ministers of his time and a political as well as a religious leader, was born Henry Macook near Maghera, County Londonderry, the fourth and youngest child of a poor tenant farmer (his holding amounted to nine acres) and his second wife. At the time of his ordination he changed his name to Cook, and later added an 'e'. Local tradition had it that his real father was a landowner in the area in whose house Mrs Macook had worked as midwife, and that this explained Cooke's aristocratic bearing and imperious manner. There may also have been some doubt about the year of his birth; according to one source he was born in 1783, not 1788.

The young Macook received all his early education from hedge schoolmasters, before making his way, the poorest of poor scholars, to Glasgow University, where

he studied for two years but left without taking a degree. He later completed the basic theological training needed to be ordained and in 1808 became assistant minister at Duneane, County Antrim; he moved presently to Donegore, and then to Killyleagh, County Down. From there he was called in 1829 to May Street in Belfast, a church built for him by admirers, where he spent the rest of his long ministry. In the same year he was awarded an honorary doctorate in Divinity by an American college, and in 1837 Dublin University gave him an LL.D. In theological matters the leading champion of orthodox Presbyterianism, he succeeded in driving out of the church the more liberal 'Arians'.

He began to emerge as a political figure in 1831, when he opposed the government's plan for a national system of primary education, intended to be non-denominational. He soon became a leading spokesman for conservative, anti-Catholic views and a staunch opponent of O'Connell. Believing that Protestants must combine against Catholic nationalism, he addressed a great meeting at Hillsborough in 1834, convened by the third Marquess of Downshire, at which he proclaimed the 'banns of marriage' between Anglicans and Presbyterians.

By 1840, Daniel O'Connell had embarked on his great campaign for the repeal of the Union. In the autumn of that year it was announced that he would visit Belfast. Even the *Northern Whig*, the newspaper of the northern liberals, expressed strong opposition to the idea. The recently established Catholic paper, the *Vindicator*, voiced strong approval, however, and had the satisfaction of announcing the forthcoming visit in January 1841. A few days later, another Belfast paper printed a challenge from Cooke to O'Connell to debate in public the issue of repeal. O'Connell dodged the challenge, however, and, abandoning plans for a triumphal progress in the north, slipped into Belfast incognito on 16 January. A 'reform' dinner held two days later attracted few Protestant liberals and next day, when O'Connell tried to address a large crowd from the balcony of the Royal Hotel, he could scarcely make himself heard. That evening, rival mobs fought it out in the streets. O'Connell left with a police escort for Donaghadee en route for Scotland. His departure was followed by a great conservative meeting at which Cooke was the hero of the hour and the chief speaker. In response to O'Connell's claim that the Catholics when in power had never persecuted Protestants he instanced 1641, 1688-89 - and 1798. The 'one argument' with which he opposed repeal, however, was the beneficial effects of the Union on Belfast: 'Look on Belfast', he concluded, 'and be a repealer, if you can'. The meeting was attended by a hundred Presbyterian clergy, and in the vote of thanks the 'banns of matrimony' proclaimed by Cooke at Hillsborough in 1834 were sanctioned by the Dean of Ross. O'Connell too claimed to have triumphed, but Cooke's supporters lauded their champion as 'the cook who dished Dan' and derided his opponent as 'the repealer repulsed'. In the same year Cooke, at the summit both of his political popularity and his religious career, was elected moderator of the Presbyterian General Assembly. He resigned from May Street in 1867 and died at the end of 1868.

This picture is a reduced version of the portrait by Sir David Macnee, painted in 1856 in Glasgow for presentation to the Assembly's College in Belfast, of which Cooke was president 1853-68. It was probably painted for his family. Daniel Macnee (1806-82) was a successful portrait painter who was elected to the newly-founded Royal Scottish Academy in 1830, became its president in 1876 and was knighted in 1877.

Sources: R. Finlay Holmes, *Henry Cooke* (1981).
            Eileen Black, *Irish Oil Paintings, 1831-1900*, Ulster Museum Catalogue (Belfast, 1997).
            DNB.

301 *Daniel O'Connell (1775-1847)*

BY GEORGE MULVANY
OIL ON CANVAS, 90 X 70 CM
NATIONAL GALLERY OF IRELAND, DUBLIN

Daniel O'Connell, the 'Liberator', was born and brought up in County Kerry. In 1791 he was sent to the Irish College of St Omer in France, transferring in 1792 to Douai. The following year he escaped from France when the anti-clerical revolutionary government suppressed the college at Douai. In 1794 he entered Lincoln's Inn in London, to read law, and was called to the Irish bar in 1798, the year of the Rebellion. His experience in France had made him an enemy of revolution in the French style. As a young lawyer in Dublin he became a freemason and joined the lawyers' corps of yeomanry, being deeply opposed to the United Irishmen. In 1800, in his first public speech, he protested against the insinuation that the Catholics approved of the Act of Union. He subsequently campaigned for Catholic Emancipation, opposing Grattan's Bill of 1813 as inadequate. The emancipation question aroused strong feelings, and O'Connell had already been involved in duels, though reluctant to fire his pistols in anger when his opponent missed. This was not good for his reputation, however, and when challenged by a Dublin merchant named John D'Esterre, a member of the Corporation which opposed emancipation, he therefore responded aggressively. Evading an attempt by D'Esterre and his ultra-Protestant friends to horse-whip him at the Four Courts, O'Connell arranged to meet his opponent in a field in Kildare on 1 February 1815 and there wounded him fatally. O'Connell himself was uneasy with his success, but his Catholic followers (including the Archbishop of Dublin, Daniel Murray, despite the fact that duelling was a reserved sin) were delighted at this triumph. Shortly afterwards, he became involved in a challenge to Robert Peel, the chief secretary, and was only prevented from meeting him in an affair of honour at Ostend when arrested and bound over in England on his way to the rendezvous.

During the following decade he campaigned for emancipation rather more constructively by the foundation of the Catholic Association and the great crusade that culminated triumphantly in 1829 with his own election to Parliament and the repeal of most of the remaining restrictions on Catholics. The mass organisation he created in the process was a new phenomenon in British politics - constitutional and non-violent in its methods, officially at least. The remarkable self-discipline with which the campaign was conducted gave the peasantry both hope and pride but in the process made O'Connell's nationalism an essentially Catholic thing. In this respect, it derived from the Defenderism of the 1790s rather than the Enlightenment idealism of the United Irishmen. Northern Presbyterians, many of whom had been fervent Irish nationalists in that fateful decade, became increasingly unsympathetic, if not hostile, to nationalism in its new form. When O'Connell moved on to attempt the repeal of the Union in the early 1840s, using the tactics that had proved so successful in the 1820s, the majority of northern Protestants united in opposing him. His confrontation with Cooke, the Presbyterian leader, in 1841 did not encourage him to revisit Belfast.

George Mulvany (1809-69) was the son of the painter Thomas James Mulvany. He was appointed Keeper of the Royal Hibernian Academy in 1845, following in the footsteps of his father. In 1854 he became director of the National Gallery of Ireland.

Sources: *DNB.*
James Kelly, *'That Damn'd Thing called Honour'.*

302 *John Kells Ingram (1823-1907)*

By SARAH PURSER (1848-1943)
PASTEL ON PAPER, 60.9 x 45.5 CM, SIGNED AND DATED 1890
ULSTER MUSEUM

John Kells Ingram was born in 1823 near Pettigo, County Donegal, where his father was a Church of Ireland clergyman. He spent his entire adult life at Trinity College, Dublin as classical scholar, mathematician and economist, was elected a Fellow of the College in 1846 and subsequently became in turn professor of Oratory, professor of Greek, librarian, senior lecturer and vice-provost. His *History of Political Economy* (1888) was translated into eight languages.

Ingram's fame in Ireland, however, rests not on his scholarly accomplishments,

which are long forgotten, but on the verses he dashed off one evening as a nineteen-year-old undergraduate. Entitled *The Memory of the Dead*, Ingram's poem is better known by its first line, 'Who fears to speak of Ninety-Eight?' It was published anonymously in *The Nation* in April 1843 and instantly became famous. Ingram did not openly admit authorship until near the end of his life, though the fact was well known in Dublin. In later life he showed little sympathy for Irish nationalism.

This lively pastel sketch was made in 1890. Sarah Henrietta Purser, one of the most important figures in the Irish arts revival, was educated in Switzerland. When her father's flourmilling business failed in 1873 she decided to make her living as a portrait painter. After studying in Dublin and in Paris she began to exhibit at the Royal Hibernian Academy and at the Royal Academy in London, helped by the patronage of the Gore-Booth family. Judicious investment in Guinness's brewery and on the Stock Exchange made her a wealthy woman. Still painting when well into her eighties, she died at the age of ninety-five.

The pastel, which came originally from one of her sketchbooks, was donated in 1931 to the Belfast Municipal Museum & Art Gallery by W.A. Ingram, son of the sitter.

Sources: Martyn Anglesea, UM catalogue entry.
                DNB.

303 *Manuscript version, untitled, of The Memory of the Dead*

PARCHMENT, 20 x 14 CM
TRINITY COLLEGE, DUBLIN

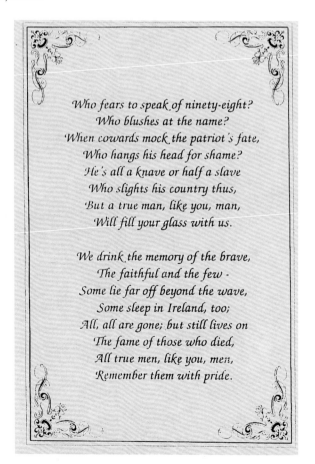

Who fears to speak of ninety-eight?
Who blushes at the name?
When cowards mock the patriot's fate,
Who hangs his head for shame?
He's all a knave or half a slave
Who slights his country thus,
But a true man, like you, man,
Will fill your glass with us.

We drink the memory of the brave,
The faithful and the few -
Some lie far off beyond the wave,
Some sleep in Ireland, too;
All, all are gone; but still lives on
The fame of those who died,
All true men, like you, men,
Remember them with pride.

INDEX

Numbers refer to catalogue entries, not pages. Bold type, e.g. **123,** indicates the presence of an illustration relating to the subject.

302